CONCISE
FLORA OF BRITAIN

FOR THE USE OF SCHOOLS

*With explanatory illustrations
and keys to identification*

by

F. K. MAKINS, M.A., F.L.S.

OXFORD
AT THE CLARENDON PRESS

Oxford University Press, Amen House, London E.C. 4

GLASGOW NEW YORK TORONTO MELBOURNE WELLINGTON
BOMBAY CALCUTTA MADRAS CAPE TOWN

Geoffrey Cumberlege, Publisher to the University

FIRST PUBLISHED 1939
REPRINTED 1945, 1948, 1952

PRINTED IN GREAT BRITAIN

PREFACE

THE object of this book is to meet the demand for a modern Flora of Britain suitable for use in schools, and by beginners generally.

Most existing Floras are not especially adapted for this purpose, while the many popular handbooks on wild flowers aim rather to satisfy the curiosity of the general public than to provide an introduction to systematic botany.

Seeing that my own aim is to help the student who already has a groundwork of botany, I have tried to find out what schools who teach botany really want and what leading botanists consider desirable in a school Flora. I expected much divergence of opinion, but, except on a few questions of nomenclature, there appears to be general agreement not only on the form a school Flora should take but on the number and choice of species to be included and the desirability or otherwise of illustrations.

I have rejected a suggestion to limit the work to 500 or so of the best-known plants. Apart from the fact that such a limit would be arbitrary and give rise to innumerable objections from many quarters, a keen student would never be satisfied with it. I have, therefore, described 1,140 species and varieties, including all except the greatest rarities. A few very rare plants, such as the Cheddar Pink and White Rockrose, have been included as they occur in easily accessible localities and are quite likely to be encountered, whereas others, often with a wider distribution but less accessible or conspicuous, have been omitted.

Many of the species described in this book have been subdivided by other authors into a multitude of subspecies, which are often given specific rank. With regard to these I have followed generally the practice of Bentham and Hooker's *British Flora* by lumping them together under aggregate species, but as the process seems to have been carried rather too far in that work I have preferred to take as a basis the list of British plants issued by the Wild Flower Society. After excluding the rarest I have extended the list to cover any marked differences that are likely to catch the eye. These I have either described separately or briefly mentioned under the aggregate description. In addition, I have included a few trees not truly naturalized but commonly seen in woods and fields.

The view is generally held that named illustrations in a Flora reduce its value to a young student. There is always the temptation to substitute an artificial thing like a drawing for the close and often laborious observation of living objects that is essential in biology. Besides, a Flora with named illustrations of species is not suitable for use in the examination room and, other things being equal, examining bodies will give preference to a book without such illustrations.

In this book, therefore, the main series of illustrations gives no clue to the identity of any plant that may be given to the student for determination. The purpose of these illustrations is solely to clear up the meanings of the technical terms given in the glossary. The drawings have all been made from living plants, mostly very common ones that any one can easily find. The smaller illustrations in the text are given as an aid to distinguishing small differences difficult for a beginner to understand from the short descriptions necessarily imposed by a book of this size.

I am grateful to all those who have favoured me with their views and suggestions and especially to Dr. W. Watson, A.L.S. (who for nearly thirty years taught botany at Taunton School), for kindly criticizing the manuscript and amending it where necessary. I am also indebted to the many kind friends who have sent me fresh specimens and helped me in numerous other ways. As the author, however, I alone am responsible for the book and for any mistakes that may appear, though I hope these will be few. To prevent mistakes and ambiguities from being repeated in future editions I hope that any one who discovers them, after a thorough test, will kindly communicate with me through the publishers. I shall also welcome any suggestions for improvement.

F. K. M.

October 1938

CONTENTS

HOW TO USE THE FLORA vii

GLOSSARY x

ILLUSTRATIONS TO GLOSSARY xvii

SYNOPSIS OF THE FAMILIES 1

ARTIFICIAL KEY TO THE FAMILIES . . . 9

DESCRIPTIONS 19

INDEX 201

HOW TO USE THE FLORA

THE chief use of a Flora such as this is to enable the student to identify plants for himself.

To take a practical example, let us suppose that we find the small pink flowers of Herb-Robert, common in every hedgerow from spring to autumn, but we do not know either the name of the plant or its family. We should begin with the key to the families on page 9.

It is a flowering plant. The figure 2 on the right-hand side of the page is repeated lower down on the left-hand side. We now have to decide whether the ovules are completely enclosed in an ovary equipped with style and stigma, or not. Seen through a lens the ovary, style, and stigma are all plainly evident. We can pass on to 3. The leaves are net-veined and there are five petals; there can be little doubt that it is a dicotyledon. We should now look at 4. Is the corolla present or absent? It is present, and poly-petalous, that is to say, it is composed of distinct petals that can be pulled off one by one without disturbing the others (it is even possible that some may fall off as we are handling the specimen). The plant must therefore be included in the first of the two alterna-tives given against 4, which leads us to 5. A distinct calyx below the pink corolla points to 6. There are less than twelve stamens (lens again), so it is possible to go straight on to 14. The pistil is syncarpous. It is true that the carpels separate in fruit, but they remain attached to the long central axis. Taking, therefore, the second of the two alternatives we go on to 17. The flower is regular, pointing to 21. Here there are three alternatives. Our plant possessing green cauline leaves can hardly be Monotropa or in the family Droseraceae, so we can proceed with confidence to 22. The number of petals and stamens rules out Cruciferae and takes us to 23. It is not a tree, shrub, or shrubby heath-like plant; it is definitely a herb, therefore it must come under 34. The ovary is superior (35), and there are five sepals (36). The leaves are compound, which indicates the family GERANIACEAE.

We should now turn to page 47, where a short description of the family Geraniaceae will be found, followed by a key to the different genera. As before, we should take the first pair of alternatives. The flowers are regular (2), the leaves opposite (3), and there are ten stamens—easily counted in young flowers though in the older ones the anthers may have dropped—while the awns of the carpels, i.e. the long extensions joining them to the central axis, are not twisted. Hence our plant must belong to the genus GERANIUM, number I in the list of genera belonging to the family.

To find the species the same process is gone through as for the family and genus. There are two flowers on each peduncle (2), they are pink and less than one inch across (3), the petals are entire (4), and the leaves are compound, with three main divisions, i.e. ternate, which proclaims the plant to be *Geranium Robertianum*. To make quite sure the result should be checked with the description given of this species.

The keys are largely artificial and are applicable only to plants described in this book. As far as possible characters that can be readily recognized by a beginner have been given as guides to identification, but it is as well to make sure that the alternative possibilities at each step have been thoroughly exhausted before going on to the next; if not, mistakes will be made and the inquirer will have to retrace his steps.

The keys and descriptions are not perfect—to eliminate every possibility of error, if such could be done, would need a much larger volume—but by their means any student gifted with patience and average intelligence should be able to identify the great majority of British plants.

A good hand-lens is essential, also a sharp knife for cutting through flowers and ovaries (a collection of old safety-razor blades has been found very useful for this purpose). For work indoors it is a good plan to mount the lens on a stand that can be moved up and down to bring the object into focus, thus freeing the hands for dissecting the smaller structures. This can best be done with a pair of needles mounted on handles.

To return to the description given of Herb-Robert, it begins with the Latin name of the plant, *G.* being an abbreviation of *Geranium*. The specific name, or 'specific epithet' as it is called, is given in full, the accent showing that in pronunciation the emphasis is on the fourth syllable and that the *a* is long. The letter L. is an abbreviation of the author of the name, Linnaeus, who named most of our common plants. The figure following the Latin name is the number of counties in which the species has so far been recorded.[1] The maximum number of counties (excluding

[1] The latest figures to which I have access are given in *The Comital Flora of the British Isles* by G. C. Druce (1932). I have not taken into account records considered doubtful by Dr. Druce unless I have been able to verify them personally or on reliable authority.

Ireland) is 112, obtained by dividing the larger counties, e.g. Yorkshire, Lincolnshire, Devon, &c., into botanical vice-counties, an arrangement first introduced by H. C. Watson in his *Topographical Botany* (1874).

Then come the common name or names, if any, and the months of flowering. Neither of these should be taken too literally. It is impossible in a work of this size to give all the common names in use, as many are purely local. The time of flowering may vary according to habitat, climatic conditions, and latitude. An exposed habitat or a cold spring retards flowering, while a sheltered habitat or a mild autumn prolongs it. Also, generally speaking, most species flower somewhat earlier in the south of England than in the north or in Scotland.

At the end of each description is given, in italics, the most likely habitat, i.e. the sort of place in which one may expect to find the plant, noting that 'cornfields' refers to any cultivated crops as distinct from meadows or pastures.

Lastly, also in italics, there is a note on frequency. The following terms are used to denote this, in the order given: very common, common, frequent, occasional, rare, and very rare. 'Local' means that the plant may be common in a few places but not generally. An 'alien' is a plant of foreign origin but now more or less established.

The sequence of Families, Genera, and Species is that of the *London Catalogue of British Plants*, 11th edition (1925), commonly used for school and private herbaria.

A knowledge of the commonest botanical terms is assumed. Where there is doubt as to the exact application in this book of any term used reference should be made to the Glossary beginning on page x and, if necessary, to the illustrations following it.

It is seldom necessary to uproot a plant in order to identify it. To pull up by the roots or to mutilate unnecessarily any plant that is not an injurious weed may deprive others of instruction and enjoyment and may also be an offence against the local by-laws.

GLOSSARY

Accumbent. Used of cotyledons lying parallel with each other and with their narrow edges touching the radicle, thus: = o.

Achene. A dry indehiscent one-seeded fruit produced from a single carpel. (Figs. 3, 4.)

Acuminate. Ending in a long point (Fig. 28).

Acute. Ending in a sharp or acute angle.

Adnate. Adhering throughout its length. (*a*, Fig. 25.)

Adpressed. Pressed closely towards the stem or some other part.

Amplexicaul. Used of a leaf, the blade of which clasps the stem. (*a*, Fig. 9.)

Apocarpous. Of separate carpels, i.e. not united into a syncarpous pistil. (Figs. 2, 6, 24, 25.)

Aril. A fleshy appendage to the seed.

Auricle. An ear-shaped lobe or projection at the base of a leaf-blade. (*a*, Fig. 9.)

Awl-shaped. Tapering evenly from base to apex and not narrowing at the base. (*a*, Fig. 15.)

Awn. A slender prolongation or appendage. (*a*, Fig. 60.)

Axil. The upper angle formed by a leaf or branch with the stem, or by a side vein with the main vein.

Axile. See Placenta.

Axillary. In the axil of a leaf.

Axis. An imaginary line passing lengthwise through the centre of a plant or organ; also used generally of any structure, such as the main stem, on or immediately around the axis.

Basilar style. A style attached to the base and not the apex of the ovary. (Figs. 21, 49.)

Berry. In the botanical sense a fleshy indehiscent fruit in which the seeds are embedded directly in the pulp without any hard coat intervening (Fig. 46), but popularly used to indicate any small fleshy fruit.

Bifid. Dividing into two. (Figs. 11, 17.)

Bisexual. With stamens and pistil in the same flower. (Fig. 2.)

Bracts. Small leaves attached to the inflorescence. (*b*, Figs. 20, 21, 25, 48, 54.)

Campanulate. Bell-shaped, e.g. a gamopetalous corolla or gamosepalous calyx wider at the top than at the bottom. (Fig. 45.)

Capitate style. A style with a small knob or swelling at the end. (*c*, Fig. 33.)

Capitulum. An inflorescence of small sessile flowers crowded together on the swollen end (receptacle) of the common stalk. (Figs. 36, 37.)

Capsule. A dry dehiscent fruit developed from two or more carpels. (Figs. 14, 16.)

Carpel. One or more special ovule-bearing structures situated in the centre of the flower and considered to be morphologically a leaf which has become specialized for the production of seed. The carpels either remain separate (Figs. 3, 4, 7, 8) or coalesce to form a syncarpous pistil. (Figs. 30, 56.)

Catkin. A tail-like or brush-like inflorescence composed of unisexual flowers enclosed in scale-like bracts, the whole often falling off as one. (Fig. 51.)

Cauline. On the stem and not from the ground. (*c*, Fig. 9.)

Ciliate. Edged with long hairs like eyelashes.

Claw. When a petal ends in a long narrow base the latter is termed a claw. (*c*, Fig. 17.)

Conduplicate. Used of cotyledons folded round the radicle, thus: ⊆o.

Connate. Joined together at the base. (Fig. 33.)

Cordate. Heart-shaped. (Fig. 1.)

Corona. Appendages at the base of petals or perianth and together forming an upright ring round the centre of the flower. (*c*, Fig. 56.)

Corymb. A flattened raceme or panicle, i.e. a raceme or panicle in which the lowest flower-stalks or branches continue to grow until they reach approximately the same level as the terminal one: therefore the outer flowers of a corymb are the first to open. (Fig. 22.)

Crenate. With rounded teeth. (Fig. 14.)

Cyme. An inflorescence in which the main axis stops growing on the production of a flower, the growth being continued by the branches. This type of inflorescence is known as *definite*, as opposed to an *indefinite* one like a raceme, in which the main axis continues to grow. If a cymose inflorescence produces branches on all sides the oldest flowers will appear in the centre, not on the edges as in a corymb; or even at the bottom if the branches greatly exceed the original flower (Fig. 34). The branches may be produced on one side only (Fig. 45) or may straighten out, giving the appearance of a raceme. Actually a cyme is the reverse of a raceme, panicle, or corymb, though it may resemble them superficially.

Decumbent. Lying on or near the ground but rising at the apex.

Decurrent. When the blade or stalk of a leaf is continued down the side of the stem. (*d*, Fig. 45.)

Dehiscent. Opening to allow seeds to escape. (Figs. 10–12, 14, 16, 27.)

Dentate. With broad triangular teeth. (Fig. 5.)

Diadelphous. When the stamens are united by their filaments into two bundles, or, as in many Papilionaceae, one stamen free and the rest united.

Dichotomous. Dividing into two and again into two and so on. (Fig. 34.)

Didynamous. With stamens in two pairs of different lengths. (Figs. 44, 48, 49.)

Digitate. A compound leaf in which all the leaflets arise from the same point at the end of the common stalk. (Fig. 23.)

Dioecious. With the sexes on different plants.

Disc, disk. A lateral projection of the receptacle, sometimes merely a narrow ring (*d*, Fig. 18). Also used of the central part of a capitulum (see page 90).

Dorsally compressed. Used of a fruit of two carpels when the joining partition between the carpels is parallel to the greatest diameter of the fruit. (Figs. 11, 12, 30.)

Drupe. A fleshy indehiscent fruit in which the seed (kernel) is enclosed in a hard shell developed from the wall of the ovary, e.g. plum and cherry. (Fig. 28.)

Entire. Without teeth or lobes.

Epicalyx. A whorl of bracts immediately outside the true calyx. (*ep*, Fig. 20.)

Epigynous. When the attachment of the perianth and stamens is above the ovary. (Figs. 22, 26, 30.)

Epipetalous. When the stamens are attached to the petals and can be pulled away with them. (Figs. 29, 39, 56.)

Exserted. Used of stamens projecting beyond the corolla. (Fig. 41.)

Exstipulate. Without stipules.

Female flower. A flower having a pistil or ovary, without any stamens. (♀, Fig. 17.)

Filament. The thread-like part of the stamen bearing the anthers at its end. (*f*, Fig. 24.)

Florets. The individual flowers in a capitulum (Figs. 38, 39, 41 *f*, 42) or in the spikelet of a grass (Figs. 59, 60).

Follicle. The dry dehiscent carpel of an apocarpous fruit. (Figs. 7, 8.)

Free-central. See **Placenta**.

Frond. The leaf of a fern or other primitive plant, bearing reproductive organs on its surface. (Fig. 61.)

Gamopetalous, gamosepalous. With united petals (*g*, Fig. 45) or sepals (*g*, Fig. 17).

Glabrous. Without hairs.

Glands. Organs of secretion, usually small swellings on the tips of hairs (Fig. 26), surface of the leaves, &c.

Glaucous. Covered with pale green or white bloom.

Globose. Shaped like a globe, globular.

Glume. A chaffy bract, as in grasses. (*g*, Figs. 59, 60.)

Hastate. Halberd-shaped, i.e. with a pair of basal pointed lobes approximately at right angles to the stalk. (Fig. 52.)

Head. Flowers or fruits crowded together at the end of a common stalk. (Figs. 3, 33.)

Herb, herbaceous. Not woody.

Hispid. Covered with stiff erect hairs.

Hoary. Covered with short close hairs.

Hypogynous. When the attachment of the perianth and stamens is below the ovary or pistil. (Figs. 2, 6.)

Imbricate. Overlapping, like the tiles of a roof. (*i*, Fig. 42.)

Imparipinnate. Pinnate, with an odd terminal leaflet. (Figs. 25, 30.)

Incumbent. Used of cotyledons lying parallel, with their broad faces towards the radicle, thus: ‖o.

Indehiscent. Not opening to allow seeds to escape; the seed then reaches the ground in various ways: e.g. by the outer coverings of the fruit rotting or being eaten or by the seed growing through them. (Figs. 13, 22, 25, 28.)

Indusium. The covering over the cluster of spore cases in a fern. (*i*, Fig. 61.)

Involucre. One or more whorls of bracts immediately below a flower, fruit, or inflorescence. (*i*, Figs. 30, 36, 37, 41, 42.)

Irregular. Used of flowers which are not symmetrical in more than two directions. (Figs. 14, 19, 44, 47, 49, 55.)

Lanceolate. Lance-shaped, i.e. with curved edges narrowing at the base and apex and at least three times longer than broad. (Fig. 27.)

Laterally compressed. Used of a fruit of two carpels when the joining partition between the carpels is right angles to the greatest diameter of the fruit. (Figs. 10, 32.)

Ligulate. Strap-shaped. A ligulate floret has the petals united into a flat one-piece corolla. (Fig. 38.)

Ligule. A small appendage at the junction of a blade of grass with its sheath. (*l*, Figs. 59, 60.)

Linear. Long and very narrow, like a blade of grass.

Lips. The two main divisions of an irregular gamopetalous corolla, the upper forming a hood or shield for the stamens and the lower a platform on which insects alight (Figs. 44, 47, 49). In orchids the term *lip* is confined to the extension forward and downward of the lowest perianth segment. (*l*, Fig. 55.)

Lobed. Divided into segments, the spaces between which do not reach the axis or centre. (Figs. 18, 22.)

Lomentum. An indehiscent fruit breaking up into one-seeded sections, sometimes with only one section fully developed. (Fig. 13.)

Lyrate. A pinnatifid leaf in which the terminal lobe is the largest. (Figs. 9, 40.)

Male flower. A flower having stamens but with the pistil absent or rudimentary. (♂, Fig. 17.)

Monadelphous. With the filaments of the stamens joined together in one bundle.

Monoecious. With unisexual flowers and both sexes on the same plant.

Mucronate. Ending abruptly in a short stiff point. (*m*, Fig. 29.)

Nerves. The most prominent veins.

Nodes. Those parts of the stem, often thickened, from which the leaves issue.

Notched. Applied to petals which are shallowly bifid at the outer end. (Figs. 23, 25, 28.)

Nut. A dry one-seeded fruit produced from more than one carpel. (Figs. 51, 53.)

Oblanceolate. Inversely lanceolate, i.e. with the narrower end towards the point of attachment. (Fig. 54.)

Oblong. With sides nearly parallel except at the base and apex. (Fig. 50.)

Obovate. Inversely ovate, i.e. with the narrower end towards the point of attachment. (Figs. 28, 43.)

Obtuse. Round-ended or ending in an obtuse angle. (Fig. 43.)

Ochrea. A stipular growth completely surrounding the stem. (*o*, Fig. 50.)

Orbicular. Roughly circular. (Fig. 31.)

Ovate. Roughly egg-shaped, with the broader end towards the point of attachment. (Figs. 17, 51.)

Ovoid. Egg-shaped in three dimensions. (*o*, Fig. 25.)

Palmate. Arranged like the fingers of a hand, i.e. arising from approximately the same point and spreading outwards. (Leaf-veins or leaflets in Figs. 18, 21, 23, 31.)

Panicle. A branched raceme, i.e. a raceme in which the main axis sends off lateral branches which may themselves branch. (Figs. 50, 60.)

Papilionaceous. 'Butterfly-shaped', like the flower of a pea. (Fig. 19.)

Pappus. The hairs or bristles which replace the calyx in some Compositae and Valerianaceae. (*p*, Figs. 35, 42.)

Parietal. See Placenta.

Paripinnate. Pinnate without an odd terminal leaflet. (Fig. 19.)

Pedicel, peduncle. Flower stalk. The former term is usually applied to the stalk of a single flower in an inflorescence. (Fig. 45.)

Peltate. Attached to the stalk by the centre or one face, as in the leaf of a garden nasturtium. (Fig. 31.)

Perfect. Used of a flower having both stamens and pistil.

Perfoliate. Describes the condition where the stem appears to pass through the leaf-blade, usually caused by the blade of the leaf clasping the stem, or by the coalescing of two opposite leaf-blades. (Fig. 33.)

Perianth. The calyx and corolla, especially when one or other is absent, or when it is not easy to say which is which. (*p*, Fig. 6.)

Perigynous. With stamens and petals inserted on the calyx in a flower with a superior ovary. (Figs. 18, 24, 28.)

Persistent. Not falling off.

Petiole. The stalk of a leaf.

Pilose. Covered with long scattered hairs.

Pinna, plural **pinnae.** The leaflets of a pinnate leaf.

Pinnate. Arranged like the divisions of a feather or herring bone, i.e. arising from opposite sides of a common axis. Used of a compound leaf with pinnate leaflets. If the leaflets of a pinnate leaf are themselves simple the leaf is *simply pinnate, once pinnate,* or *1-pinnate* (Fig. 19.) If, however, they are divided into secondary pinnate leaflets the leaf is *bipinnate, twice pinnate,* or *2-pinnate* (Fig. 61), and so on.

Pinnatifid. Pinnately lobed. (Figs. 9, 22, 40, 42.)

Placenta. The particular part of the ovary on which the ovules are borne. The arrangement of the placentas, known as *placentation,* is of the greatest importance in classification. The three main kinds of placentation are: *parietal,* in which the placentas are situated on the outer walls of the ovary (Fig. 14); *axile,* in which the placentas are situated in the centre of an ovary of two or more cells, i.e. at the junction of the inner walls (Fig. 56); and *free-central,* in the centre of a one-celled ovary, i.e. without any inner walls. (Fig. 17.)

Pod. A dry dehiscent fruit developed from a single carpel. (Fig. 19.)

Polypetalous, polysepalous. With separate petals and sepals, so that each can be pulled off without disturbing the others or tearing the whole. When a flower drops its petals separately it is invariably polypetalous.

Pome. An indehiscent fruit derived from a syncarpous pistil which becomes completely embedded in a fleshy mass produced by the growth of the receptacle, e.g. apple, pear, and hawthorn. (Fig. 22.)

Procumbent. Spreading near the ground.

Prostrate. Lying on the ground.

Pubescent. Covered with soft short hairs, downy.

Raceme. An inflorescence of stalked flowers in which the main axis continues to grow, therefore the terminal flower is the last to be developed, the others appearing before and below it. (Figs. 9, 27.)

Radical. Growing direct from the root or rhizome, i.e. at ground-level. (Figs. 11, 36.)

Receptacle. The swollen head of the flower-stalk upon which the floral organs or, in the case of a capitulum, the flowers, are inserted. In many of the Rosaceae the receptacle develops into a cup enclosing the pistil while the stamens, petals, and sepals grow from the rim. (*r*, Figs. 2, 6, 22, 37.)

Recurved, reflexed, revolute. Curved downwards or backwards (*se*, Fig. 28.)

Regular. Used of a flower that is symmetrical in all directions. (Figs. 20, 22, 23, &c.)

Reniform. Kidney-shaped. (Fig. 49.)

Rhizome, rootstock. An underground, or partly underground, rooting stem. (*r*, Fig. 58.)

Rotate. Used of a gamopetalous corolla without or with a very small tube and having segments spreading in all directions. (*r*, Fig. 46.)

Runcinate. Pinnatifid, with lobes pointing backwards. (Fig. 40.)

Runners. Creeping and usually rooting branches of the stem. (*ru*, Figs. 23, 31.)

Saccate. Having a bag-like protuberance or pouch, i.e. a very short spur. (*s*, Fig. 47.)

Sagittate. Arrow-shaped, i.e. with two basal lobes or points directed backwards. (*s*, Figs. 9, 57.)

Samara. A dry indehiscent winged fruit. (Figs. 18, 51.)

Scape. The stalk of a flower or inflorescence growing direct from the ground and bare of leaves. (*s*, Figs. 11, 36.)

Scarious. Dry and papery, not green.

Scorpioid cyme. A cyme in which the subsequent flowers after the first develop on one side only, giving a curved or rolled-up appearance to the whole inflorescence. (Fig. 45.)

Serrate. With small fine teeth like a saw. (Figs. 20, 21, 25, 28, &c.)

Sessile. Without a stalk.

Silicula. A short and broad two-valved capsule divided by a thin partition on the edges of which the seeds are borne. (Figs. 9–11.)

Siliqua. Like a silicula but long and narrow. (Fig. 12.)

Sinuate. Indented by shallow rounded bays and not by teeth. (Figs. 18, 53.)

Solitary. Used of flowers when only one is found at the end of the stem or in the axil of a normal leaf. (Figs. 36, 44.)

Sorus. Cluster of spore-bearing organs in a fern.

Spadix. A fleshy spike of closely-packed flowers. (Fig. 57.)

Spathe. A large leaf-like bract enclosing or attached to a flower or inflorescence. (*sp*, Figs. 56, 57.)

Spathulate. Shaped like a spatula, i.e. broadest near the outer end and gradually narrowing to the base. (Fig. 36.)

Spike. A raceme of sessile flowers. (Figs. 48, 59.)

Spur. A hollow prolongation, usually slender, of a petal or sepal and often secreting honey. (*s*, Fig. 44.)

Stellate. Star-shaped, arranged like the rays or points of a star.

Stipules. Pair of appendages, often leaf-like, at the base of a leaf-stalk. (*s* Figs. 14, 19, 21, 28.)

Subulate. See Awl-shaped.

Syncarpous. Of united carpels. See Carpel.

Ternate. Used of a compound leaf with three leaflets. (Fig. 20.)

Tomentose. Completely covered with short matted hairs.

Tube. That part of a gamopetalous corolla or gamosepalous calyx below the lobes. (*t*, Figs. 39, 48, 56.)

Tubercle. A small rounded projection. (*t*, Fig. 50.)

Umbel. An inflorescence in which the flower-stalks all arise from one point. (Figs. 28, 30.)

Unisexual. With stamens and pistil in separate flowers. (Fig. 17.)

Urceolate. Pitcher-shaped, i.e. a corolla wider in the middle than above or below. (Fig. 43.)

Valvate. Side by side, not overlapping.

Valve. The sections into which a capsule separates to allow the seeds to escape. (*v*, Figs. 10, 12, 14.)

Viscid. Sticky.

Vittae. Oil tubes between the ribs on the fruit of most Umbelliferae. (*v*, Fig. 30.)

Wavy. Used of the margin of a leaf that is crinkled or folded in a vertical plane, as distinct from sinuate where the curvature is in a horizontal plane. (Fig. 50.)

Whorl. A group of three or more flowers, leaves, stems, or other organs arising from the same level on all sides of the main axis. (Fig. 29.)

Winged. With one or more thin flat projections.

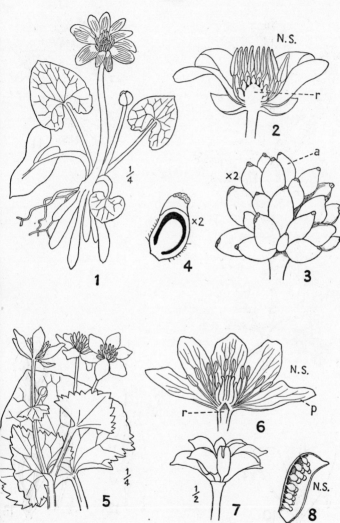

b

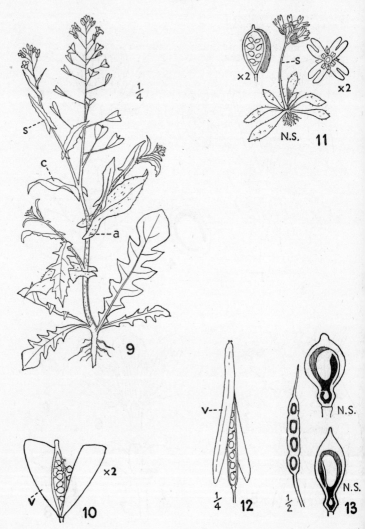

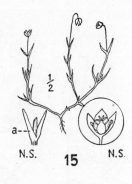

14

15

16

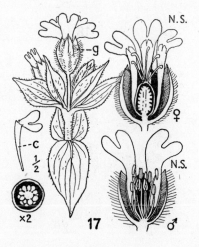

17

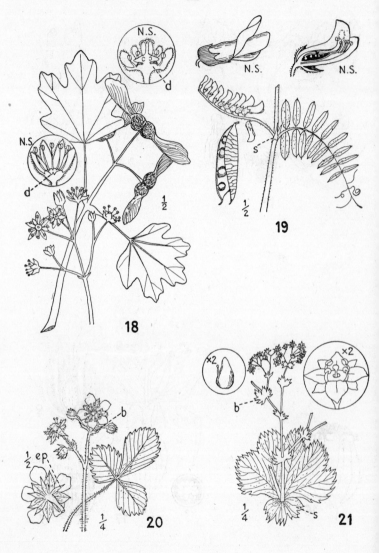

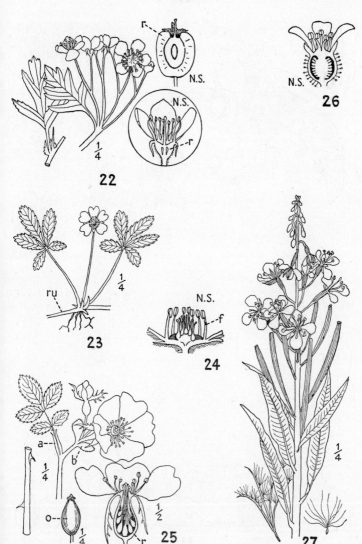

r

N.S.

N.S.

r

22

N.S.

26

ru

23

N.S.

f

24

a

b

o

r

25

r

27

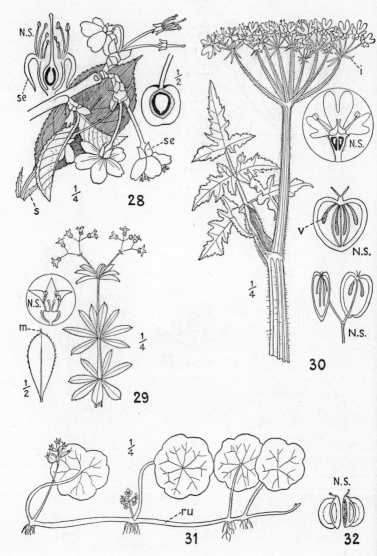

N.S.

se

½

se

28

s

i

N.S.

v

N.S.

N.S.

30

¼

N.S.

m

½

29

¼

¼

ru

31

N.S.

32

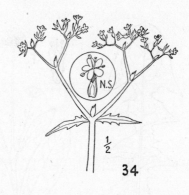

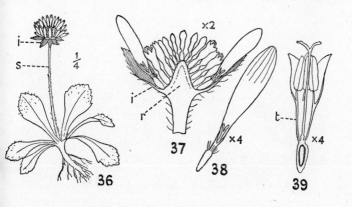

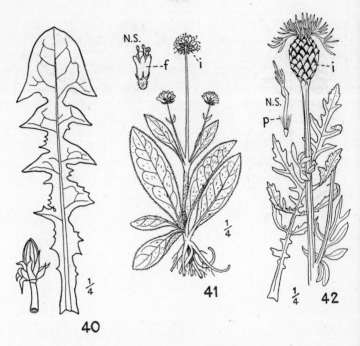

40

41

42

43

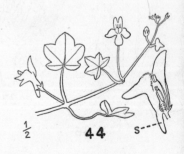

44

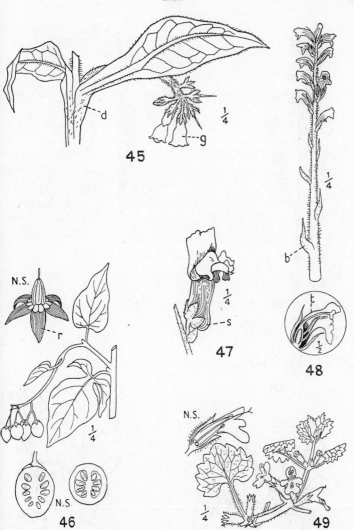

45

d

g   ¼

N.S.

r

¼

N.S.

46

47

s   ¼

48

t

½

b

¼

N.S.

¼   49

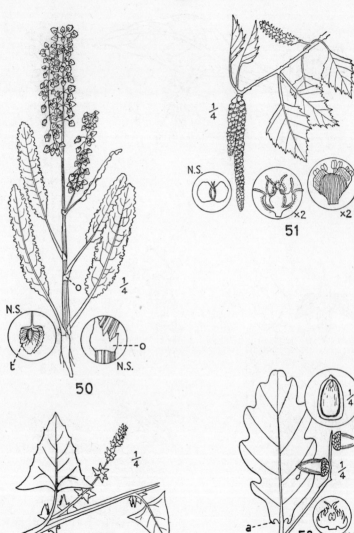

N.S.

×2

×2

51

N.S.

¼

o

¼

o

N.S.

50

t

52

¼

¼

¼

a

53

N.S.

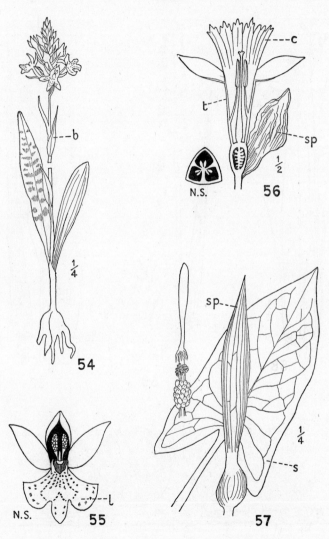

b

c

t

sp

N.S.

½

56

¼

54

sp

¼

s

N.S.

l

55

57

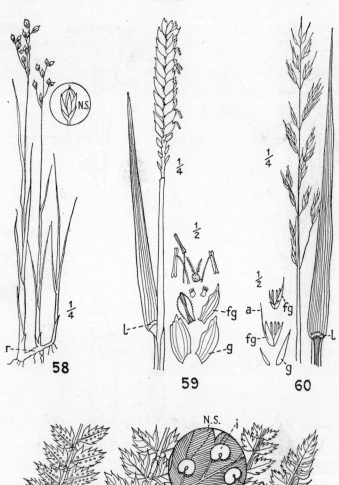

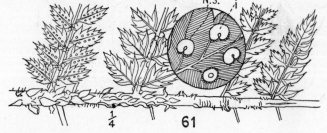

SYNOPSIS OF THE FAMILIES

I. *DICOTYLEDONS*

Leaves usually net-veined. Parts of the flower usually in fours or fives, some multiple of four or five, or a large indefinite number. Vascular bundles regularly arranged near the circumference of the stem. Cotyledons two.

A. POLYPETALAE

Flowers usually with calyx and corolla. Petals not united and the stamens seldom attached to them.

* *Stamens hypogynous* (THALAMIFLORAE)

1. **Ranunculaceae.** Page 19.
   (Buttercup Family.) Stamens usually numerous. Carpels usually several to many. Fruit of achenes or follicles.
2. **Berberidaceae.** Page 23.
   (Barberry Family.) Stamens six. Carpel one. Fruit a berry.
3. **Nymphaeaceae.** Page 23.
   (Water-lily Family.) Water plants with large floating leaves. Stamens numerous.
4. **Papaveraceae.** Page 24.
   (Poppy Family.) Sepals two, deciduous. Petals four. Stamens numerous. Fruit a capsule.
5. **Fumariaceae.** Page 25.
   (Fumitory Family.) Flowers small, irregular. Stamens six. Fruit a nut or capsule.
6. **Cruciferae.** Page 25.
   (Wallflower Family.) Flowers regular. Petals four. Stamens six, four long and two short. Fruit a two-valved capsule (siliqua or silicula) or lomentum.
7. **Resedaceae.** Page 35.
   (Mignonette Family.) Flowers small, irregular. Stamens numerous. Fruit a capsule.
8. **Cistaceae.** Page 35.
   (Rockrose Family.) Leaves opposite. Sepals five, three large and two very small. Petals five. Stamens numerous. Fruit a three-valved capsule.
9. **Violaceae.** Page 36.
   (Violet Family.) Leaves alternate, stipulate. Flowers irregular. Stamens five, the anthers more or less united into a tube. Fruit a three-valved capsule.
10. **Polygalaceae.** Page 37.
    (Milkwort Family.) Flowers irregular. Stamens eight, in two bundles. Fruit a flattened capsule.
11. **Frankeniaceae.** Page 37.
    (Sea-heath Family.) Heath-like shrub with small regular flowers. Stamens four to five. Placentation parietal. Fruit a capsule.

12. **Caryophyllaceae.**   Page 38.
    (Pink Family.) Herbs with opposite entire leaves and regular flowers. Stamens usually five or ten. Placentation free-central. Fruit a capsule.
13. **Portulaceae.**   Page 43.
    (Portulaca Family.) Herbs with opposite entire leaves. Sepals two. Placentation free-central. Fruit a three-valved capsule.
14. **Tamaricaceae.**   Page 44.
    (Tamarisk Family.) Trees or shrubs with minute alternate scale-like leaves. Stamens four to five. Fruit a capsule.
15. **Elatinaceae.**   Page 44.
    (Waterwort Family.) Leaves opposite, entire. Petals three or four. Stamens six or eight. Ovary with three or more cells. Fruit a capsule.
16. **Hypericaceae.**   Page 44.
    (St. John's Wort Family.) Leaves opposite, entire. Stamens numerous, in three or five bundles. Styles three or five. Placentation axile. Fruit a capsule.
17. **Malvaceae.**   Page 46.
    (Mallow Family.) Leaves alternate, palmately veined. Petals five, joined to the staminal tube. Stamens numerous, united into a tube. Fruit of numerous carpels arranged in a ring.
18. **Tiliaceae.**   Page 46.
    (Lime Family.) Trees with small regular flowers. Stamens numerous. Fruit a nut.
19. **Linaceae.**   Page 47.
    (Flax Family.) Leaves entire. Stamens four or five. Styles four or five, with capitate stigmas. Fruit a capsule.
20. **Geraniaceae.**   Page 47.
    (Crane's-bill Family.) Stamens five or ten. Fruit of five carpels with a persistent axis.

** *Stamens perigynous or epigynous, or attached to an outgrowth from the receptacle* (CALYCIFLORAE)

† *Ovary usually superior*

21. **Aquifoliaceae.**   Page 50.
    (Holly Family.) Evergreen shrubs with alternate leaves and small regular flowers. Sepals, petals, and stamens four or five. Fruit a drupe.
22. **Celastraceae.**   Page 51.
    (Spindle-tree Family.) Shrubs with opposite leaves and small regular flowers. Stamens four or five, inserted on a fleshy growth surrounding the ovary. Seeds attached to a fleshy aril.
23. **Rhamnaceae.**   Page 51.
    (Buckthorn Family.) Shrubs with small regular flowers. Stamens four or five, opposite the petals. Fruit a drupe.
24. **Aceraceae.**   Page 51.
    (Maple Family.) Trees or shrubs with opposite leaves and small regular flowers. Stamens eight, attached to a small growth surrounding the ovary. Fruit a double samara.

25. **Hippocastanaceae.** Page 52.
     (Horse Chestnut Family.) Trees or shrubs with opposite digitate leaves and showy irregular flowers. Fruit a leathery capsule.
26. **Papilionaceae.** Page 52.
     (Pea Family.) Flowers irregular. Stamens ten, filaments united. Carpel one. Fruit a pod.
27. **Rosaceae.** Page 60.
     (Rose Family.) Flowers regular. Stamens usually numerous, attached to the calyx.
28. **Saxifragaceae.** Page 67.
     (Saxifrage Family.) Flowers regular. Stamens eight or ten, attached to the calyx. Fruit a capsule.
29. **Ribesiaceae.** Page 69.
     (Gooseberry Family.) Shrubs with small regular flowers. Stamens five. Ovary inferior. Fruit a berry.
30. **Crassulaceae.** Page 70.
     (Stonecrop Family.) Leaves fleshy. Flowers regular. Carpels separate, superior. Fruit of follicles.
31. **Droseraceae.** Page 71.
     (Sundew Family.) Herbs with radical glandular leaves and small regular flowers. Stamens five, hypogynous. Fruit a capsule.
32. **Haloragaceae.** Page 71.
     (Marestail Family.) Water plants with opposite or whorled leaves and minute axillary flowers. Fruit a capsule or nut.
33. **Lythraceae.** Page 72.
     (Loosestrife Family.) Leaves opposite or whorled. Stamens six or twelve, attached to the calyx. Fruit a two-valved capsule.

†† *Ovary always inferior*

34. **Onagraceae.** Page 72.
     (Willow-herb Family.) Petals two or four. Stamens two, four, or eight. Fruit a capsule.
35. **Cucurbitaceae.** Page 74.
     (Cucumber Family.) Climbing or trailing plants with regular unisexual flowers. Fruit a berry.
36. **Umbelliferae.** Page 74.
     (Parsley Family.) Herbs with small regular flowers in umbels. Stamens five, styles two. Carpels two, separating in fruit.
37. **Araliaceae.** Page 83.
     (Ivy Family.) Woody plants with small regular flowers in umbels. Stamens five. Fruit a drupe.
38. **Cornaceae.** Page 84.
     (Dogwood Family.) Leaves opposite, entire. Petals four. Stamens four. Style one. Fruit a drupe.

B. GAMOPETALAE

Flowers usually with both calyx and corolla. Petals united.

* *Ovary inferior*

39. **Adoxaceae.** Page 84.
     (Moschatel Family.) Herbs with small green flowers. Stamens eight or ten. Fruit a berry.

40. **Caprifoliaceae.** Page 84.

    (Honeysuckle Family.) Woody plants with opposite leaves. Stamens five. Fruit a berry.

41. **Rubiaceae.** Page 86.

    (Bedstraw Family.) Herbs with whorled leaves and small regular flowers. Fruit a berry or pair of indehiscent carpels.

42. **Valerianaceae.** Page 88.

    (Valerian Family.) Leaves opposite. Flowers small, irregular. Stamens three or one. Fruit an achene, with pendulous seed.

43. **Dipsaceae.** Page 89.

    (Teasel Family.) Florets in an involucrate capitulum. Stamens four, anthers free. Fruit an achene, with pendulous seed.

44. **Compositae.** Page 90.

    (Daisy Family.) Florets in an involucrate capitulum. Stamens five, anthers united into a tube. Fruit an achene, with erect seed.

45. **Campanulaceae.** Page 107.

    (Harebell Family.) Stamens five, attached to the base of the corolla. Ovary 2–5-celled, placentation axile. Fruit a capsule.

46. **Vacciniaceae.** Page 109.

    (Whortleberry Family.) Woody plants with small nodding flowers. Calyx and corolla 4–5-lobed. Stamens twice as many as corolla lobes. Fruit a berry.

** *Ovary superior*

† *Stamens hypogynous or nearly so*

47. **Ericaceae.** Page 109.

    (Heather Family.) Stamens usually twice as many as corolla lobes. Style one. Fruit a capsule or berry.

48. **Plumbaginaceae.** Page 112.

    (Thrift Family.) Stamens five. Styles five. Fruit a nut.

†† *Stamens epipetalous*

49. **Primulaceae.** Page 112.

    (Primrose Family.) Herbs. Style one, with capitate stigma. Placentation free-central. Fruit a capsule.

50. **Oleaceae.** Page 115.

    (Privet Family.) Trees or shrubs with opposite leaves. Stamens two. Fruit a berry or samara.

51. **Apocynaceae.** Page 115.

    (Periwinkle Family.) Woody plants with opposite entire leaves. Sepals and petals five. Ovary of two separate carpels with one style. Fruit of follicles.

52. **Gentianaceae.** Page 115.

    (Gentian Family.) Herbs with regular showy flowers. Sepals, petals, and stamens four, five, or eight. Ovary one-celled, placentation parietal. Fruit a capsule.

53. **Polemoniaceae.** Page 116.

    (Phlox Family.) Stamens five. Ovary three-celled. Fruit a capsule.

54. **Boraginaceae.** Page 117.

> (Forget-me-not Family.) Herbs with rough alternate entire leaves. Stamens five. Ovary four-cleft, with basilar style. Fruit of four nutlets.

55. **Convolvulaceae.** Page 120.

> (Convolvulus Family.) Twining or trailing plants with alternate leaves (absent in *Cuscuta*) and funnel-shaped or bell-shaped flowers. Ovary with two to four cells. Fruit a capsule.

56. **Solanaceae.** Page 121.

> (Nightshade Family.) Leaves alternate. Sepals, petals, and stamens five. Ovary two-celled, with axile placentation. Fruit a berry or capsule.

57. **Scrophulariaceae.** Page 121.

> (Foxglove Family.) Stamens typically four, didynamous (five in Verbascum and two in Veronica). Ovary two-celled, with axile placentation. Fruit a capsule.

58. **Orobanchaceae.** Page 127.

> (Broomrape Family.) Brownish parasitic herbs. Flowers irregular. Stamens four, didynamous. Fruit a capsule.

59. **Lentibulariaceae.** Page 128.

> (Butterwort Family.) Marsh plants with irregular flowers. Stamens two. Placentation free-central. Fruit a capsule.

60. **Verbenaceae.** Page 129.

> (Vervain Family.) Leaves opposite. Stamens four, didynamous. Ovary with two or four cells, with one ovule in each cell. Fruit of four nutlets.

61. **Labiatae.** Page 129.

> (Deadnettle Family.) Leaves opposite. Stamens usually four and didynamous, rarely two. Ovary four-cleft, with basilar style. Fruit of four nutlets.

62. **Plantaginaceae.** Page 136.

> (Plantain Family.) Leaves radical. Flowers small, usually in spikes. Sepals, petals, and stamens four. Fruit a capsule or nut.

C. INCOMPLETAE

Flowers with only one perianth whorl (usually sepal-like) or none.[1] An artificial subdivision including all those dicotyledons not falling into A or B.

* *Flowers not in catkins*

(See also the anomalous families 81 and 82)

63. **Illecebraceae.** Page 137.

> (Knawel Family.) Low herbs with usually opposite entire leaves. Stamens five or less. Ovary superior, one-celled. Fruit a small nut.

64. **Chenopodiaceae.** Page 138.

> (Goosefoot Family.) Herbs with exstipulate and usually alternate leaves. Stamens five or less. Ovary superior, one-celled. Fruit of a single seed enclosed in a persistent perianth.

[1] One or both whorls of the perianth may be suppressed in some Polypetalae and Gamopetalae.

65. **Polygonaceae.** Page 141.
    (Dock Family.) Herbs with alternate leaves and ochreate stipules. Stamens five to eight. Ovary superior, one-celled. Fruit a small nut.

66. **Aristolochiaceae.** Page 144.
    (Birthwort Family.) Leaves alternate. Sepals three, stamens six or twelve. Ovary inferior, with three or six cells. Fruit a capsule.

67. **Thymeleaceae.** Page 145.
    (Daphne Family.) Woody plants with alternate exstipulate leaves. Stamens eight, inserted on the calyx tube. Ovary superior, one-celled. Fruit a drupe.

68. **Elaeagnaceae.** Page 145.
    (Sea-buckthorn Family.) Shrubs covered with silvery scales. Stamens four. Ovary superior. Fruit a berry.

69. **Loranthaceae.** Page 145.
    (Mistletoe Family.) Shrubby parasites on the branches of trees. Flowers unisexual. Fruit a berry.

70. **Santalaceae.** Page 146.
    (Sandalwood Family.) Parasites on the roots of other plants. Stamens four or five, opposite the sepals. Ovary inferior. Fruit a small nut.

71. **Euphorbiaceae.** Page 146.
    (Spurge Family.) Plants usually with milky juice. Flowers unisexual (apparently bisexual in Euphorbia). Ovary superior, with two or three cells. Fruit a capsule.

72. **Buxaceae.** Page 147.
    (Box Family.) Trees or shrubs with unisexual monoecious flowers. Stamens four. Ovary superior, styles three. Fruit a capsule.

73. **Ulmaceae.** Page 148.
    (Elm Family.) Trees with small bisexual flowers. Ovary superior, one-celled. Fruit a samara.

74. **Urticaceae.** Page 148.
    (Nettle Family.) Herbs with small unisexual flowers. Ovary superior, one-celled. Fruit an achene.

** ** *Male flowers, at least, in catkins* (AMENTIFERAE)

75. **Platanaceae.** Page 149.
    (Plane Family.) Trees with alternate palmately lobed leaves. Flowers unisexual, monoecious, in globular catkins. Fruit a mass of nutlets.

76. **Juglandaceae.** Page 149.
    (Walnut Family.) Trees with alternate aromatic leaves. Flowers monoecious. Fruit a large drupe.

77. **Myricaceae.** Page 149.
    (Sweet Gale Family.) Aromatic shrubs with alternate simple leaves. Flowers dioecious. Fruit a resinous nut.

78. **Betulaceae.** Page 150.
    (Birch Family.) Trees with monoecious flowers. Fruit winged, or a persistent woody cone, or a nut seated in a leafy cup.

79. **Fagaceae.** Page 151.
    (Beech Family.) Trees with monoecious flowers. Nut enclosed in a spiny husk or seated in a woody cup.
80. **Salicaceae.** Page 152.
    (Willow Family.) Trees with dioecious catkins. Fruit a two-valved capsule with tufted seeds.

*** *Flowers not in catkins* (Anomalous families)

81. **Empetraceae.** Page 154.
    (Crowberry Family.) Heath-like shrubs with unisexual flowers. Stamens three. Fruit a berry-like drupe.
82. **Ceratophyllaceae.** Page 155.
    (Hornwort Family.) Submerged aquatic herbs with whorled leaves and minute unisexual flowers. Stamens numerous. Fruit a small nut.

II. *MONOCOTYLEDONS*

Leaves usually parallel-veined. Parts of the flower usually in threes or some multiple of three. Vascular bundles irregularly arranged in the stem. Cotyledon one.

* *Ovary inferior*

83. **Hydrocharidaceae.** Page 155.
    (Frogbit Family.) Water plants with regular unisexual flowers. Petals three. Fruit indehiscent.
84. **Orchidaceae.** Page 156.
    (Orchid Family.) Flowers irregular. Stamens one or two, adhering to the pistil. Ovary one-celled, placentation parietal. Fruit a capsule.
85. **Iridaceae.** Page 160.
    (Iris Family.) Flowers regular. Stamens three. Ovary three-celled, placentation axile. Fruit a capsule.
86. **Amaryllidaceae.** Page 160.
    (Daffodil Family.) Flowers regular. Stamens six. Ovary three-celled, placentation axile. Fruit a capsule.
87. **Dioscoreaceae.** Page 161.
    (Black Bryony Family.) Twining plants with small unisexual flowers. Stamens six. Ovary three-celled. Fruit a berry.

** *Ovary superior*

88. **Liliaceae.** Page 161.
    (Lily Family.) Flowers regular. Stamens usually six. Ovary three-celled, placentation axile. Fruit a capsule or berry.
89. **Juncaceae.** Page 163.
    (Rush Family.) Stiff grass-like herbs with small brown flowers. Perianth of six calyx-like segments. Stamens six. Fruit a capsule.
90. **Typhaceae.** Page 166.
    (Reedmace Family.) Water or marsh plants with unisexual flowers in heads or spikes.

91. **Araceae.** Page 166.
> (Arum Family.) Flowers sessile on a spadix enclosed in or attached to a spathe. Fruit a berry.

92. **Lemnaceae.** Page 167.
> (Duckweed Family.) Tiny floating plants without stems. Stamen one, carpel one.

93. **Alismaceae.** Page 167.
> (Water-plantain Family.) Marsh or water plants with conspicuous flowers and numerous carpels. Fruit of achenes or follicles.

94. **Naiadaceae.** Page 168.
> (Pondweed Family.) Marsh or water plants. Flowers small, in spikes or axillary. Carpels several, distinct in fruit.

95. **Cyperaceae.** Page 170.
> (Sedge Family.) Grass-like or rush-like herbs with solid stems and entire sheaths. Flowers small, in spikes, each flower enclosed in one bract (glume). Fruit an achene.

96. **Gramineae.** Page 180.
> (Grass Family.) Stem hollow, swollen at the nodes; sheaths split on one side. Flowers small, in spikes or panicles, each flower enclosed in two or more bracts (glumes). Fruit an achene (caryopsis).

III. *GYMNOSPERMS*

Ovules borne on open carpels, i.e. not enclosed in an ovary. Style and stigma therefore none.

97. **Coniferae.** Page 192.
> (Pine Family.) Resinous trees or shrubs with needle-like leaves and unisexual flowers, the males in catkins.

IV. *CRYPTOGAMS*

Seedless plants. Reproduction by spores borne in spore-cases (sporangia).

98. **Filices.** Page 193.
> (Fern Family.) Herbs with underground stems and conspicuous aerial leaves bearing the sporangia.

99. **Equisetaceae.** Page 198.
> (Horsetail Family.) Herbs with hollow aerial stems and whorled branches. Sporangia in terminal spikes.

100. **Lycopodiaceae.** Page 199.
> (Clubmoss Family.) Creeping moss-like plants with minute leaves. Sporangia axillary.

101. **Isoetaceae.** Page 200.
> (Quillwort Family.) Submerged tufted plants. Sporangia radical.

102. **Marsiliaceae.** Page 200.
> (Pillwort Family.) Submerged plants with creeping stems. Sporangia radical.

ARTIFICIAL KEY TO THE FAMILIES

AND ANOMALOUS GENERA AND SPECIES

[*Names in square brackets indicate families and genera outside their proper class owing to the absence by suppression of some normal feature.*]

Flowering plants with seeds[1] (PHANEROGAMS) 2
Flowerless plants without seeds (CRYPTOGAMS) 144

   2 Ovules completely enclosed in an ovary usually with style and
      stigma (ANGIOSPERMS) 3
     Ovules not enclosed in an ovary, style and stigma none (GYMNO-
      SPERMS) . . . . . . **Coniferae** (p. 192)

   3 Leaves usually net-veined. Parts of the flower usually in fours
     or fives, some multiple of 4 or 5, or a large indefinite
     number.[2] (DICOTYLEDONS) 4
     Leaves usually parallel-veined.[3] Parts of the flower usually
     in threes or some multiple of 3.[4] (MONOCOTYLEDONS) . 112

I. *DICOTYLEDONS*[5]

   4 Corolla present or absent; if present, polypetalous, with
     stamens seldom attached to it 5
     Corolla nearly always present, gamopetalous, stamens usually
     attached to it[6] (GAMOPETALAE) 43

   5 Flowers with a corolla as well as a calyx (POLYPETALAE) . 6
     Flowers without a corolla though calyx, if present, sometimes
     petaloid (INCOMPLETAE) 81

A. POLYPETALAE

Corolla polypetalous

   6 Stamens more than twelve 7
     Stamens less than twelve 14

   7 Stamens united into a columnar tube . **Malvaceae** (p. 46)
     Stamens perigynous or epigynous . . **Rosaceae** (p. 60)
     Stamens hypogynous 8

   8 Petals more than sixteen, aquatic plants with floating
     leaves . . . . . **Nymphaeaceae** (p. 23)
     Petals normally less than sixteen 9

---

[1] The duckweeds (Lemnaceae) flower so rarely that it may be impossible without previous acquaintance with the family to recognize them as flowering plants.
[2] In some dicotyledons, e.g. Berberis, Lythrum, Rumex, Polygonum, the floral parts may be 6 or 9.
[3] Net-veined in the monocotyledons Arum, Tamus, and Paris.
[4] In some monocotyledons, e.g. Paris and Potamogeton, the floral parts are in fours.
[5] If the flowers are in an involucrate capitulum having the appearance of a single flower, e.g. daisy and dandelion, refer to 75.
[6] Apparently gamopetalous in Trifolium, Polygala, and Malvaceae. Do not mistake coloured sepals for petals.

9	Pistil apocarpous	**Ranunculaceae** (p. 19)
	Pistil syncarpous	10
10	Flowers irregular	**Resedaceae** (p. 35)
	Flowers regular	11
11	Sepals two, deciduous . . .	**Papaveraceae** (p. 24)
	Sepals five, usually persistent . .	12
12	A tree, flowers in small clusters attached to a long leaf-like bract	**Tilia** (p. 46)
	Herb or shrub	13
13	Style one, sepals unequal . .	**Cistaceae** (p. 35)
	Styles three or five, sepals equal .	**Hypericaceae** (p. 44)
14	Pistil apocarpous	15
	Pistil syncarpous	17
15	Carpels numerous . . .	**Ranunculaceae** (p. 19)
	Carpels two to twelve	16
16	Carpels superior . . .	**Crassulaceae** (p. 70)
	Carpels inferior (enclosed in calyx tube) .	**Rosaceae** (p. 60)
17	Flowers irregular	18
	Flowers regular or nearly so . .	21
18	Stamens ten, filaments joined together to form a tube round the ovary, flowers papilionaceous .	**Papilionaceae** (p. 52)
	Stamens eight, in two bundles of four each	**Polygalaceae** (p. 37)
	Stamens six, in two bundles of three each	**Fumariaceae** (p. 25)
	Stamens five, free	19
19	Flowers in umbels, ovary inferior .	**Umbelliferae** (p. 74)
	Flowers not in umbels, ovary superior .	20
20	Leaves stipulate	**Violaceae** (p. 36)
	Leaves exstipulate	**Impatiens** (p. 50)
21	Plant not green (leaves reduced to scales)	**[Monotropa]** (p. 111)
	Leaves all radical, long-stalked and covered with long glandular bristles . . .	**Droseraceae** (p. 71)
	Plant not having all the above characters	22
22	Stamens six, four long and two short; calyx and corolla 4-partite	**Cruciferae** (p. 25)
	Plant without the above characters . .	23
23	Prostrate shrubby heath-like plant . .	24
	Tree or shrub	25
	Herb	34
24	Flowers unisexual, fruit a berry .	**[Empetraceae]** (p. 154)
	Flowers bisexual, fruit a capsule .	**Frankeniaceae** (p. 37)
25	Ovary superior	26
	Ovary inferior	32
26	Leaves compound, digitate .	**Hippocastanaceae** (p. 52)
	Leaves simple	27
27	Leaves palmately lobed, opposite .	**Aceraceae** (p. 51)
	Leaves without both the above characters together .	28

28 Leaves minute, scale-like . . . Tamaricaceae (p. 44)
   Leaves not minute and scale-like 29

29 Stem with spines in threes . . . Berberis (p. 23)
   Stem without spines, or spines solitary . . . 30

30 Stamens opposite the minute petals . . Rhamnaceae (p. 51)
   Stamens alternate with the petals 31

31 Leaves opposite, finely toothed . . . Euonymus (p. 51)
   Leaves alternate, usually with large spiny teeth . Ilex (p. 50)

32 Petals four, leaves opposite . . . . Cornus (p. 84)
   Petals five, leaves alternate 33

33 Climbing by aerial roots . . . . Hedera (p. 83)
   Not climbing . . . . . . Ribes (p. 69)

34 Ovary superior 35
   Ovary inferior 41

35 Sepals two . . . . . Portulaceae (p. 43)
   Sepals six to twelve (intermediate ones often very
    small) . . . . . Lythraceae (p. 72)
   Sepals three to five (sometimes divided) . . 36

36 Leaves in a whorl of four . . . [Paris] (p. 163)
   Leaves compound or distinctly lobed . Geraniaceae (p. 47)
   Leaves simple 37

37 Leaves opposite 38
   Leaves alternate or radical 40

38 Ovary and capsule one-celled, styles not capitate . . . . . Caryophyllaceae (p. 38)
   Ovary and capsule several-celled, styles capitate . 39

39 Water plant . . . . . Elatinaceae (p. 44)
   Land plant . . . . . Linaceae (p. 47)

40 Style one . . . . . [Pyrola] (p. 111)
   Styles two or absent . . . Saxifragaceae (p. 67)
   Styles five . . . . . Linaceae (p. 47)

41 Petals two or four, fruit a capsule . . Onagraceae (p. 72)
   Petals four, fruit a berry . . . . Cornus (p. 84)
   Petals five 42

42 Flowers in umbels . . . . Umbelliferae (p. 74)
   Flowers not in umbels . . . Saxifragaceae (p. 67)

B. GAMOPETALAE
Corolla gamopetalous

43 Ovary superior 44
   Ovary inferior 70

44 Stamens more numerous than the corolla lobes . . 45
   Stamens equal in number to the corolla lobes or fewer 47

45 Flowers irregular 18
   Flowers regular 46

46 Pistil apocarpous, leaves succulent . . [Cotyledon] (p. 70)
   Pistil syncarpous, leaves not succulent . Ericaceae (p. 109)

47 Style basilar from four-cleft ovary 48
   Style terminal or absent 49

48 Leaves all opposite, aromatic; flowers usually irregular and
   in whorls . . . . **Labiatae** (p. 129)
   Leaves mostly alternate, roughly hairy; flowers regular and
   in scorpioid cymes . . . . . **Boraginaceae** (p. 117)

49 Stamens three . . . .[Montia] (p. 44)
   Stamens five 50
   Stamens two, four, six, or eight 59

50 Styles five . . . . . **Plumbaginaceae** (p. 112)
   Style one 51

51 Twining   or   prostrate   plant   with   alternate
   leaves . . . . . . **Convolvulaceae** (p. 120)
   Plant not twining, or prostrate with opposite leaves . . 52

52 Stamens opposite the corolla lobes . . **Primulaceae** (p. 112)
   Stamens alternate with the corolla lobes 53

53 Leaves opposite 54
   Leaves alternate 56

54 Trailing plant with evergreen leaves; ovary double, with one
   style . . . . **Apocynaceae** (p. 115)
   Ovary single 55

55 Procumbent   evergreen   shrub   with   very   small
   leaves . . . . **Loiseleuria** (p. 111)
   Herb . . . . . . **Gentianaceae** (p. 115)

56 Water plant . . . . . . **Gentianaceae** (p. 115)
   Land plant 57

57 Leaves pinnately compound . . **Polemonium** (p. 117)
   Leaves simple 58

58 Petals yellow . . . . . . **Verbascum** (p. 122)
   Petals not yellow, or yellow with a network of purple
   veins . . . . **Solanaceae** (p. 121)

59 Tree or shrub 60
   Herb 61

60 Stamens two . . . . . . **Oleaceae** (p. 115)
   Stamens four . . . . . [Aquifoliaceae] (p. 50)

61 Stamens two 62
   Stamens more than two 63

62 Petals four, corolla rotate . . . **Veronica** (p. 124)
   Petals five, corolla spurred . . **Lentibulariaceae** (p. 128)

63 Stamens of equal length 64
   Stamens didynamous 68

64 Leaves all radical 65
   Cauline leaves present 66

65 Stamens longer than corolla . . **Plantaginaceae** (p. 136)
   Stamens shorter than corolla . . . **Limosella** (p. 124)

66 Leaves opposite . . . . **Gentianaceae** (p. 115)
   Leaves alternate 67

67 Leaves minute, entire . . . **Centunculus** (p. 114)
  Leaves not minute, crenate . . . **Sibthorpia** (p. 124)
68 Leafless brownish plant . . . **Orobanchaceae** (p. 127)
  Leaves green 69
69 Corolla regular or nearly so . . . **Verbena** (p. 129)
  Corolla irregular . . . **Scrophulariaceae** (p. 121)
70 Cauline leaves whorled . . . **Rubiaceae** (p. 86)
  Cauline leaves, if any, not whorled 71
71 Shrubby 72
  Herbaceous 73
72 Stamens five . . . . . **Caprifoliaceae** (p. 84)
  Stamens eight or ten . . . **Vacciniaceae** (p. 109)
73 Climber . . . . . **Cucurbitaceae** (p. 74)
  Not a climber 74
74 Flowers in an involucrate capitulum 75
  Flowers not in an involucrate capitulum . . . 78
75 Anthers united 76
  Anthers free 77
76 Anthers united into a tube round the style, fruit an
    achene . . . . **Compositae** (p. 90)
  Anthers united at base only, fruit a capsule **Jasione** (p. 107)
77 Stamens four . . . . . **Dipsaceae** (p. 89)
  Stamens five . . . . . **Phyteuma** (p. 107)
78 Stamens three or one . . . **Valerianaceae** (p. 88)
  Stamens eight or ten . . . **Adoxaceae** (p. 84)
  Stamens five 79
79 Leaves compound . . . . **Sambucus** (p. 84)
  Leaves simple 80
80 Stamens inserted at base of corolla tube **Campanulaceae** (p. 107)
  Stamens inserted on sides of corolla tube . **Samolus** (p. 114)

C. INCOMPLETAE

Corolla absent

81 Calyx present (sometimes petaloid) 82
  Calyx absent, perianth completely wanting or reduced to
    minute scales 105
82 Parasite on trees . . . **Loranthaceae** (p. 145)
  Flowers unisexual, though the two kinds of flowers may be
    near together 83
  Flowers bisexual, with both pistil and stamens in the same
    calyx 91
83 Aquatics with opposite or whorled leaves [**Haloragaceae**] (p. 71)
  Land plants; or aquatics with alternate leaves . . 84
84 Herbs 85
  Tree, shrub, or shrubby plant 90

85 Stipules ochreate . . . . **Rumex (p. 143)**
    Stipules not ochreate, or none 86

86 Climbing plant with opposite, palmately lobed
    leaves . . . . . . **Humulus (p. 148)**
    Not climbing 87

87 Stamens five or less 88
    Stamens nine or more 89

88 Stamens five . . . . . **Atriplex (p. 140)**
    Stamens four . . . . . **Urticaceae (p. 148)**

89 Leaves pinnately compound . . . **[Poterium] (p. 65)**
    Leaves simple . . . . . **Euphorbiaceae (p. 146)**

90 Leaves with silvery scales on under side, branches often
    spiny . . . . . . **Hippophae (p. 145)**
    Procumbent heath-like shrub . . **Empetraceae (p. 154)**
    Leaves broad, glossy green on both sides . **Buxaceae (p. 147)**

91 Pistil of two or more separate carpels 92
    Pistil syncarpous or of one carpel 93

92 Stamens hypogynous . . . **[Ranunculaceae] (p. 19)**
    Stamens perigynous or epigynous . . **[Rosaceae] (p. 60)**

93 Ovary superior 94
    Ovary inferior 103

94 Style one or none 95
    Styles more than one 99

95 Shrub or tree 96
    Herb 97

96 Stamens eight . . . . . **Daphne (p. 145)**
    Stamens four or five . . . . **[Rhamnus] (p. 51)**

97 All the leaves toothed or lobed . . . **[Rosaceae] (p. 60)**
    Leaves, at least the upper ones, entire . . . 98

98 Stamens two . . . . . **[Lepidium] (p. 33)**
    Stamens six . . . . . **[Lythraceae] (p. 72)**
    Stamens four or five . . . **[Primulaceae] (p. 112)**

99 Tree or shrub with opposite palmately lobed
    leaves . . . . . **[Aceraceae] (p. 51)**
    Tree with alternate leaves . . **Ulmaceae (p. 148)**
    Herb 100

100 Stipules ochreate . . . . **Polygonaceae (p. 141)**
    Stipules not ochreate, or none 101

101 Leaves, at least some of them, alternate **Chenopodiaceae (p. 138)**
    Leaves all opposite 102

102 Capsule several-seeded . . . **[Caryophyllaceae] (p. 38)**
    Capsule one-seeded . . . **Illecebraceae (p. 137)**

103 Aquatics with whorled leaves . . **[Haloragaceae] (p. 71)**
    Leaves not whorled 104

104 Leaves compound or palmately lobed . . **[Rosaceae] (p. 60)**
    Leaves linear . . . . . **Thesium (p. 146)**
    Leaves broad, cordate, entire . . **Aristolochiaceae (p. 144)**
    Leaves broad, with tapering base . **[Chrysosplenium] (p. 69)**

105 Leaves opposite or whorled 106
    Leaves alternate 108
106 Tree with pinnately compound leaves . [Fraxinus] (p. 115)
    Aquatic plant 107
107 Leaves entire or pinnately lobed . [Haloragaceae] (p. 71)
    Leaves toothed . . . Ceratophyllaceae (p. 155)
108 Leaves pinnately compound . . . Juglans (p. 149)
    Leaves palmately lobed . . . Platanus (p. 149)
    Leaves simple, pinnately veined or lobed . . . 109
109 Shrub with exstipulate strongly aromate leaves Myrica (p. 150)
    Leaves stipulate, not aromatic 110
110 Dioecious . . . . . Salicaceae (p. 152)
    Monoecious 111
111 Fruit with woody involucre or husk . . Fagaceae (p. 151)
    Fruit without woody involucre or husk . Betulaceae (p. 150)

II. *MONOCOTYLEDONS*

112 Floating or submerged aquatics 113
    Erect aquatics or land plants 129

(a) FLOATING OR SUBMERGED AQUATICS

(As a water habitat tends to blot out the differences between the various classes of vegetation, this section of the key covers those dicotyledonous and cryptogamic plants which might, owing to their minute or otherwise anomalous flowers, be easily mistaken for monocotyledons.)[1]

113 Minute free-floating frondose plants seldom exceeding ¼ inch
        across . . . . . Lemnaceae (p. 167)
    Plants distinctly differentiated into stem and leaves . . 114
114 Leaves all radical 115
    Cauline leaves present 119
115 Leaves broad or toothed . Hydrocharidaceae (p. 155)
    Leaves linear, entire 116
116 Rootstock creeping . . . [Pilularia] (p. 200)
    Rootstock not creeping 117
117 Leaves subulate, about ½ inch long . [Subularia] (p. 31)
    Leaves often more or less flattened and longer . . 118
118 Leaves swollen at their bases and containing sporan-
        gia . . . . . [Isoetes] (p. 200)
    Leaves not swollen at their bases and not containing
        sporangia . . . . . [Littorella] (p. 137)
119 Leaves whorled 120
    Leaves not whorled 122

[1] Aquatic dicotyledons with conspicuous flowers are not covered by this section, though their submerged portions may possibly be mistaken for lower plants. The only way they can be recognized is to see them in flower.

120 Leaves forked . . . [Ceratophyllum] (p. 155)
    Leaves pinnately divided . . [Myriophyllum] (p. 71)
    Leaves not divided 121

121 Leaves about ½ inch long, flat, crowded, in whorls of
    three . . . . . . Elodea (p. 155)
    Leaves long, linear, not crowded, in whorls of five or
    more . . . . [Chara¹]

122 Leaves opposite, seldom exceeding one inch . . 123
    Leaves opposite or alternate, mostly much longer . 126

123 Surface leaves in a rosette, lower leaves linear, stamen
    one . . . . . [Callitriche] (p. 72)
    Surface leaves not in a rosette, leaves all spathulate, stamens
    three to six 124

124 Flowers white, petals 5, stamens 3 . . .[Montia] (p. 44)
    Flowers pink or green, stamens 6 125

125 Petals three, pink . . .[Elatine hexandra] (p. 44)
    Petals absent or very minute . . [Peplis] (p. 72)

126 Linear leaves all submerged; floating leaves, if any, ovate or
    oblong . . . . . Naiadaceae (p. 168)
    Linear leaves floating on the surface of the water . . 127

127 Leaves cylindrical, hollow . . Juncus bulbosus (p. 165)
    Leaves flat 128

128 Flowers in sessile globose heads . Sparganium (p. 166)
    Flowers in solitary terminal spikelets . Scirpus fluitaus (p. 172)

(b) ERECT AQUATIC OR TERRESTRIAL MONO-
COTYLEDONS

129 Flowers on a spadix inside or attached to a large leaf-like
    spathe . . . . . Araceae (p. 166)
    Spathe none, or if present, spadix none . . . 130

130 Ovary inferior, perianth distinct 131
    Ovary superior 136

131 Climber with broad net-veined leaves Dioscoreaceae (p. 161)
    Not a climber 132

132 Leaves toothed . . . . Stratiotes (p. 155)
    Leaves entire 133

133 Flowers irregular, ovary 1-celled . Orchidaceae (p. 156)
    Flowers regular, ovary 2-3-celled . . . 134

134 Flowers on a spadix . . . . Acorus (p. 167)
    Flowers not on a spadix 135

135 Stamens three . . . . Iridaceae (p. 160)
    Stamens six . . . . Amaryllidaceae (p. 160)

136 Perianth present 137
    Perianth absent or merely of scales or hairs . . 141

¹ An alga; not included in this flora.

137 Perianth of eight narrow segments; leaves broad, in a single
    whorl .   .   .   .   **Paris** (p. 163)
    Perianth of four segments   .   **Potamogeton** (p. 169)
    Perianth of six segments .   .   138
138 Ovary apocarpous   139
    Ovary syncarpous .   .   .   140
139 Perianth petaloid .   .   **Alismaceae** (p. 167)
    Perianth calyx-like .   .   **Triglochin** (p. 168)
140 Perianth petaloid .   .   **Liliaceae** (p. 161)
    Perianth calyx-like, chaffy .   **Juncaceae** (p. 163)
141 Flowers enclosed by chaffy bracts (glumes) .   . 142
    Flowers in dense heads or spike, without bracts . 143
142 Leaf-sheath split on one side; each flower enclosed in two or
    more bracts .   .   .   **Gramineae** (p. 180)
    Leaf-sheath not split; each flower enclosed in one
    bract .   .   .   **Cyperaceae** (p. 170)
143 Fruit a berry, leaves usually broad .   **Araceae** (p. 166)
    Fruit dry, leaves linear .   .   **Typhaceae** (p. 166)

III. *GYMNOSPERMS*

Ovules not enclosed in an ovary, style and stigma none
                               Coniferae (p. 192)

IV. *CRYPTOGAMS*

144 Plants with underground stems and large aerial
    leaves .   .   .   .   **Filices** (p. 193)
    Plants with minute leaves on aerial or partly submerged stems 145
    Plants usually submerged, with long cylindrical or subulate
    leaves with spore-cases at their bases .   147
145 Stems creeping or decumbent, rooting at the
    base .   .   .   **Lycopodiaceae** (p. 199)
    Stem erect; branches, if present, whorled .   146
146 Stem hollow, jointed, with a toothed sheath at each joint,
    fructification in a terminal spike . **Equisetaceae** (p. 198)
    Stem with crowded whorls of leaves, flowers axil-
    lary .   .   .   **[Hippuris]** (p. 71)
147 Stem creeping, spore-cases conspicuous . **Pilularia** (p. 200)
    Stem not creeping, spore-cases concealed by the leaf-
    bases .   .   .   **Isoetes** (p. 200)

Family 1. RANUNCULA'CEAE

Perianth segments free. Stamens usually numerous (few in *Myosurus*), hypogynous. Pistil superior, apocarpous.

Climbing shrub with opposite leaves . . . Clematis I
Herb with alternate or radical leaves . . . 2

  2 Carpels one-seeded, fruit of achenes . . . 3
    Carpels several-seeded, fruit of follicles . . . 7

  3 Carpels in a long spike; leaves radical, linear . . Myosurus V
    Carpels in a globular or cylindrical head . . 4

  4 Perianth of distinct sepals and petals . . . 5
    Perianth segments all alike 6

  5 Flowers red . . . . . Adonis IV
    Flowers yellow or white . . . Ranunculus VI

  6 Flowers small, in panicles or racemes . . Thalictrum II
    Flowers large, solitary . . . . Anemone III

  7 Flowers irregular 8
    Flowers regular 9

  8 Perianth spurred . . . . Delphinium XI
    Perianth not spurred . . . . Aconitum XII

  9 Perianth spurred . . . . Aquilegia X
    Perianth not spurred 10

10 Flowers green or greenish yellow . . . Helleborus IX
    Flowers bright yellow 11

11 Leaves compound or deeply divided . . Trollius VIII
    Leaves with shallow lobes or none . . Caltha VII

I. *CLEM'ATIS*

C. Vital'ba L. 79. Traveller's Joy, Old Man's Beard. July–Aug. Shrubby. Climbing by petioles. Leaves opposite, compound, pinnate, leaflets often coarsely toothed or lobed. Flowers small, greenish-white, in panicles; perianth segments 4–6; carpels numerous, developing into achenes each with a long feathery persistent style. *Hedges on calcareous soil; common, especially in the south.*

II. *THALIC'TRUM*

Leaves compound. Perianth segments 4–5, shorter than the conspicuous stamens. Achenes few, furrowed, without long appendages.

Plant not exceeding 6 inches, flowers in a simple raceme   T. alpinum
Plant 1 foot or more, flowers in a panicle 2

2 Flowers mostly drooping, leaflets as broad as long . T. minus
  Flowers mostly erect, leaflets longer than broad . T. flavum

T. alpi'num L. 30. Alpine Meadow-rue. June–Aug. Leaves mostly radical. Flowers in a raceme on a simple stem. *Mountains in the north.*

T. mi′nus L. 69. Lesser Meadow-rue. June–Aug. Leaflets small, roundish. Flowers drooping, in a broad panicle. *On dry limestone, rare but locally abundant.*

T. fla′vum L. 76. Common Meadow-rue. June–Aug. Leaflets large, narrow, acute. Flowers erect, in compact panicles. *Damp meadows, frequent.*

III. *ANEM′ONE*

Leaves compound, long-stalked. Flowers solitary, long-stalked, with a leafy involucre some distance below the flower; perianth segments usually 6, white or coloured, longer than the stamens. Achenes numerous.

A. Pulsatil′la L. 19. Pasque-flower. April–June. Flowers large, purple, silky outside. Achenes with long feathery awns. *On chalk and limestone, rare.*

A. nemoro′sa L. 109. Wood Anemone, Wind Flower. March–May. Flowers white. Awns not feathery. *Woods, common.*

IV. *ADO′NIS*

A. an′nua L. (A. autumna′lis L.) 11. Pheasant's-eye. June–Sept. Leaves dissected into linear segments. Flowers solitary; sepals 5, green or reddish; petals 5–8, scarlet with dark spot at base. Fruit a cylindrical head of rather large achenes. *Cornfields, rare.*

V. *MYOSU′RUS*

M. min′imus L. 44. Mousetail. April–June. Leaves radical, linear, entire. Flowers small, yellowish-green, radical, long-stalked; sepals 5, shortly spurred; petals 5, very narrow; achenes in a long spike. *Damp places, rare.*

VI. *RANUN′CULUS*

Flowers white or yellow; sepals 3–5, petals 5–9 or more each with a nectary at its base; carpels 1-seeded, numerous. Fruit a globular or cylindrical head of beaked achenes.

Flowers white	2
Flowers yellow	4

2 Aquatic plant with finely divided submerged leaves   R. aquatilis
   Plants of wet places without finely divided leaves . . . 3

3 Petals about as long as sepals, lobes of leaf widest at
   base . . . . R. hederaceus
   Petals twice as long as sepals, lobes of leaf not widest at
   base . . . . R. Lenormandi

4 Leaves not compound or markedly lobed 5
   Leaves compound or distinctly lobed 7

5 Leaves cordate; sepals 3, petals 6–9 or more, root tuberous   R. Ficaria
   Leaves lanceolate 6

6 Leaves stalked, peduncles furrowed . . . R. Flammula
   Leaves sessile, peduncles not furrowed . . R. Lingua

7 Carpels covered with tubercles or prickles 8
  Carpels smooth or tuberculate only at edge 9

8 Carpels prickly, leaves glabrous . . . . R. arvensis
  Carpels tuberculate, leaves hairy . . . . R. parviflorus

9 Sepals reflexed 10
  Sepals spreading 12

10 Petals very small, carpels in a conical or cylindrical head R. sceleratus
   Petals conspicuous, carpels in a globular head . . . 11

11 Flowers bright glossy yellow, carpels without tubercles, rootstock
     bulbous . . . . R. bulbosus
   Flowers pale yellow, carpels tuberculate at edge . R. sardous

12 Stems creeping, terminal leaf segment stalked . R. repens
   Stem not creeping, leaf segments all sessile . . . 13

13 Plant hairy, achenes glabrous . . . . . R. acris
   Plant glabrous or nearly so, achenes downy . . R. auricomus

R. aquat'ilis L. 89. Water Crowfoot. May–Aug. Leaves mostly
finely cut into linear segments, but the floating leaves, if any, are
deeply divided into broad lobes. Flowers white, solitary, axillary.
Ponds and streams, common.

R. Lenorman'di F. Schultz. 61. Ivy-leaved Water Crowfoot. April–
Sept. Leaves all reniform or shallowly lobed, the lobes narrowing at
the base. Flowers white, petals twice as long as sepals. *Wet mud,
frequent.*

R. hedera'ceus L. 112. Ivy-leaved Water Crowfoot. April–Sept.
Like the preceding species, but lobes of leaves broadest at base and
petals about as long as sepals. *Wet mud, common.*

R. sclera'tus L. 102. Celery-leaved Crowfoot. May–Sept. Glabrous.
Stem thick and hollow. Leaves deeply divided. Flowers yellow, very
small. Carpels in a conical or cylindrical head. *Wet places, frequent.*

R. Flamm'ula L. 112. Lesser Spearwort. June–Sept. Stem decumbent, rooting at base. Lower leaves ovate, long-stalked, upper lanceolate or linear. Flowers yellow, peduncles furrowed. *Marshy ground,
common.*

R. Lin'gua L. 82. Greater Spearwort. June–Sept. Stem with runners.
All the leaves lanceolate, sessile or nearly so. Flowers large, yellow,
peduncles not furrowed. *Marshy ground, occasional.*

R. auri'comus L. 91. Goldilocks. April–June. Glabrous or nearly
so. Radical leaves orbicular or reniform. Flowers bright yellow;
achenes downy. *Woods and hedgebanks, frequent.*

R. a'cris L. 112. Acrid Buttercup. May–Oct. Tall hairy plant.
Lower leaves long-stalked, deeply divided into palmate segments;
upper ones short-stalked or sessile, divided into a few linear segments.
Flowers large, bright yellow, sepals spreading, peduncle not furrowed.
Achenes glabrous. *Meadows and waysides, common.*

R. re'pens L. 112. Creeping Buttercup. April–Sept. Differs from *R. acris* chiefly in its creeping runners and furrowed peduncles. Leaves ternate, with broad segments, the middle one stalked. *Meadows and waysides, common, usually in damper places than R. acris.*

R. bulbo'sus L. 109. Bulbous Buttercup. April–June. Distinguished from the two preceding species by its bulbous rootstock, reflexed sepals, and smaller leaves. *Meadows, common.*

R. sardo'us Crantz (**R. hirsu'tus** Curtis). 82. Pale Hairy Buttercup. June–Oct. Like the preceding species but the flowers are much smaller and of a paler yellow. Carpels tuberculate near the edge. *Cornfields and waste places, occasional.*

R. parviflo'rus L. 62. Small-flowered Buttercup. May–July. Hairy. Stems weak, prostrate or ascending. Radical leaves orbicular or reniform, lobed or toothed. Flowers very small. Carpels covered with small tubercles. *Meadows and waste places, occasional.*

R. arven'sis L. 74. Corn Buttercup. May–Aug. Glabrous or nearly so. Erect. Leaves finely cut, pale green. Flowers small, pale yellow. Carpels prickly. *Cornfields, mostly in S. England, occasional.*

R. Fica'ria L. 112. Lesser Celandine, Pilewort. Feb.–May. Root tuberous. Leaves mostly radical, cordate, smooth and shining. Flowers glossy yellow, sepals 3, petals 8 or more. Carpels large, in a globular head. *Shady banks, common.*

VII. *CAL'THA*

C. palus'tris L. 112. Marsh Marigold, King-cups. March–June. Glabrous. Leaves orbicular or reniform, crenate, radical ones long-stalked, cauline short-stalked or sessile. Flowers large, golden-yellow; perianth segments 5, all alike. Fruit of 5–10 follicles. *Marshy places, common.*

VIII. *TROL'LIUS*

T. europae'us L. 53. Globe-flower. June–July. Glabrous. Leaves palmately compound. Flowers large, globular, golden-yellow; sepals 5–15, large and yellow; petals as many, small and linear. Fruit of several follicles. *Damp woods and mountain pastures in the north, frequent.*

IX. *HELLEB'ORUS*

Leaves digitate, pale green. Sepals 5, large, greenish; petals 8–10, minute, tubular. Fruit of several large follicles.

H. vir'idis L. 35. Green Hellebore, Bear's-foot. March–April. Flowers usually 3 or 4, sepals spreading. *Meadows and copses, rare.*

H. foet'idus L. 23. Stinking Hellebore, Setterwort. Feb.–April. Flowers many, in a large panicle with large ovate bracts; sepals converging. *Stony places in southern half of England, rare.*

X. *AQUILE'GIA*

A. vulga'ris L. 59. Columbine. May–July. Leaves biternate; leaflets broad, 3-lobed, glaucous. Flowers large, blue or purple, drooping; perianth segments 10, all coloured, the inner ones spurred; carpels 5. Fruit of 5 follicles. *Open woods and copses, especially on limestone, occasional.*

XI. *DELPHIN'IUM*

D. Aja'cis L. 38. Larkspur. June–July. Leaves palmately divided into narrow segments. Flowers blue, reddish, or white, in terminal racemes; perianth segments 5, one outer segment with a long spur; carpel 1. *A rare weed of cornfields.*

XII. *ACONI'TUM*

A. Napel'lus L. 8. Monkshood, Wolfsbane. May–July. Leaves palmately divided into linear segments. Flowers large, blue, irregular; perianth segments 7–10, all coloured, the uppermost outer one forming a large helmet-shaped hood enclosing two erect curved inner segments; carpels 3. Fruit of 3 follicles. *Damp shady places in W. England and S. Wales, rare (common in gardens).* POISONOUS.

FAMILY 2. **BERBERIDA'CEAE**

Perianth segments about 12, in 2 whorls of 6 each, all coloured and free. Stamens 6, hypogynous, opposite the inner perianth segments and opening by lidded valves. Pistil of a single carpel containing 1 or more ovules at the bottom, stigma large and flat.

Ber'beris vulga'ris L. 101. Common Barberry. May–June. Branchlets angular, grey, armed with spines in threes. Leaves alternate or in tufts in the axils of the spines, finely and sharply toothed. Flowers yellow, in drooping racemes. Fruit a coral-red berry. *Hedges and woods, often planted.*

FAMILY 3. **NYMPHAEA'CEAE**

Water plants with large floating leaves. Flowers large, solitary; perianth segments numerous; stamens numerous, hypogynous; pistil superior or half inferior, many-celled or apocarpous.

I. *NU'PHAR*

N. lu'teum Sm. 93. Yellow Waterlily. June–Sept. Leaves large, glabrous, deeply cordate. Flowers yellow, on stalks above water-level, 5 or 6 outer perianth segments much larger than the inner ones. *In still or slowly moving water, common.*

II. *NYMPHAE'A*

N. alba L. 94. White Waterlily. June–Aug. Leaves like those of the yellow waterlily. Flowers white, floating on the surface of the water, the 4 outer perianth segments greenish on the back and larger than the inner ones. *Less common than the yellow waterlily.*

FAMILY 4. PAPAVERA'CEAE

Herbs with milky juice. Sepals 2, deciduous. Petals 4, crumpled in bud. Stamens numerous, hypogynous. Ovary superior, 1-celled, with numerous parietal placentas giving the appearance of a many-celled ovary. Fruit a capsule opening by pores or valves.

Ovary and fruit globular or club-shaped 2
Ovary and fruit linear 3
2 Stigmas large and sessile . . . . Papaver I
Stigmas small, on a short style . . Meconopsis II
3 Flowers more than 1 inch in diameter . . Glaucium III
Flowers less than 1 inch in diameter . . Chelidonium IV

I. *PAPA'VER*

Capsule globular or club-shaped, topped by a sessile disk on which the stigmas radiate like the spokes of a wheel. Flowers large and showy, dropping their petals easily.

Capsule smooth 2
Capsule bristly 4
2 Flowers bluish white, leaves glaucous . . P. somniferum
Flowers red, leaves green 3
3 Capsule short and broad . . . . . P. Rhoeas
Capsule long and narrow . . . . . P. dubium
4 Capsule short and broad . . . . . P. hybridum
Capsule long and narrow . . . . . P. Argemone

P. somnif'erum L. Opium Poppy. June–Aug. Leaves glabrous, glaucous, amplexicaul. Flowers large, bluish white, with purple blotch at base of each petal. Capsule large, globular. *An escape from gardens.*

P. Rhoe'as L. 101. Common Red Poppy. June–Aug. Hairy. Leaves deeply divided into pinnate lobes. Flowers large, bright red. Capsule broad, smooth. *Cornfields and waste places, common.*

P. du'bium L. 109. Long-headed Poppy. June–July. Differs from the preceding species chiefly in the shape of the capsule, which is long and narrow. *Less common than the last.*

P. Argemo'ne L. 96. Rough-headed Poppy. June–July. Flowers small, pale red, petals dark at base. Capsule narrow, bristly. *Cornfields and waste places, occasional.*

P. hy'bridum L. 46. June–July. Flowers purplish, with dark blotch at base of each petal. Capsule broad, bristly. *Light soils, rare.*

II. *MECONOP'SIS*

M. cam'brica Vig. 19. Welsh Poppy. June–Aug. Flowers large, pale yellow; stigma small, stalked. Capsule narrow. *Rocky woods and shady places in W. England and Wales, occasional.*

III. *GLAU'CIUM*

G. fla'vum Crantz. 52. Horned Poppy. June–Sept. Stout and glaucous. Leaves thick, pinnately lobed. Flowers large, yellow, short-stalked. Capsule linear, very long (6 inches or more). *Sea-shores, occasional.*

IV. *CHELIDO'NIUM*

C. ma'jus L. 96. Greater Celandine. May–Aug. Stem full of yellow juice. Leaves compound, thin, glaucous below. Flowers small, yellow. Capsule linear, seeds crested. *Old walls and hedgebanks; common in England and Wales, less so in Scotland.*

FAMILY 5. FUMARIA'CEAE

Glabrous herbs with small, much-divided leaves. Flowers irregular; sepals 2, very small; petals 4, in 2 pairs, the outer united at base and spurred; stamens 6, hypogynous; ovary superior, 1-celled, with 2 parietal placentas.

Flowers yellowish-white; fruit elongated, many-seeded .	Corydalis I
Flowers pink or purple; fruit roundish, 1-seeded . .	Fumaria II

I. *CORYDA'LIS*

C. lu'tea DC. Yellow Fumitory. May–Aug. Stem erect or spreading. Leaflets broad, thin, pale green, lobed. Flowers yellow, in short racemes. *On walls. An escape from gardens.*

C. clavicula'ta DC. 96. White Climbing Fumitory. June–Sept. Climbs by tendrils. Leaflets small, narrow-ovate. Flowers white, in very short racemes. *Stony hill-sides, occasional.*

II. *FUMA'RIA*

F. officinalis L. 110. Fumitory. April–Oct. Stems tufted and spreading. Leaflets very small. Flowers pink or purplish, in longish racemes. Fruit a small globular 1-seeded pod. *Cornfields and dry waste places, common.*

FAMILY 6. CRUCIF'ERAE

Leaves alternate, exstipulate.* Sepals 4, petals 4. Stamens 6, 4 long and 2 short.† Ovary superior, 2-celled, with a single style and a capitate or 2-lobed stigma.

Fruit a 2-valved capsule, 2- or more-seeded .	.	.	.	2
Fruit indehiscent, 1-seeded or jointed .	.	.	.	28
2 Fruit long and narrow (siliqua) .		.	.	3
Fruit short and broad (silicula) .	.	.	.	17
3 Flowers normally yellow .	.	.	.	4
Flowers white, pink, or purple .	.	.	.	12

---

* Apparently stipulate in *Cardamine impatiens.*
† Only 2 stamens in the rare casual, *Lepidium ruderale.*

4 Leaves entire or with a very few small teeth 5
Lower leaves coarsely toothed, lobed or compound . . 6

5 Flowers small, not scented . . . . Erysimum XIII
Flowers large, sweet-scented . . . . Cheiranthus II

6 Fruit with a long beak . . . . . Brassica XV
Fruit with a very short or no beak 7

7 Fruit ½ inch long or less 8
Fruit ¾ inch long or more 9

8 Valves of fruit with a prominent rib . . . Brassica XV
Valves of fruit not ribbed . . . . . Nasturtium III

9 Cauline leaves sessile, sagittate . . . . . Arabis V
Cauline leaves stalked, not sagittate 10

10 Glabrous, stem deeply furrowed . . . Barbarea IV
Hairy; or stem not or slightly furrowed 11

11 Seeds in a single row . . . . Sisymbrium XI
Seeds in a double row . . . . Diplotaxis XVI

12 Stigma 2-lobed 13
Stigma capitate 14

13 Leaves grey, entire, sinuate or lobed . . . Matthiola I
Leaves green, toothed . . . . . Hesperis X

14 Leaves all simple 15
Some or all leaves compound 16

15 Upper leaves sessile . . . . . . Arabis V
Leaves all stalked . . . . . Alliaria XII

16 Seeds in two rows in each cell of fruit . . Nasturtium III
Seeds in one row . . . . . Cardamine VI

17 Flowers yellow, leaves entire . . . Alyssum VII
Flowers yellow, leaves toothed . . . Nasturtium III
Flowers not yellow 18

18 Prostrate . . . . . Coronopus XVIII
Erect or ascending 19

19 Minute water plant with linear, cylindrical leaves . Subularia XIV
Land plant with flat leaves 20

20 Fruit triangular or obcordate . . . Capsella XVII
Fruit ovate or globose 21

21 Petals unequal 22
Petals equal 23

22 Leaves radical, forming a rosette . . . Teesdalia XXII
Leaves mostly cauline . . . . . Iberis XXI

23 Fruit globose or cylindrical, or dorsally compressed, i.e. with
the valves parallel to the partition between them . . 24
Fruit laterally compressed, i.e. with the valves at right angles
to the partition 26

24 Glabrous . . . . . . Cochlearia IX
Hairy 25

25 Each cell of fruit with 4 seeds or fewer . . . Alyssum VII
   Each cell with more than 4 seeds . . . . Draba VIII
26 Each cell of fruit 1-seeded . . . . Lepidium XIX
   Each cell with 2 or more seeds 27
27 Leaves simple . . . . . . Thlaspi XX
   Leaves compound . . . . Hutchinsia XXIII
28 Trailing, leaves all compound . . . Coronopus XVIII
   Erect or ascending, leaves mostly simple . . . 29
29 Fruit long, cylindrical, beaked, many-jointed . Raphanus XXVI
   Fruit short, 1-jointed 30
30 Fruit long-ovoid, angular, acute . . . . Cakile XXV
   Fruit globose, not angular, obtuse . . . Crambe XXIV

I. *MATTHI'OLA*

Leaves grey with down. Flowers large, purple, fragrant, petals clawed, stigma 2-lobed.

M. sinua'ta Br. 10. Sea Stock. June–Aug. Stem spreading. Lower leaves sinuate or lobed. *Sandy sea-shores in S. and W. England, Wales, and Ireland, rare.*

M. inca'na Br. 8. Stock, Gilliflower. May–June. Stem erect. Leaves all entire. *Sea-cliffs on south coast of England, rare.*

II. *CHEIRAN'THUS*

C. Chei'ri L. 93. Wallflower. April–May. Leaves green, lanceolate, entire. Flowers large, yellow, fragrant, stigma 2-lobed. *Walls, usually an escape from gardens.*

III. *NASTUR'TIUM*

Leaves glabrous. Fruit short, cylindrical or ovoid, seeds in two rows.

Flowers white . . . . N. officinale
Flowers yellow 2
2 Fruit ovoid . . . . N. amphibium
   Fruit cylindrical or linear 3
3 Petals longer than sepals . . . . . N. sylvestre
   Petals not longer than sepals . . . . N. palustre

N. officina'le Br. 112. Watercress. May–Oct. Leaves pinnately compound, leaflets entire or sinuate. Flowers white. Fruit curved upwards. *Brooks, common.*

N. sylves'tre Br. 76. June–Aug. Root creeping. Leaves pinnately compound, leaflets toothed. Flowers small, yellow. Fruit straight. *Wet places, frequent.*

N. palus'tre DC. 90. June–Sept. Root fibrous. Leaves deeply pinnatifid, lobes toothed. Flowers very small, yellow, petals not longer than sepals. Fruit very short, almost ovoid. *Wet places, frequent.*

N. amphib'ium Br. 54. Water Rocket. June–Sept. Tall and erect.
Leaves mostly simple, lanceolate, toothed, or pinnatifid. Flowers
yellow, larger than in the two preceding species. Fruit very small,
ovoid, with a long style. *Wet places, occasional.*

IV. *BARBARE'A*

B. vulga'ris Br. 107. Wintercress. May–Aug. Erect, stiff, and glabrous; stem deeply grooved. Leaves lyrate. Flowers numerous, bright
yellow. Fruits linear, semi-erect, crowded in long racemes. Cotyledons
accumbent. *Waysides, common.*

V. *AR'ABIS*

Usually hairy plants with radical leaves in a rosette, stem leaves sessile.
Flowers white or yellowish. Fruit linear.

Cauline leaves with rounded or pointed base	. . . .	2
Cauline leaves with tapering base	. . . .	3
2 Cauline leaves glabrous or nearly so, flowers yellowish	A. glabra	
Cauline leaves hairy, flowers white . . .	A. hirsuta	
3 Radical leaves entire or faintly toothed . . .	A. Thaliana	
Radical leaves pinnately lobed or coarsely toothed	. . .	4
4 Several flowering stems to each plant . . .	A. petraea	
One flowering stem to each plant . . .	A. stricta	

A. petrae'a Lam. 20. Northern Rockcress. July–Aug. Stems tufted,
decumbent. Radical leaves pinnately lobed, nearly glabrous. Flowers
few, large, white or purplish. Fruits spreading. *Mountains in the north.*

A. stricta Huds. 3. Bristol Rockcress. April–May. Stem simple, erect
about 6 inches high. Radical leaves dark green, hairy, pinnately lobed
or coarsely toothed. Flowers white, with erect petals. Fruits erect.
Avon gorge near Bristol, very rare.

A. hirsu'ta Scop. 100. Hairy Rockcress. May–Aug. Stem about
1 foot high, one or several from each plant. Cauline leaves hairy,
clasping the stem. Flowers small, white. Fruits thin, erect, crowded
in a long raceme. *Walls, hedgebanks, and dry meadows, frequent.*

A. gla'bra Bernh. (A. perfolia'ta Lam.). 42. Tower Mustard. May–
July. Tall glabrous erect plant with yellowish flowers and sagittate
cauline leaves. Fruits long, erect, crowded in a long raceme. *Hedgebanks and waysides, occasional.*

A. Thalia'na L. (Sisym'brium Thalia'num Gay). 107. Thale
Cress. April–May. Stem simple or branched, rising from a rosette
of radical leaves. Cauline leaves few, small, with tapering base. Flowers
small, white. Fruits spreading. *Old walls and dry banks, frequent.*

VI. *CARDAMI'NE*

Leaves pinnately compound. Flowers white or lilac. Fruit linear, the
valves acting as springs and shooting the seeds some distance.

Flowers large, with spreading petals		2
Flowers small, with erect petals		3

2 Erect, upper leaves with linear leaflets . . . C. pratensis
  Decumbent, leaflets all broad . . . . . C. amara

3 Leaves apparently stipulate . . . . . C. impatiens
  Leaves exstipulate . . . . . . C. hirsuta

C. ama'ra L. 79. Large Bittercress. May–June. Stems spreading. Leaflets all ovate or orbicular, toothed. Flowers white, with violet anthers. *Damp meadows and riversides, occasional.*

C. praten'sis L. 112. Cuckoo-flower, Ladies' Smock. April–June. Stem erect. Upper leaves with narrow entire leaflets. Flowers lilac, with yellow anthers. *Damp meadows, shady lanes, and riversides, common.*

C. hirsu'ta L. 112. Hairy Bittercress. March–Oct. Radical leaves in a rosette. Flowering stems several, spreading or erect. Leaflets ovate or orbicular, with scattered hairs. Flowers small, white, with erect petals and 4 stamens. *Waste ground, very common.*

   C. flexuo'sa (With.), a more luxuriant variety growing in damper places, is distinguished by the wavy flowering stems, 6 stamens and slender style.

C. impa'tiens L. 31. Narrow-leaved Bittercress. June–Aug. Stem erect, nearly simple. Petiole continued into two small stipule-like appendages. Leaflets narrow, coarsely toothed. Petals minute. *Moist calcareous soils, chiefly in W. England, rare.*

VII. *ALYS'SUM*

Hairy, with stellate or forked hairs. Leaves small, entire. Filaments often winged or toothed. Fruits ovate or orbicular, with convex 1–4-seeded valves.

A. alyssoi'des L. (**A. calyci'num** L.) May–June. Hairs stellate. Leaves oblanceolate, crowded. Flowers yellow. *Escape from gardens.*

A. marit'imum L. Sweet Alyssum. June–Sept. Hairs forked. Leaves linear or lanceolate. Flowers white, fragrant. *Escape from gardens.*

VIII. *DRA'BA*

Small hairy plants with tufted rosettes of simple radical leaves from which arise the slender flowering stems. Fruits ovate to lanceolate in outline, many-seeded.

Flowering stems leafless, petals deeply bifid . . . . D. verna
Flowering stems leafy, petals entire or notched . . . 2

2 Petals notched . . . . D. incana
  Petals entire . . . . D. muralis

D. mura'lis L. 25. April–May. Green and hairy. Cauline leaves clasping the stem. Flowers small, white. Fruit ovate. *Walls and rocks, rare.*

D. inca'na L. 30. Hoary Whitlow-grass. June–July. Grey-green with stellate hairs. Cauline leaves not clasping the stem. Flowers small, white. Fruit lanceolate, slightly twisted. *Scotland and N. England, local.*

D. ver'na L. (**Eroph'ila vulga'ris** DC.) 111. Common Whitlow-grass. March–May. Leaves all radical. Flowers white, petals deeply bifid. Fruits ovate, long-stalked. *Walls and rocks, common.*

IX. *COCHLEA'RIA*

Leaves simple, glabrous, thick, radical ones long-stalked. Flowers white. Fruit globular or ovoid.

C. officina'lis L. 85. Scurvy-grass. May–Aug. Low spreading plant. Radical leaves cordate or ovate, smooth. Flowers in racemes. Fruit globose or ovoid. *Sea-shores and mountains, frequent.*

C. Armora'cia L. 89. Horseradish. May–Aug. Root long. Stem erect, up to 3 ft. high. Radical leaves very large, oblong, rough. Flowers small, in numerous racemes forming a terminal panicle. Fruit ovoid, long-stalked. *Naturalized in waste places, frequent.*

X. *HES'PERIS*

H. matrona'lis L. Dame's Violet. May–Aug. Tall plant with large simple toothed leaves and showy purple (sometimes white) flowers, fragrant in the evening. Calyx erect, the two lateral sepals saccate. Petals spreading. Stigma with two erect lobes. Fruit linear, constricted between the seeds. *Escape from gardens, rare.*

XI. *SISYM'BRIUM*

Flowers small, yellow. Fruit linear, seeds in one row, cotyledons incumbent.

Fruits short, adpressed	S. officinale
Fruits long, not adpressed	2
2 Stem hairy	3
Stem glabrous or nearly so	4
3 Leaves 2-pinnatifid	S. Sophia
Leaves 1-pinnatifid	S. orientale
4 Fruits erect	S. Irio
Fruits wide-spreading	S. altissimum

S. officina'le Scop. 111. Hedge Mustard. April–July. Branches rigid, spreading like a candelabrum. Leaves lyrate, downy. Flowers very small. Fruit about ½ inch long, closely pressed to stem, in long slender racemes. *Waysides, common.*

S. orienta'le L. April–Sept. Stem hispid, leaves pinnatifid, the terminal lobe very long, narrow, and hastate. Fruit linear, erect. *Waste places, a frequent alien.*

S. altis'simum L. 96. June–Aug. Lower leaves runcinate; upper narrow, sessile, with a few hairs. Flowers pale yellow. Fruit linear, wide-spreading. *Waste places, a frequent alien.*

S. Sophi'a L. 79. Flixweed. July–Aug. Slender plant with finely divided leaves. Fruit an inch long, spreading. *Waysides, occasional.*

S. I'rio L. 13. London Rocket. June–Aug. Stiff glabrous plant with deeply pinnatifid or compound leaves and long slender spreading fruits. *Waysides, rare.*

XII. *ALLIAR'IA*

A. officina'lis Andrz. (**Sisym'brium Alliaria** Scop.) 101. Garlic Mustard, Jack-by-the-Hedge. April–June. Erect. Leaves simple, broad, dark green, coarsely toothed, long-stalked, smelling of garlic when rubbed. Flowers white. Fruits long, stiff, and spreading. *Hedgebanks, very common.*

XIII. *ERYS'IMUM*

Flowers small, yellow. Cotyledons incumbent.

E. Cheiranthoi'des L. 73. Treacle Mustard. June–Aug. Tall and narrow. Leaves entire or slightly toothed. Fruit linear, 4-angled. *Cornfields and waste places, occasional.*

E. orienta'le Br. Hare's-ear Treacle Mustard. June–Sept. Leaves ovate, entire, glabrous and glaucous, embracing stem with rounded auricles. Flowers pale yellow or whitish. Fruit linear. *Waste places, an occasional alien.*

XIV. *SUBULA'RIA*

S. aquat'ica L. 32. Awlwort. July–Aug. A small plant 1 or 2 inches high and submerged in water. Leaves all radical, cylindrical, awl-shaped. Flowers few, very small, white. Fruit very small, ovoid. *In the shallow edges of mountain tarns in Scotland, N. England, and N. Wales.*

XV. *BRAS'SICA*

Somewhat coarse plants with lyrate leaves and yellow flowers. Fruit with a distinct beak, seeds in one row, cotyledons conduplicate.

Fruits closely pressed to stem	B. nigra
Fruits spreading	2
2 Sepals erect or slightly spreading . . .	3
Sepals wide-spreading	5
3 Upper leaves deeply divided	B. monensis
Upper leaves not divided	4
4 Upper leaves auricled	B. campestris
Upper leaves not auricled	B. oleracea
5 Beak flat, longer than fruit	B. alba
Beak conical, shorter than fruit . . .	B. Sinapis

B. olera′cea L. 16. Wild Cabbage. May–Aug. Lower leaves lyrate, very large, glabrous and glaucous; upper leaves small, sessile. Flowers large, pale yellow. Fruit long, linear, spreading, beak very small. *Sea cliffs, rare.*

    Cultivated varieties include the cabbage, cauliflower, and kale.

B. campes′tris L. 111. Field Cabbage. May–Aug. Lower leaves lyrate, green, slightly glaucous and hispid; upper ones clasping the stem. Flowers large, bright yellow. Fruit long, linear, beak long and thin. *Waste places and edges of fields, frequent.*

    Cultivated varieties include the turnip, swede, and rape.

B. monen′sis Huds. 17. Isle of Man Cabbage. June–Sept. Stem prostrate. Leaves mostly radical, pinnately lobed or compound, glabrous or with a few stiff hairs. Flowers large, pale yellow. Fruit long, linear, spreading; beak long, usually containing a few seeds. *Sea-coasts in the west and north, rare.*

B. ni′gra Koch. (**Sina′pis nigra** L.) 68. Black Mustard. May–Aug. Lower leaves lyrate. Fruit about ½ inch long, cylindrical, with a prominent rib on each valve, closely pressed to stem, beak small. *Hedgebanks and cornfields, occasional.*

B. Sina′pis Visiani. (**Sina′pis arven′sis** L.) 112. Charlock. May–Oct. Coarse and hispid. Lower leaves lyrate. Fruit with a long conical beak, spreading. *Waysides, common.*

B. al′ba Boiss. (**Sina′pis alba** L.) 99. White Mustard. May–Oct. Lower leaves lyrate. Fruit covered with white hairs; beak very long, flattened. *Waysides and cornfields, common.*

XVI. *DIPLOTAX′IS*

Very like *Brassica*, with which it is often united. Differs in the seeds being in two distinct rows. Sepals spreading. Fruit compressed.

D. tenuifo′lia DC. (**Brassica tenuifolia** Boiss.) 49. Wall Rocket, Wall Mustard. June–Sept. A bushy perennial 1–2 feet high with woody base and leafy stem. Leaves glabrous, coarsely toothed or lobed, having a disagreeable smell when rubbed. Flowers pale yellow. Fruits long and slender, spreading. *Old walls, occasional.*

D. mura′lis DC. (**Brassica muralis** Boiss.) 70. Wall Rocket, Stinkweed. July–Sept. An annual 6–12 inches high with leafless flowering stems. Leaves mostly radical, coarsely toothed or lobed, having a disagreeable smell when rubbed. Flowers pale yellow. Fruits slender, spreading. *Waste ground, slag heaps, railway sidings, frequent.*

XVII. *CAPSELL′A*

C. Bursa-pasto′ris Medik. 112. Shepherd's Purse. March–Oct. Radical leaves lanceolate, toothed or lyrate; cauline leaves auricled, clasping stem. Flowers small, white. Fruits flat, triangular or heartshaped, many-seeded. *Very common.*

XVIII. *CORONO'PUS*

Small straggling herbs with small pinnately compound leaves and short racemes of minute white flowers. Fruit of two round pods set side by side, each with a single seed.

C. did'ymus Sm. **(Senebie'ra didyma** Sm.) 62. Lesser Wart-cress. May–Aug. Pods rough but not deeply wrinkled, slender-stalked. *Waste ground, occasional.*

C. Ruel'lii All. **(Senebie'ra Coronopus** Poir.) 83. Swine-cress, Wart-cress. May–Aug. Pod deeply wrinkled, short-stalked or sessile. *Waste ground, frequent.*

XIX. *LEPID'IUM*

Flowers small, white, very numerous, often in corymbose racemes. Fruit ovate or ovoid, with one seed in each cell.

Fruit winged at top		2
Fruit not winged		3
2 Style longer than notch of fruit, anthers violet .	.	L. Smithii
Style shorter than notch of fruit, anthers yellow	.	L. campestre
3 Upper leaves linear, small	.	L. ruderale
Upper leaves broad, large . . .	.	4
4 Upper leaves auricled and clasping the stem	.	L. Draba
Upper leaves with tapering base . . .	.	L. latifolium

L. latifo'lium L. 24. Dittander. July–Aug. A stout erect pale-green perennial with a large loose panicle of sweet-scented flowers. Leaves ovate or broadly lanceolate, glabrous. Fruit very small. *Waste ground near the sea, rare.*

L. rudera'le L. 56. Narrow-leaved Cress. May–June. Much branched and wiry, glabrous. Upper leaves linear, less than one inch long; lower leaves pinnatifid, with linear segments. Flowers minute, petals none, stamens two. Fruit very small, slightly notched at top. *Waste ground near the sea, rare.*

L. campes'tre Br. 90. Pepperwort. May–Aug. Stem solitary, erect, branched at top. Leaves oblong or lanceolate, hairy. Flowers very small, anthers yellow. Fruit winged at top, style very short. *Fields and waysides, occasional.*

L. Smith'ii Hook. 97. Pepperwort. May–Aug. Stems several, decumbent at base. Leaves lanceolate, hairy. Flowers with violet anthers. Fruit winged at top, style long. *Fields and waysides, frequent.*

L. Dra'ba L. 26. Hoary Cress. May–July. Downy. Leaves ovate, upper ones clasping the stem and auricled at the base. Flowers white, the racemes forming a broad flat corymb. Fruit ovoid, style conspicuous. *Waste places, rare, but spreading.*

XX. *THLAS'PI*

Leaves simple, glabrous, upper ones clasping the stem. Flowers small, white or lilac. Fruit flat, winged, orbicular or obovate, with two or more seeds in each cell.

Fruit large (about ½ inch across) . . . . T. arvense
Fruit small (about ¼ inch across) 2
2 Fruit longer than broad . . . . . . T. alpestre
Fruit as broad as long . . . . . T. perfoliatum

T. arven'se L. 96. Penny Cress, Mithridate Mustard. May–July. Radical leaves lanceolate, soon disappearing; cauline leaves auricled. Fruit large, circular, deeply notched, and with a broad flat wing all round. *Cornfields, occasional.*

T. perfolia'tum L. 4. May. Radical leaves ovate; cauline leaves amplexicaul. Fruit small, obovate, shallowly notched. *Stony places in the Midlands, rare.*

T. alpes'tre L. 16. June–Aug. Radical leaves ovate, cauline leaves with small auricles. Fruit small, narrow, with a shallow notch. *Mountains, rare.*

XXI. *IBE'RIS*

I. ama'ra L. 20. Candytuft. July–Aug. Leaves linear or lanceolate, toothed or entire. Flowers white or pink, two of the petals much larger than the other two. Fruit flat, orbicular or ovate, winged, one seed in each cell. *Cornfields on limestone, rare.*

XXII. *TEESDA'LIA*

T. nudicau'lis Br. 82. May–June. Small plant with a rosette of pinnately compound leaves. Flowers white, two of the petals larger than the other two. Fruit flat, orbicular, winged, two seeds in each cell. *Sandy and gravelly places, occasional.*

XXIII. *HUTCHIN'SIA*

H. petrae'a Br. 16. March–May. Small plant. Leaves very small, pinnately compound. Flowers very small, white. Fruit ovate, two seeds in each cell. *Limestone rocks in W. England, Wales, and Dumfries, rare.*

XXIV. *CRAM'BE*

C. marit'ima L. 39. Sea-kale. June–Sept. Stout erect plant. Leaves ovate, coarsely toothed, thick, and glaucous. Flowers white. Fruit globular, indehiscent, one-seeded. *Sandy sea-shores, occasional.*

XXV. *CAKI'LE*

C. marit'ima Scop. 68. Sea Rocket. June–Aug. Leaves thick, pinnately lobed, segments narrow. Flowers white or lilac. Fruit indehiscent, spindle-shaped, one-seeded. *Sandy sea-shores, frequent.*

XXVI. *RAPH'ANUS*

R. Raphanis'trum L. 111. Wild Radish. April–Sept. Lower leaves lyrate, with stiff hairs. Flowers white, pale yellow, or lilac, usually with purple veins. Fruit a several-jointed, furrowed pod with a long beak. *Cornfields, frequent.*

    R. marit'imus (Sm.) is a rare seaside variety with yellow flowers and short-beaked pods.

FAMILY 7. **RESEDA'CEAE**

Herbs with alternate exstipulate leaves and small irregular greenish-yellow or white flowers in terminal spikes or racemes. Stamens numerous, hypogynous. Ovary superior, 1-celled. Fruit a capsule opening at the top before the seeds are ripe.

RESE'DA

R. lu'tea L. 58. Wild Mignonette. June–Aug. Leaves pinnately divided into linear segments. Flowers small, in long racemes, sepals and petals usually 6. *Waste places, occasional.*

R. lu'teola L. 98. Weld, Dyer's Weed. June–Aug. Leaves linear or lanceolate, glabrous. Flowers in long narrow spikes, sepals and petals usually 4. *Waste places, frequent.*

FAMILY 8. **CISTA'CEAE**

Leaves opposite. Sepals 5, 3 large and 2 very small. Petals 5. Stamens numerous, hypogynous. Ovary superior, 1-celled. Fruit a capsule opening by longitudinal valves.

HELIAN'THEMUM

Stem woody, capsule 3-valved.

Leaves without stipules, flowers small .	.	.	.	H. canum
Leaves with stipules, flowers large	.	.	.	2
2 Flowers yellow .	.	.	.	H. Chamaecistus
Flowers white .	.	.	.	H. appeninum

H. ca'num Baumg. 9. Hoary Rockrose. May–July. Leaves not longer than ½ inch, without stipules. Flowers small, yellow. *Wales and NW. England, rare.*

H. Chamaecis'tus Mill. (**H. vulga're** Gaertn.) 93. Common Rockrose. June–Sept. Leaves about 1 inch long, green above, white below, stipulate. Flowers large, yellow. *Dry pastures on calcareous soils, common.*

H. appeni'num Lam. and DC. (**H. polifo'lium** Mill.) 2. White Rockrose. June–Aug. Leaves grey on both sides, margins much recurved. Flowers white. *N. Somerset and S. Devon, rare.*

Family 9. VIOLA'CEAE

Leaves alternate, stipulate. Sepals 5, with small appendages at base; petals 5, irregular, the lowest one spurred. Stamens 5, the anthers more or less united into a tube round the single style. Ovary superior, 1-celled. Fruit a capsule opening by 3 longitudinal valves.

VI'OLA

Lateral petals not overlapping the upper ones, stipules not leafy	.	2
Lateral petals overlapping the upper ones, stipules leafy	. .	8
2 Sepals obtuse	. .	3
Sepals acute	. .	5
3 Leaves reniform, hairless, slightly crenate	. .	V. palustris
Leaves cordate, with hairs, conspicuously crenate	. .	4
4 Flowers sweet-scented, stem with runners	. .	V. odorata
Flowers scentless, runners very short or none	. .	V. hirta
5 Leaves with tapering base	. .	V. lactea
Leaves with cordate or rounded base	. .	6
6 Leaves longer than broad, flowers terminal (a)	.	V. canina
Leaves as broad as long, flowers on lateral branches below a barren tuft (b)	.	7

 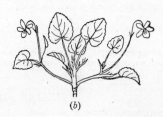

(a) (b)

7 Spur straight, darker than petals	. . .	V. sylvestris
Spur curved, not darker than petals	. . .	V. Riviniana
8 Petals small, shorter than the sepals	.	V. arvensis
Petals large, longer than the sepals .	. .	9
9 Stems above ground several, branching	. .	V. tricolor
Stems above ground one or two, simple	. .	V. lutea

V. odora'ta L. 86. Sweet Violet. March–April. Stem with runners. Leaves broadly cordate, crenate, slightly hairy. Flowers violet or white, scented, sepals obtuse, bracts above middle of stalk. *Hedge-banks and woods, common.*

V. hir'ta L. 76. Hairy Violet. March–June. Runners none or very short. Leaves narrowly cordate, crenate, very hairy. Flowers violet, not scented, sepals obtuse, bracts below middle of stalk. *Pastures and woods on calcareous soil, common.*

V. palus'tris L. 103. Marsh Violet. April–June. Leaves reniform, glabrous, obtuse, crenatures indistinct. Flowers pale violet, sepals obtuse, stigma not hooked. *Wet places, common in the north, less so in the south.*

V. sylves'tris Lam. 63. Wood Violet. April–May. Leaves cordate, acute. Flowers lilac, sepals acute, spur darker than the petals. *Woods and hedgebanks, frequent.*

V. Rivinia'na Reichb. 112. Common Dog Violet. March–June. Leaves roundly cordate, stipules fringed with long teeth. Flowers violet, spur usually a paler shade of the same colour but sometimes yellowish, sepals acute. *Hedgebanks and woods, common.*

V. cani'na L. 101. Yellow-spurred Dog Violet. April–June. Leaves narrowly cordate, stipules entire or with a few short teeth. Flowers violet, spur yellow, sepals acute. *Heaths and sand-dunes, locally common.*

V. lac'tea Smith. 27. Milky Violet. April–June. Leaves ovate or lanceolate. Flowers whitish, sepals acute. *Heaths, rare.*

V. tri'color L. 43. Pansy. May–Sept. Leaves ovate, crenate, obtuse. Flowers large, blue and yellow. *Cornfields, occasional.*

V. arven'sis Murr. 110. Field Pansy, Heartsease. May–Sept. Leaves oblong-lanceolate, crenate or serrate. Flowers small, yellow, white, or purplish. *Cornfields, common.*

V. lu'tea Huds. 66. Yellow Mountain Pansy. June–July. Stems one or two, simple. Leaves ovate or cordate. Flowers large, yellow. *Mountain pastures.*

Family 10. POLYGALA'CEAE

Leaves entire, mostly alternate. Flowers irregular; stamens 8, in two bundles each with 4 anthers; ovary superior, 2-celled, flat, style and stigma 1. Fruit a somewhat fleshy capsule.

POLYG'ALA

P. vulga'ris L. 101. Milkwort. May–Sept. Leaves lanceolate or linear, the lower ones smaller than the upper. Flowers blue, pink, or white, drooping in terminal racemes. Capsule orbicular. *Dry pastures, common.*

   P. serpylla'cea (Weihe) has the lower leaves opposite.

P. calca'rea F. Schultz. 20. May–July. Leaves obovate or oblanceolate, the lower ones in a rosette and larger than the upper. *Chalk hills, rare.*

Family 11. FRANKENIA'CEAE

Sepals and petals 4–5. Stamens 4–5, hypogynous. Ovary superior, 1-celled. Fruit a capsule opening by longitudinal valves.

Franke'nia lae'vis L. 10. Sea Heath. July–Aug. Low spreading heath-like shrub with small entire opposite or whorled leaves with recurved margins. Flowers small, pink, with a tubular calyx and spreading petals. *Salt marshes on south-east coasts of England.*

FAMILY 12. CARYOPHYLLA'CEAE

Herbs with opposite entire leaves. Sepals and petals usually 5, sometimes 4. Stamens usually 5 or 10, hypogynous. Ovary superior, 1-celled, with free-central placentation. Fruit a 1-celled capsule.

Sepals united, capsule stalked	2
Sepals free, capsule sessile	4
2 Calyx with bracts at base	Dianthus I
Calyx without bracts at base	3
3 Styles 2	Saponaria II
Styles 3–4	Silene III
Styles 5	Lychnis IV
4 Leaves with small white scaly stipules . . .	5
Leaves without stipules	6
5 Styles 3	Spergularia XI
Styles 4–5	Spergula X
6 Petals entire	7
Petals bifid or notched	9
7 Styles 3	Arenaria VIII
Styles 4–5	8
8 Capsule opening by 4–5 valves . . .	Sagina IX
Capsule opening by 8 teeth . . .	Moenchia VI
9 Styles 3	Stellaria VII
Styles 4–5	10
10 Leaves up to 2 inches or more in length, capsule splitting to base	Stellaria aquatica
Leaves small, capsule opening by short teeth at the top	Cerastium V

I. DIAN'THUS

Stiff plants with linear leaves. Calyx tubular, 5-toothed, clasped by bracts at the base. Petals 5, toothed or jagged. Stamens 10. Styles 2.

Flowers clustered	2
Flowers solitary or in pairs	3
2 Bracts broad, scarious	D. prolifer
Bracts narrow, herbaceous . . .	D. Armeria
3 Bracts with short points, flowers scented . .	D. caesius
Bracts with long points, flowers not scented	D. deltoides

D. Arme'ria L. 50. Deptford Pink. July–Aug. Leaves downy. Flowers small, pink or red, with white dots, in terminal clusters, bracts narrow. *Waste places, rare.*

D. deltoi'des L. 59. Maiden Pink. June–Sept. Leaves green, about ½ inch long. Flowers small, pink, solitary or in pairs, scentless. *Hilly pastures, rare.*
There is a glaucous variety with white flowers.

D. cae'sius L. 1. Cheddar Pink. June–July. Leaves glaucous. Flowers large, pink, solitary, scented. *Cheddar cliffs, Somerset.*

D. pro'lifer L. 8. Proliferous Pink. June–Aug. Leaves glabrous. Flowers small, pink, in compact terminal heads; bracts broad, concealing the calyx. *Hilly pastures, rare.*

II. *SAPONA'RIA*

S. officina'lis L. 71. Soapwort. Aug.–Sept. Leaves ovate, 3-nerved. Flowers pale pink or white, in dense cymes or heads, styles two. *Hedges and banks of streams, occasional.*

III. *SILE'NE*

Sepals united into a 5-toothed calyx. Petals 5, narrowed at base into a claw. Stamens 10. Styles 3.

Calyx glabrous	.	2
Calyx hairy	.	4
2 Stems very short, plant moss-like	S. acaulis
Stems elongated, plant not moss-like . . .	. 3
3 Flowers in cymes	. S. Cucubalus
Flowers mostly solitary	. S. maritima
4 Flowers small, axillary	. S. anglica
Flowers large, terminal	. S. noctiflora

S. Cucu'balus Wibel (**S. infla'ta** Sm.) 105. Bladder Campion. June–Sept. Glaucous and usually glabrous. Leaves ovate, pointed. Flowers white, in loose terminal cymes; calyx inflated, net-veined. *Cornfields and waysides, common.*

S. marit'ima With. 81. Sea Campion. June–Sept. Leaves small, thick, crowded at base of stem. Flowers white, mostly solitary. *Seashores and by mountain streams, frequent.*

S. ang'lica L. 72. English Catchfly. June–Sept. Leaves small. Flowers small, pink or white, sessile or nearly so, usually all turned to one side. *Cornfields, occasional.*

S. acau'lis L. 23. Moss Campion. July–Aug. Grows in dense moss-like tufts. Leaves linear, glabrous. Flowers small, numerous, reddish-purple. *Mountains.*

S. noctiflo'ra L. 66. Night Catchfly. July–Sept. Leaves large. Flowers large, pink or white, in few-flowered dichotomous cymes, calyx hairy and sticky. *Cornfields, occasional.*

IV. *LYCH'NIS*

Sepals united into a 5-toothed calyx. Petals 5, narrowed at base into a claw, with a small double or notched scale at base of lamina. Stamens 10. Styles 5.

Calyx teeth longer than corolla	.	L. Githago
Calyx teeth shorter than corolla . . .	.	. 2
2 Flowers white	. L. alba
Flowers red or pink	.	. 3
3 Petals deeply divided into linear segments .	. L. Flos-cuculi
Petals bifid	. L. dioica

L. al′ba Mill. (**L. vesperti′na** Sibth.) 106. White Campion. May–
Sept. Leaves ovate, hairy. Flowers white, generally unisexual and
dioecious. *Hedgebanks and waste places, common.*

L. dioi′ca L. (**L. diur′na** Sibth.) 112. Red Campion. April–Oct.
Like the preceding species but flowers pink or red. *Damp hedgebanks,
very common.*

L. Flos-cu′culi L. 112. Ragged Robin. May–Sept. Leaves lanceolate.
Flowers red or pink, petals cut into linear segments. *Damp places, less
common than the two preceding species.*

L. Githa′go Scop. 102. Corn Cockle. June–Sept. Very hairy. Leaves
long, lanceolate or linear. Flowers large, purplish-red, solitary, calyx
continued into linear teeth exceeding the petals. *Cornfields, locally
common.*

V. *CERAS′TIUM*

Leaves small, hairy, exstipulate. Flowers usually small, white, in
terminal forked cymes; sepals 4–5, free; petals 4–5 or 0, bifid; stamens
10 or 5. Capsule opening by teeth at the top.

Petals much longer than the sepals 2
Petals not or scarcely longer than the sepals 3
2 Leaves lanceolate or linear, acute . . . C. arvense
  Leaves ovate, obtuse . . . . . . C. alpinum
3 Hairs not gland-tipped . . . . . C. vulgatum
  Hairs gland-tipped 4
4 Bracts with scarious margins . . . C. semidecandrum
  Bracts without scarious margins 5
5 Fruiting peduncles shorter than calyx . . . C. viscosum
  Fruiting peduncles longer than calyx . . C. tetrandrum

C. tetran′drum Curtis. 85. April–Oct. Leaves ovate. Bracts without
scarious margins. Pedicels longer than calyx. Parts of the flower
usually in fours. *Waste places near the sea, frequent.*

C. semidecan′drum L. 97. April–June. Hairs gland-tipped. Bracts
with narrow scarious margins. Stamens mostly 5. Pedicels longer
than calyx, reflexed immediately after flowering. *Dry waste places,
common.*

C. visco′sum L. (**C. glomera′tum** Thuill.) 112. Large Mouse-ear
Chickweed. April–Sept. Hairs gland-tipped. Leaves broadly ovate.
Bracts without scarious margins. Stamens mostly 10. Capsule curved,
pedicel shorter than calyx. *Damp places, common.*

C. vulga′tum L. (**C. trivia′le** Link.) 112. Common Mouse-ear
Chickweed. April–Sept. Differs from all the others in the almost
complete absence of glandular hairs. Leaves oblong, dark green. Fruiting pedicels longer than calyx. *One of the commonest weeds.*

C. alpi′num L. 20. Alpine Mouse-ear Chickweed. June–Aug. Leaves
ovate, obtuse. Flowers large, petals deeply bifid, much longer than the
sepals. *Moist places in mountains, locally common.*

C. arven'se L. 79. Field Mouse-ear Chickweed. April–Aug. Leaves
linear-lanceolate, acute. Flowers large, petals much longer than sepals.
Dry fields and banks, occasional.

VI. *MOENCH'IA*

M. erec'ta Gaertn. 60. April–June. Leaves linear, glabrous and
glaucous. Flowers white, long-stalked, 4-parted. Capsule opening by
8 teeth. *Dry places, occasional.*

VII. *STELLA'RIA*

Leaves exstipulate. Flowers white; sepals 5, free; petals 5, deeply
bifid; stamens usually 10; styles usually 3. Capsule with 5–6 teeth (sometimes 3).

Lower leaves stalked	**2**
Leaves all sessile	**4**
2 Stem with hairs on one side only	S. media
Stem with hairs all round, or glabrous	**3**
3 Styles 5	S. aquatica
Styles 3	S. nemorum
4 Petals divided half-way	S. Holostea
Petals divided nearly to base	**5**
5 Leaves short, ovate or lanceolate, petals shorter than sepals	S. uliginosa
Leaves long and very narrow, petals as long as sepals .	**6**
6 Flowers numerous: bracts small, fringed with hairs .	S. graminea
Flowers solitary or few: bracts large, glabrous . .	S. glauca

S. aquat'ica Scop. 62. Water Stitchwort. July–Sept. Stem weak,
furrowed. Leaves ovate or cordate; upper ones sessile, 2 inches or
more in length. Petals deeply bifid. Styles 5. Capsule opening by
longitudinal valves. *Streams and wet ditches in the southern half of
England, frequent.*

S. nem'orum L. 54. Wood Stitchwort. May–Aug. Like the preceding
species but stem cylindrical and styles 3. *Moist woods, mostly in the
north, occasional.*

S. me'dia Vill. 112. Chickweed. Feb.–Nov. Stem cylindrical, with
a line of hairs down one side. Leaves small, ovate, nearly glabrous,
lower ones stalked. Flowers small; petals deeply bifid, shorter than
the sepals; stamens 3–5. *One of the commonest weeds on moist soils.*
    S. neglec'ta (Weihe) is larger and taller, with 10 stamens. *S.
Boraea'na* (Jord.) has no petals.

S. Holos'tea L. 111. Greater Stitchwort. April–June. Stems weak,
4-angled, rough. Leaves lanceolate or linear, long-pointed, sessile,
rough on the edges. Flowers large, petals divided half-way to base,
twice as long as sepals. *Hedgebanks and woods, common.*

S. glau'ca With. 69. Marsh Stitchwort. May–Sept. Usually glaucous.
Stems weak, 4-angled, smooth. Leaves linear-lanceolate, margins
smooth. Flowers large, solitary or few, petals divided nearly to base,
longer than the sepals which are strongly 3-nerved. Bracts leafy,
glabrous. *Wet places, occasional.*

S. gramin'ea L. 110. Lesser Stitchwort. May–Aug. Stem angular, glabrous. Leaves linear-lanceolate, $1\frac{1}{2}$ to 2 inches long. Flowers small, numerous, in panicled cymes, petals deeply bifid, sepals strongly 3-nerved. *Hedgebanks and heaths, frequent.*

S. uligino'sa Murr. 112. Bog Stitchwort. May–Aug. Stem weak, 4-angled, glabrous. Leaves narrowly ovate or lanceolate, seldom more than 1 inch long. Flowers small, petals deeply bifid, shorter than the sepals. *Wet places, common.*

VIII. *ARENA'RIA*

Leaves exstipulate. Flowers small, white; petals 5, entire; sepals 5, free; styles 3. Capsule opening by 3–6 longitudinal valves.

Leaves ovate	2
Leaves linear	4
2 Leaves thick and fleshy	A. peploides
Leaves thin	3
3 Lower leaves stalked, $\frac{1}{2}$ inch or more in length . .	A. trinervia
Leaves all sessile, less than $\frac{1}{4}$ inch in length .	A. serpyllifolia
4 Petals longer than sepals	A. verna
Petals shorter than sepals	A. tenuifolia

A. ver'na L. 28. Vernal Sandwort. May. Leaves stiff, awl-shaped. Petals longer than sepals. Capsule opening in 3 valves. *Mountains, rare.*

A. tenuifo'lia L. 42. Fine-leaved Sandwort. May–June. Like the preceding species but petals shorter than sepals. *Walls and dry places, rare.*

A. triner'via L. 103. Three-nerved Sandwort. April–July. Stems spreading. Leaves ovate, pale green, 3-nerved, mostly stalked. Flowers small, white; petals entire, rather shorter than the sepals. Capsule opening in 6 valves. *Moist shady places, common.*

A. serpyllifo'lia L. 112. Thyme-leaved Sandwort. April–Aug. Leaves very small, ovate, sessile. Flowers very small, petals much shorter than the sepals. Capsule opening in 6 valves. *Walls and dry places, common.*

A. peploi'des L. 81. Sea Purslane. May–Aug. Leaves ovate, thick, pale green. Petals about as long as sepals. Capsule opening in 3–4 valves. *Sandy places near the sea, common.*

IX. *SAGI'NA*

Small tufted plants with linear or awl-shaped leaves. Flowers minute, sepals 4–5, petals 4–5 or o, stamens 4–10, styles 4–5. Fruit a capsule opening in 4–5 valves.

Parts of the flower in fours	2
Parts of the flower in fives	3

Branches prostrate, pedicels deflexed after flowering   S. procumbens
Branches ascending, pedicels erect after flowering   .   S. apetala
Petals longer than the sepals   .   .   .   .   S. nodosa
Petals not longer than the sepals   .   .   .   S. subulata

apet′ala Ard. 91. Erect Pearlwort. May–Sept. Stems ascending. Flowers very minute, all erect; sepals 4, spreading in fruit; petals none. *Walls and dry places, common.*
   In *S. cilia′ta* (Fries) the sepals are glandular and adpressed to the capsule. *S. marit′ima* (Don.) is a seaside variety with blunt fleshy leaves.

procum′bens L. 112. Common Pearlwort. May–Sept. Stems prostrate. Flowers erect at first, afterwards deflexed, sepals and petals 4. *Paths and waste places, common.*

subula′ta Presl. 66. June–Sept. Often with glandular hairs. Flowers white, conspicuous, sepals and petals 5. *Heaths, local.*

nodo′sa Fenzl. 106. Knotted Pearlwort. July–Sept. Leaves glabrous in whorl-like clusters. Flowers few, conspicuous, sepals and petals 5, petals longer than the sepals. *Damp places, frequent.*

X. *SPER′GULA*

arven′sis L. 109. Corn Spurrey. June–Sept. Stems slender, ascending or erect. Leaves long, linear, in opposite clusters, with minute scarious stipules at each node. Flowers small, white, on long stalks which turn down after flowering; sepals 5; petals 5; entire; styles 5. Fruit a 5-valved capsule. *Cornfields, common.*

XI. *SPERGULA′RIA*

Stems prostrate. Leaves linear, stipulate, with smaller ones usually clustered in their axils. Flowers small, pinkish; petals 5, entire; styles 3. Fruit a 3-valved capsule.

ru′bra Presl. 104. Sand Spurrey. June–Sept. Leaves flat, acute. Seeds wingless. *Sandy and gravelly heaths, common.*

sali′na Presl. 77. Sea Spurrey. July–Sept. Leaves cylindrical, fleshy. Sepals more than half as long as capsule. Seeds often winged. *Salt marshes, locally frequent.*

   S. margina′ta (Kittel) has larger capsules about twice as long as the sepals, and seeds all with a broad wing.

FAMILY 13.   PORTULA′CEAE

Herbs with opposite entire leaves. Sepals 2, petals 5. Ovary superior, -celled, with free-central placentation. Fruit a capsule opening by 3 longitudinal valves.

Stamens 5   .   .   .   .   Claytonia I
Stamens 3   .   .   .   .   Montia II

I. *CLAYTO'NIA*

C. perfo'liata Donn. 42. May–July. Radical leaves ovate, long
stalked. Flowers small, white, in clusters or short racemes, each flower
ing stem passing through a leaf formed by the union of two opposit
leaves. *Garden weed, locally common.*

II. *MONTIA*

M. fonta'na L. 61. Water Blinks. April–Aug. A small green glabrou
plant forming dense tufts. Leaves small, obovate, glabrous. Flower
small, white, in the axils of the upper leaves. *Wet places, frequent.*

Family 14. TAMARICA'CEAE

Shrubs with minute alternate scale-like leaves. Flowers very small
pink or white, in crowded spikes, often forming conspicuous panicles
sepals and petals 5; stamens 5, hypogynous; ovary superior, 1-celled
styles 3. Fruit a 3-valved capsule, each seed with a tuft of cottony hairs

TAMARIX

T. ang'lica Webb. 10. English Tamarisk. Aug.–Oct. Shrub 3–6 ft
high with erect or spreading branches. *South coast of England.*
   Other species of tamarisk have been introduced and mixed with th
above, e.g. *T. parviflora* (DC.) in which the flowers are 4-merous an
appear in early summer, and *T. gallica* (L.) differing from *T. anglic*
in very slight particulars.

Family 15. ELATINA'CEAE

Leaves opposite. Stamens 4–10, hypogynous. Ovary superior, 3–5
celled, stigmas capitate. Fruit a 3–5-valved capsule with several seeds.

ELAT'INE

E. hexan'dra DC. 31. Waterwort. Aug. Minute water or marsh
plant with creeping stems and opposite entire leaves. Flowers ver
small, pink, globular, petals 3, stamens 6, styles 3. *In the mud of ponds
rare.*

Family 16. HYPERICA'CEAE

Leaves opposite, entire, exstipulate, often gland-dotted. Flower
yellow; sepals and petals 5; stamens numerous, hypogynous, in 3–!
bundles; ovary superior, 3–5-celled, styles 3–5. Fruit a capsule openin
by 3–5 longitudinal valves.

HYPER'ICUM

Leaves with numerous transparent dots 2
Leaves without or with very few transparent dots 7
2 Sepals without or with few glands on margin 3
Sepals with numerous glandular teeth 4

| Stem 2-edged | . | . | . | . | . | . | H. perforatum |
| Stem 4-angled | . | . | . | . | . | . | H. tetrapterum |

| Stem glabrous | . | . | . | . | . | . | . 5 |
| Stem hairy | . | . | . | . | . | . | . 6 |

| Leaves 1 inch or more long | . | . | . | . H. montanum |
| Leaves ½ inch or less | . | . | . | . H. pulchrum |

| Leaves ovate or oblong, stem tall and erect | . | . H. hirsutum |
| Leaves orbicular, woolly, stem diffuse | . | . | H. elodes |

| Stem decumbent or prostrate, leafy | . | . | H. humifusum |
| Stem erect | . | . | . | . | . | . | . 8 |

| Stamens in 3 bundles | . | . | . | . | . | . H. dubium |
| Stamens in 5 bundles | . | . | . | . | . H. Androsaemum |

I. Androsae'mum L. 80. Tutsan. June–Aug. Shrubby. Leaves large, ovate, sessile, without transparent dots. Flowers few, sepals large and leaf-like, stamens in 5 bundles, styles 3. *Waysides and copses, occasional.*

I. perfora'tum L. 102. Common St. John's Wort. July–Sept. Leaves oblong, sessile, with numerous transparent dots, seldom more than ¾ inch long. Flowers many, stamens in 3 bundles, styles 3. *Waysides and copses, common.*

I. tetrap'terum Fries. 103. Square-stalked St. John's Wort. July–Sept. Stem sharply 4-angled or slightly winged. Leaves up to 1 inch long, ovate, sessile, clasping the stem at base, dotted with transparent glands. Flowers numerous, sepals narrow. *Wet places, common.*

I. du'bium Leers. (**H. macula'tum** Crantz). 87. July–Aug. Like the preceding species but leaves with very few transparent dots and the stem only slightly 4-angled.

I. humifu'sum L. 105. Trailing St. John's Wort. July–Aug. Stems decumbent or prostrate, crowded with small lanceolate or narrowly ovate leaves with very few transparent dots. Flowers few, small, pale yellow. *Heathy places, frequent.*

I. pul'chrum L. 111. Slender St. John's Wort. July–Aug. Tall and narrow. Leaves small, cordate, clasping the stem, gland-dotted. Flowers numerous, sepals with black glandular teeth, petals tipped with red. *Heathy places, frequent.*

I. hirsu'tum L. 92. Hairy St. John's Wort. July–Aug. Stems hairy. Leaves ovate, hairy, short-stalked, dotted with glands. Flowers numerous; sepals fringed with black glands. *Woods and shady banks, frequent.*

I. monta'num L. 51. Mountain St. John's Wort. July–Aug. Stems stiff, erect, glabrous. Leaves ovate, glabrous, gland-dotted, clasping the stem. Sepals with black glands. *Limestone hills, rare.*

I. elo'des L. 64. Marsh St. John's Wort. July–Aug. Stems spreading, woolly. Leaves orbicular, woolly on both sides, clasping the stem. Flowers few, pale yellow, sepals with glandular teeth. *Wet places in the west, frequent.*

FAMILY 17. MALVA'CEAE

Leaves alternate, palmately nerved. Flowers regular; petals 5, unite
at base to staminal tube; stamens numerous, united into a tube roun
the pistil; ovaries superior, arranged in a ring, styles long and protrudin
through the staminal tube. Seeds kidney-shaped, one or more to eac
carpel.

Involucre of 5 or more bracts forming an outer calyx . Althaea
Involucre of 3 bracts . . . . . . Malva I

I. *ALTHAE'A*

A. officina'lis L. 32. Marsh Mallow. Aug.–Sept. Tall and erect
Stem and leaves covered with velvety down. Leaves ovate or slightl
3-lobed. Flowers pink; involucral bracts, about 8, much shorter tha
calyx. *Salt marshes and waste places, occasional.*

II. *MAL'VA*

Calyx of 5 united sepals, involucral bracts 3.

Stem prostrate, flowers small, lilac . . . M. rotundifoli
Stem erect, flowers large, purple, pink or white . . . .
2 Cauline leaves deeply lobed . . . . . M. moschat
Cauline leaves shallowly lobed . . . . . M. sylvestri

M. moscha'ta L. 92. Musk Mallow. June–Sept. Cauline leaves deepl
divided into pinnatifid lobes, radical leaves shallowly lobed. Flower
large, pink or white. Carpels rounded on back. *Waysides and railwa
embankments, frequent.*

M. sylves'tris L. 102. Common Mallow. June–Oct. Leaves large
rough, long-stalked, shallowly lobed. Flowers large, reddish purple
Carpels 10, flat on back. *Roadsides and waste places, common.*

M. rotundifo'lia L. 90. Dwarf Mallow. June–Sept. Stems procum
bent or prostrate. Leaves shallowly lobed. Flowers small, lilac. Car
pels 15, rounded on back. *Roadsides and waste places, frequent.*

FAMILY 18. TILIA'CEAE

Leaves alternate, stipulate. Sepals 5, valvate, deciduous. Petals 5
Stamens numerous, hypogynous. Ovary superior.

TILIA

Trees with small fragrant whitish-green flowers in small cluster
attached to a long leaf-like bract. Ovary 5-celled. Fruit a small nut.

T. platyphyl'los Scop. 8. Large-leaved Lime. July. Leaves large
broadly cordate, acuminate, sharply toothed, pubescent beneath. Frui
with prominent ribs. *Commonly planted and possibly native in old woods
T. vulga'ris* (Hayne), the so-called Common Lime, is also com
monly planted. It differs in the leaves being glabrous beneath excep
for axil tufts, and the ribs on the fruit are much less prominent.

T. corda'ta Mill. 29. Small-leaved Lime. July–Aug. Leaves broadly cordate, toothed, acuminate, glabrous beneath except for woolly tufts in the vein-axils, and not more than 2½ inches across. *Old woods, rare.*

FAMILY 19. LINA'CEAE

Leaves entire, exstipulate. Sepals and petals 4–5; stamens as many as petals, hypogynous; ovary superior, 4–5-celled; styles 4–5, with capitate stigmas. Fruit a capsule separating into 4–5 carpels.

Parts of the flower in fours	Radiola I
Parts of the flower in fives	Linum II

I. *RADI'OLA*

R. linoi'des Roth. (**R. Millegra'na** Sm.) 89. Allseed. June–Sept. Minute erect plant with tufts of numerous forked stems. Leaves minute, opposite, ovate. Flowers minute, globular; petals 4, white; calyx with 8–12 teeth. *Damp sandy and peaty places, occasional.*

II. *LI'NUM*

Sepals, petals and stamens 5, free.

Flowers white, leaves opposite	L. catharticum
Flowers blue, leaves alternate	2
2 Sepals obtuse	L. perenne
Sepals acute	3
3 Stem erect, simple; flowers large . . .	L. usitatissimum
Stem decumbent, branching at base, flowers small .	L. bienne

L. cathar'ticum L. 112. Purging Flax. May–Oct. Stem and branches very thin. Leaves small, opposite, ovate. Flowers very small, white. *Meadows and heaths, very common.*

L. peren'ne L. 16. Perennial Flax. July–Aug. Stems tufted. Leaves linear or lanceolate. Flowers large, bright blue, sepals obtuse. *Calcareous heaths, rare.*

L. bien'ne Mill. (**L. angustifo'lium** Huds.) 41. Biennial or Pale Flax. May–Oct. Stem decumbent, branching from base. Leaves linear or lanceolate. Flowers small, pale blue. *Calcareous pastures, occasional.*

L. usitatis'simum L. Common Flax, Linseed. July–Aug. Annual with simple erect stems. Leaves lanceolate. Flowers large, pale blue, sepals acute. *Escape from cultivation.*

FAMILY 20. GERANIA'CEAE

Herbs with mostly opposite, stipulate, and divided or compound leaves. Sepals and petals usually 5, stamens 5–10. Ovary superior, 5-celled, styles 5. Fruit a capsule separating into 5 carpels leaving a persistent axis (a 5-valved capsule in *Oxalis*).

Flowers irregular	Impatiens IV
Flowers regular	2

2 Leaves radical or alternate . . . . . Oxalis II.
  Leaves opposite . . . .

3 Stamens 10, awns of carpels not twisted in fruit . Geranium
  Stamens 5, awns of carpels twisted in fruit . . Erodium I.

I. GERA'NIUM

Flowers regular, red, pink, or purple; stamens 10, hypogynous, united at the base, 5 shorter than the other 5; pistil 5-lobed, ending in a long beak. Carpels attached to central axis by long awns which curl upwards as the fruit ripens and scatter the seeds.

Peduncles 1-flowered . . . . . . G. sanguineum
Peduncles 2 or more flowered 2

2 Flowers blue, 1 inch or more across . . . G. pratense
  Flowers red, pink, or purplish, less than 1 inch across . . 3

3 Petals entire 4
  Petals notched 9

4 Leaves ternate (compound) . . . . G. Robertianum
  Leaves lobed (simple) 5

5 Flowers more than ½ inch across 6
  Flowers less than ½ inch across 7

6 Sepals mucronate . . . . . . G. phaeum
  Sepals long-awned . . . . . . G. sylvaticum

7 Glabrous . . . . G. lucidum
  Hairy 8

8 Leaves broadly lobed; peduncles shorter than leaves G. rotundifolium
  Leaves narrowly lobed; peduncles longer than leaves G. columbinum

9 Petals much longer than the sepals . . . G. pyrenaicum
  Petals scarcely longer than the sepals 10

10 Segments of lower leaves not divided to base . . . 11
   All leaves divided to base 12

11 Carpels glabrous, transversely wrinkled . . . G. molle
   Carpels hairy, keeled . . . . . G. pusillum

12 Peduncles shorter than neighbouring leaves . G. dissectum
   Peduncles longer than neighbouring leaves . G. columbinum

G. sanguin'eum L. 62. Bloody Crane's-bill. June–Aug. Leaves orbicular, divided to base into narrow segments. Flowers about 1½ inches in diameter, bright rosy-purple, solitary, sepals awned. *Dry rocky places, occasional.*

G. phae'um L. 60. Dusky Crane's-bill. June–July. Leaves divided into broad acute lobes, unequally serrate. Flowers about ¾ inch across, dark purple, sepals mucronate. *Hilly woods and fields, occasional.*

G. sylvat'icum L. 61. Wood Crane's-bill. June–Aug. Leaves divided almost to base into acute pinnatifid lobes. Flowers about ¾ inch across, rosy purple, sepals awned. *Moist woods and fields, chiefly in the north.*

G. praten'se L. 97. Meadow Crane's-bill. June–Aug. Leaves divided almost to base into acute pinnatifid lobes. Flowers an inch or more across, blue or purplish-blue, sepals awned. Fruits drooping. *Meadows and waysides, frequent.*

G. pyrena'icum L. 74. Mountain Crane's-bill. May–Sept. Lower leaves divided about half-way into broad obtuse segments, upper leaves more deeply and narrowly cut. Flowers rather more than ½ inch across, purple or purplish-red; petals notched, about twice as long as sepals; sepals mucronate. *Waste places, occasional.*

G. mol'le L. 112. Dove's-foot Crane's-bill. April–Oct. Leaves orbicular, divided about half-way into broad obtuse segments. Flowers small, reddish-purple, petals deeply notched, not longer than the mucronate sepals. Carpels glabrous, transversely wrinkled. *Waste places, common.*

G. pusil'lum L. 86. Small-flowered Crane's-bill. May–Sept. Leaves small, orbicular, divided rather more than half-way into broad obtuse segments. Flowers small, reddish-purple, petals slightly notched, sepals mucronate. Carpels hairy, keeled on back. *Waysides and cornfields, occasional.*

G. rotundifo'lium L. 29. June–July. Leaves large, hairy, orbicular, divided less than half-way into broad obtuse segments. Flowers small, pink, petals entire, sepals mucronate. *Old walls and waste places, rare.*

G. dissect'um L. 111. Jagged-leaved Crane's-bill. May–Aug. Leaves orbicular, divided to base into linear segments. Flowers very small, reddish-purple, on stalks much shorter than the neighbouring leaves; sepals very hairy, awned. Carpels hairy, not keeled. *Waysides, common.*

G. columbi'num L. 77. Long-stalked Crane's-bill. May–Sept. Leaves divided to base into linear segments. Flowers about ½ inch across, purplish-pink, on stalks much longer than neighbouring leaves, sepals awned. *Hedgebanks and dry fields, frequent.*

G. lu'cidum L. 98. Shining Crane's-bill. April–Aug. Leaves orbicular or reniform, divided rather more than half-way into broad obtuse segments, glabrous and shining. Flowers small, pink; petals entire, clawed. *Walls and waste places, common.*

G. Robertia'num L. 112. Herb-Robert. May–Nov. Leaves ternately compound, leaflets stalked. Flowers pink, red, purplish, or white, about ½ inch across; petals entire, clawed; sepals awned. *Waysides and stony places, very common.*

II. *ERO'DIUM*

Very like *Geranium* but the leaves are pinnately, not palmately divided, while the flowers have only 5 fertile stamens. Fruit with a long beak, the awns of the carpels twisted in fruit.

Leaves simple . . . . E. maritimum
Leaves compound, pinnate 2

Leaflets deeply pinnatifid . . . . E. cicutarium
Leaflets toothed or shortly lobed . . . E. moschatum

E. cicuta'rium L'Hér. 111. Stork's-bill. May–Sept. Tufted, hairy, and somewhat sticky, often musky-scented like the following species. Leaflets deeply cut. Flowers small, reddish-purple, in pairs or umbels. *Waste ground, frequent.*

E. moscha'tum L'Hér. 33. Musky Stork's-bill. May–Sept. Hairy and smelling strongly of musk. Leaflet ovate, coarsely toothed or shortly pinnatifid. Flowers small, bluish-purple, in umbels. *Sandhills and heaths near the sea, rare.*

E. marit'imum L'Hér. 33. Sea Stork's-bill. May–Sept. Small, hairy, and sticky. Leaves simple, ovate, toothed or lobed, small. Peduncles 2-flowered. Flowers small, reddish-purple. Beak short. *Sandy places near the sea, locally common.*

III. *OX'ALIS*

Leaves trifoliate (like clover), alternate or radical, leaflets entire. Sepals and petals 5, stamens 10. Fruit a 5-valved capsule, not beaked.

O. Acetosel'la L. 112. Wood Sorrel. April–June. Leaves all radical, long-stalked. Flowers white, solitary. *Common in woods.*

O. cornicula'ta L. 35. June–Sept. Leaves cauline, alternate, long-stalked. Flowers yellow, in pairs. *Escape from gardens.*

IV. *IMPA'TIENS*

Leaves simple, alternate, toothed, exstipulate. Flowers irregular perianth segments all coloured, the largest one spurred; stamens 5 filaments short and thick, anthers touching; ovary superior, 5-celled style none. Fruit a capsule, the valves curling inwards and scattering the seeds.

I. Noli-tan'gere L. 41. Yellow Balsam, Touch-me-not. July–Sept. Flowers yellow, spur widely bent back and entire. *Shady places in N. England and N. Wales, rare.*

I. biflo'ra Walt. 17. Orange Balsam. July–Aug. Flowers orange brown, spur closely bent back and notched. *Along the river Wey in Surrey and a few other streams, rare.*

FAMILY 21. AQUIFOLIA'CEAE

Sepals and petals usually 4. Stamens 4, alternate with the petals and adhering to the base of the corolla. Ovary superior, 4-celled, capped by a sessile stigma. Fruit a berry-like 2–4-seeded drupe.

I'LEX

I. Aquifo'lium L. 107. Holly. May–Aug. Shrub or small tree. Leaves alternate, stiff, leathery and glossy, spiny-pointed, and either with a wavy margin armed with spiny teeth, or entire. Flowers small, white or greenish-white, unisexual or bisexual, monoecious or dioecious, in axillary clusters. Fruit bright red. *Hedges and woods, common.*

Family 22. CELASTRA'CEAE

Stamens few, alternate with the petals and inserted on a fleshy disk surrounding the ovary. Ovary superior, several-celled, seed with an aril.

EUON'YMUS

E. europae'us L. 79. Spindle Tree. May–June. Shrub or small tree with green 4-angled branchlets. Leaves opposite, ovate, or lanceolate, minutely toothed. Flowers small, yellowish-green; petals 4, stamens 4; ovary sunk in the disk, style 1. Fruit a red fleshy 4-valved capsule, seeds enclosed in an orange-coloured aril. *Hedges and open woods, common.*

Family 23. RHAMNA'CEAE

Sepals 4–5. Petals 4–5 or 0. Stamens as many as petals and opposite to them, perigynous. Ovary several-celled, style very short. Fruit (in the British species) a small berry-like 3–4-seeded drupe.

RHAM'NUS

Shrub or small tree with simple leaves. Flowers small, green, in axillary clusters.

R. cathar'ticus L. 61. Common Buckthorn. May–June. Branches often ending in a spine. Leaves opposite or nearly so, finely toothed, with 3–4 pairs conspicuous lateral veins. Flowers dioecious; sepals and petals four. Fruit small, black. *Hedges, occasional.*

R. Fran'gula L. 72. Alder Buckthorn. Berry-bearing Alder. May–July. Spines none. Leaves alternate, entire, with 6 or more pairs parallel veins. Flowers bisexual, sepals and petals 5. Fruit small, dark purple. *Hedges, occasional.*

Family 24. ACERA'CEAE

Shrubs or trees with opposite and, in the British species, palmately lobed leaves. Flowers small, greenish-yellow, in axillary racemes; sepals 5, petals 5 or 0; stamens about 8, on a small disk; ovary superior, 2-lobed and 2-celled, the lobes expanding into wings in the fruit, styles 2. Fruit a double samara.

A'CER

A. Pseudo-plat'anus L. Sycamore. May–June. Leaves large, the lobes with numerous sharp teeth. Flowers in long drooping racemes. Wings of fruit spreading at an angle. *Commonly planted and naturalized.*

A. campes'tre L. 66. Common Maple. May–June. Leaves small, lobes sinuate, with few or no teeth. Flowers in short erect racemes. Wings of fruit spreading horizontally. *Hedges and open woods, common in S. England.*

Family 25. HIPPOCASTANA'CEAE

Trees or shrubs with opposite digitate leaves, stipules none. Flowers irregular, in terminal panicles; sepals and petals 4–5; stamens about 7; ovary superior, 3-celled, surrounded by a narrow disk; style and stigma 1. Fruit a large leathery capsule splitting into three valves and usually holding one large seed.

AE'SCULUS

A. **Hippocast'anum** L. Horse-chestnut. May–June. Leaflets 5–7, large, obovate or oblanceolate, unequally serrate, acuminate. Flowers white, tinged with pink, petals clawed. Fruit covered with spines. *Commonly planted but not naturalized.*

Family 26. PAPILIONA'CEAE

Leaves alternate, stipulate, usually compound. Flowers irregular; sepals united into a tube; petals 5, the upper one is known as the *standard*, the lateral ones as the *wings*, while the lowest form a boat-shaped *keel*, usually free but sometimes united (e.g. *Trifolium*); stamens 10, either all united in a tube round the ovary or 9 united and 1 free; ovary superior, 1-celled, ovules attached to the upper side, style simple. Fruit a pod, either indehiscent or splitting longitudinally into two valves.

Filaments all united in lower half (monadelphous)	. . .	2
Uppermost filament free (diadelphous)	. . .	6
2 Leaves of mature plant simple or none	. . .	3
Leaves compound	. . .	4
3 Calyx much shorter than corolla, without bracts	.	Genista I
Calyx nearly as long as corolla, with bracts	. .	Ulex II
4 Leaves pinnate .	. . .	Anthyllis IX
Lower leaves ternate .	. . .	5
5 Calyx 2-lipped	. . .	Cytisus III
Calyx regular, 5-cleft .	. . .	Ononis IV
6 Leaves pinnate; or ternate, with stipules as large as leaflets	.	7
Leaves ternate, stipules small	. . .	13
7 Leaves imparipinnate .	. . .	8
Leaves paripinnate (with tendril or point in place of terminal leaflet) or replaced by simple leaf-like branches or stipules	.	12
8 Peduncle with terminal leaf	. . .	9
Peduncle without terminal leaf	. . .	10
9 Flowers yellow .	. . .	Lotus X
Flowers pink .	. .	Ornithopus XII
10 Flowers in heads or umbels	. .	Hippocrepis XIII
Flowers in racemes	. . .	11
11 Flowers pink .	. .	Onobrychis XIV
Flowers yellow or purple	. . .	Astragalus XI
12 Style hairy on lower side or both .	. .	Vicia XV
Style hairy on upper side only	. .	Lathyrus XVI

13 Flowers in long one-sided racemes . . . Melilotus VII
    Flowers in short racemes or heads 14
14 Pod much curved, corolla deciduous . . . Medicago VI
    Pod straight or nearly so 15
15 Pod scarcely longer than calyx. Flowers usually in globose or
    cylindrical heads . . . . . . Trifolium VIII
    Pod much longer than calyx. Flowers few, white . Trigonella V

I. *GENIS'TA*

Low woody plants with simple leaves. Flowers yellow, calyx 5-toothed, stamens monadelphous. Pod longer than calyx.

Stem with spines . . . . G. anglica
Stem without spines 2
2 Petals and fruit glabrous . . . . . G. tinctoria
   Petals and fruit hairy . . . . G. pilosa

G. ang'lica L. 89. Needle Furze, Petty Whin. May–June. Stem spiny. Leaves ovate or lanceolate. Flowers yellow. Pod much inflated. *Heaths, occasional.*

G. pilo'sa L. 7. Hairy Greenweed. May–June. Leaves obovate or lanceolate. Flowers yellow, axillary, petals hairy. Pod short, hairy. *Heaths in S. England, rare.*

G. tincto'ria L. 75. Dyer's Greenweed. June–Aug. Leaves oblong or lanceolate, nearly glabrous. Flowers yellow. Pod long and narrow, glabrous. *Fields and copses, frequent.*

II. *U'LEX*

Branchlets green, furrowed and very spiny. Leaves small, simple, usually reduced to scales. Flowers yellow; calyx yellow, nearly as long as corolla; stamens monadelphous. Pod scarcely longer than calyx.

U. europae'us L. 112. Furze, Gorse, Whin. Feb.–June. Calyx very hairy, bracts at base conspicuous. *Heaths and uplands, common.*

U. mi'nor Roth. (**U. na'nus** Forst.) 67. Dwarf Furze. Aug.–Sept. Calyx nearly glabrous, bracts at base minute. *Heaths, locally common.* *U. Gal'lii* Planch. is similar but larger, and with stronger spines.

III. *CYT'ISUS*

C. scopar'ius Link. 110. Common Broom. April–June. Shrub with long green angled branches. Lower leaves ternate, stalked, upper ones sessile and often simple. Flowers large, yellow, slender-stalked, axillary; calyx 2-lipped, petals broad, stamens monadelphous, style very long and rolled inwards. Pod long, black, hairy on the edges. *Dry hills, common.*

IV. *ONO'NIS*

Leaves ternate, leaflets toothed, stipules attached to the petioles. Flowers pink, solitary, axillary; stamens monadelphous. Pod short, inflated.

O. re'pens L. **(O. arven'sis** L.) 101. Rest-harrow. June–Sept. Prostrate or ascending, usually without spines. Pod as long as the calyx. *Poor pastures and sandy places, common.*

O. spino'sa L. 71. Spiny Rest-harrow. July–Sept. Small woody plant with erect spiny stems. Leaflets smaller and narrower than in the preceding species. Pod shorter than the calyx. *Sandy and chalky pastures, frequent.*

V. *TRIGONEL'LA*

T. purpuras'cens L. **(T. ornithopodioi'des** DC.) 37. Fenugreek. June–Aug. Stems spreading 2–3 inches, closely matted, glabrous. Leaves ternate; leaflets obcordate, toothed. Flowers small, white or pinkish, axillary, stamens diadelphous, petals persistent in fruit. Pod long and narrow, slightly curved, glabrous. *Dry sandy places, rare.*

VI. *MEDICA'GO*

Leaves ternate; leaflets toothed, the middle one stalked. Calyx 5-toothed, stamens diadelphous. Pod small, curved or spirally twisted.

Flowers blue or purple	M. sativa
Flowers yellow, greenish, or variegated	2
2 Ripe pod small, black, 1-seeded, not prickly . .	M. lupulina
Ripe pod larger, not black	3
3 Pod curved, not prickly	M. falcata
Pod spirally twisted, prickly	4
4 Pod flattened, netted	M. hispida
Pod nearly globular, not netted	M. arabica

M. sati'va L. Lucerne. June–Aug. Leaflets oblanceolate, hairy. Flowers blue or purple, in short racemes. Pod smooth, spirally twisted. *Escape from cultivation.*

M. falca'ta L. 5. Sickle Medick. June–Aug. Perennial with procumbent or ascending stems. Leaflets oblanceolate, hairy. Flowers yellow or greenish, in short racemes. Pod flat and curved like a sickle or ring. *Dry banks and waste places in S. and E. England, rare.*

M. lupuli'na L. 109. Black Medick, Nonsuch. April–Nov. Leaflets obovate, hairy. Flowers small, yellow, in small heads; peduncles longer than petioles. Pod black when ripe, spirally twisted, 1-seeded. *Fields and waysides, very common.*

M. his'pida Gaertn. **(M. denticula'ta** Willd.) 67. May–Aug. Leaflets obovate, glabrous. Flowers small, yellow, in small heads, peduncles scarcely longer than petioles. Pod light brown when ripe, prickly netted. *Cornfields and waste places near the sea in S. and E. England, rare.*

M. arab'ica All. **(M. macula'ta** Sibth.) 53. Spotted Medick. April–Sept. Leaflets obovate, glabrous, usually with a dark spot in the centre. Flowers small, yellow, in small heads on peduncles shorter than petioles. Pod light brown when ripe, prickly, furrowed on the edge, not netted. *Meadows and waste places near the sea, frequent.*

VII. *MELILO'TUS*

Leaves ternate, stipules small; leaflets toothed, middle one stalked.
Flowers yellow or white, in one-sided racemes; stamens diadelphous.
Pod small, thick, longer than the calyx.

Flowers white . . . . M. alba
Flowers yellow 2
2 Pod ribbed, glabrous . . . . . . M. arvensis
  Pod netted, hairy . . . . M. altissima

M. altis′sima Thuill. 86. Common Melilot. May–Aug. Leaflets
lanceolate. Flowers yellow. Pod netted, hairy. *Waste places, frequent.*

M. al′ba Desr. 75. White Melilot. June–Aug. Leaflets nearly linear.
Flowers white. *Waste places near the sea, rare.*

M. arven′sis Wallr. 55. July–Sept. Leaflets ovate. Flowers yellow.
Pod transversely ribbed, glabrous. *SE. England, rare.*

VIII. *TRIFO'LIUM*

Leaves ternate; stipules large, adhering to the petiole. Flowers red,
white, or yellow, in globose or cylindrical heads or in few-flowered
clusters; corolla persistent in fruit; stamens diadelphous. Pod small,
enclosed in the calyx.

Flowers white 2
Flowers yellow 4
Flowers red, pink, or purple 6
2 Flower-heads sessile . . . . . . T. scabrum
  Flower-heads stalked 3
3 Flower-heads small, flowers not reflexed after fad-
    ing   T. subterraneum
  Flower-heads large, flowers reflexed after fading . T. repens
4 Flowers 20–50 in a head . . . . . T. procumbens
  Flowers 15 or less in a head 5
5 Flowers 2–6 in a head, stalked . . . . T. filiforme
  Flowers 10–15 in head, sessile . . . . T. dubium
6 Flower-heads sessile 7
  Flower-heads stalked 10
7 Flowers ½ inch long or more . . . . T. pratense
  Flowers very small 8
8 Glabrous . . . . T. glomeratum
  Hairy 9
9 Lateral veins stand out in strong relief on under-side of leaflet;
    calyx teeth spreading or recurved after flowering   T. scabrum
  Not like above . . . . T. striatum
10 Flowers stalked, reflexed after fading . . . T. hybridum
  Flowers sessile, not reflexed after fading 11
11 Stems prostrate, rooting at the nodes, calyx inflated after
    flowering . . . . T. fragiferum
  Stems erect or ascending, calyx not inflated . . . 12

12 Flower-heads cylindrical 13
   Flower-heads globose or ovoid 14
13 Flower-heads crimson . . . . . T. incarnatum
   Flower-heads pale pink, soft and feathery . . T. arvense
14 Flowers ¼ inch or less . . . . . T. squamosum
   Flowers ½ inch or more 15
15 Calyx hairy all over, stipules broad, connate . . T. pratense
   Calyx hairy only on the teeth, stipules narrow, free T. medium

T. subterra′neum L. 46. May–June. Leaflets obovate, hairy. Flower-heads small, white, stalked, the whole head turning down towards the ground after fading. Fruiting calyx with star-shaped linear teeth. *Dry pastures in S. England, occasional.*

T. praten′se L. 112. Red Clover. May–Oct. A rather coarse straggling plant with long hairy stems. Leaflets elliptical, usually with a lighter V-shaped patch in the middle. Flower-heads large, reddish-purple, sessile between two leaves or shortly stalked, turning brown after flowering, calyx very hairy. *Meadows and waysides, very common.*

T. me′dium L. 108. Zigzag Clover. June–Sept. Like the preceding species but the leaflets are lanceolate and the hairs on the calyx are confined to the teeth. *Meadows and waysides, frequent.*

T. squamo′sum L. (**T. marit′imum** Huds.) 22. Sea Clover. June–Aug. Leaflets oblanceolate, stipules long and narrow. Flower-heads small, stalked, globose or ovoid, pale pink. *Near the sea in S. England, rare.*

T. incarna′tum L. 37. Crimson Clover. May–July. Leaflets broad. Flower-heads stalked, cylindrical, rich crimson (sometimes white). *Escape from cultivation.*

T. arven′se L. 102. Hare's-foot Clover. June–Sept. Stipules and leaflets small and narrow. Flower-heads stalked, cylindrical; flowers pale pink, half hidden by the hairy teeth of the calyces. *Sandy ground, especially near the sea, frequent.*

T. stria′tum L. 86. Knotted Clover. June–July. Small tufted plant. Leaflets obovate, hairy. Flower-heads sessile, small, pale red, globose or ovoid, calyx hairy. *Dry pastures, frequent.*

T. sca′brum L. 59. Rough Clover. May–Aug. Like the preceding species but the veins on the under-side of the leaflets are much more prominent, and the calyx teeth are broader and recurved after flowering. *Dry pastures, occasional.*

T. glomera′tum L. 21. Clustered Clover. May–June. Small and glabrous. Leaflets broadly obovate. Flower-heads sessile, very small, pink, globose. Calyx teeth recurved after flowering. *Dry pastures in S. and E. England, rare*

T. hy′bridum L. 86. Alsike Clover. June–Sept. Large glabrous plant with broadly obovate leaflets often with a V-shaped patch in the centre. Flower-heads large, red, long-stalked; flowers stalked, reflexed after fading. *Cornfields and waysides, common.*

T. re'pens L. 112. White or Dutch Clover. May–Sept. Stems creeping and rooting at the nodes. Leaves with very long stalks; leaflets nearly orbicular, toothed. Flower-heads large, white tinged with pink, on very long stalks; flowers reflexed after fading. *Meadows and waysides, very common.*

T. fragif'erum L. 72. Strawberry Clover. July–Aug. Like the preceding species but the flowers are red and the calyx much inflated in fruit. *Dry pastures, occasional.*

T. procum'bens L. 107. Hop Trefoil. June–Aug. Leaflets small, obovate. Flower-heads small, lemon-yellow, short-stalked; flowers numerous (up to 50). *Meadows and waysides, common.*

T. du'bium Sibth. (**T. mi'nus** Sm.) 112. Lesser Yellow Clover. June–Aug. Like the preceding species but smaller. Flowers bright yellow, about 10–15 in each head. *Meadows and waysides, common.*

T. filifor'me L. 70. Slender Yellow Clover. May–July. Like the preceding two species but the leaflets are even smaller and there are only two or three (rarely more) flowers in each head, which is of a deeper yellow. *Dry pastures and waste places, occasional.*

IX. *ANTHYL'LIS*

A. Vulnera'ria L. 110. Kidney Vetch, Lady's Fingers. May–Aug. Leaves pinnate, hairy; leaflets entire, the terminal one the largest. Flowers usually yellow, in terminal heads, each head with a divided involucre-like bract beneath; stamens all united; calyx inflated. Pod enclosed within the calyx. *Dry pastures, frequent.*

X. *LO'TUS*

Leaves ternate, with two stipules at the base of the petiole nearly as large as the leaflets and giving the appearance of a pinnate leaf with 5 leaflets. Flowers yellow, in an umbellate cyme at the end of a long axillary peduncle with a terminal leaf. Stamens diadelphous. Pod long and narrow.

L. cornicula'tus L. 112. Bird's-foot Trefoil. May–Sept. Leaflets obovate. Calyx teeth straight in bud. *Meadows and hedgebanks, very common.*
 L. ten'uis (Waldst. and Kit.) is a variety with linear-lanceolate leaflets.

L. uligino'sus Schk. (**L. ma'jor** Scop.). 104. July–Sept. Like the preceding species but larger, taller, and more erect. Calyx teeth spreading in bud. *Moist places, frequent.*

XI. *ASTRAG'ALUS*

Leaves pinnate, with 11 or more leaflets. Flowers in short racemes at the end of long axillary peduncles without a terminal leaf; stamens diadelphous. Pod cylindrical, divided by a longitudinal partition.

A. dan'icus Retz. (**A. hypoglot'tis** DC.) 47. Purple Milk-vetch. June–July. Leaflets 20 or more, ovate, small. Flowers bluish-purple. Pod about ½ inch. *Dry pastures, rare.*

A. glycyphyl'los L. 67. Milk-vetch. June–Sept. Stems prostrate, zigzag. Leaflets about 8–12, ovate, large. Flowers yellow. Pod long, erect, curved. *Copses and dry pastures, rare.*

XII. *ORNITH'OPUS*

O. perpusil'lus L. 86. Bird's-foot. May–Aug. Leaves pinnate; leaflets 10 or more pairs, small, ovate, softly hairy. Flowers small, pink or white, in a few-flowered umbel at the end of a long axillary peduncle with a terminal leaf; stamens diadelphous. Pods long, curved, constricted between the seeds. *Dry pastures, occasional.*

XIII. *HIPPOCRE'PIS*

H. como'sa L. 49. Horseshoe Vetch. May–July. Leaves pinnate, glabrous, with 9–15 small oblong leaflets. Flowers yellow, in an apparent umbel at the end of a long axillary peduncle without a terminal leaf; stamens diadelphous. Pods long, flattened, with curved joints. *Dry pastures on calcareous soil, occasional.*

XIV. *ONOBRY'CHIS*

O. viciaefo'lia Scop. 35. Sainfoin. May–Sept. Leaves pinnate; leaflets about 6–12 pairs, oblong or lanceolate, about an inch long. Flowers pink, in a raceme at the end of a long axillary peduncle without a terminal leaf; stamens diadelphous. Pod prickly, 1-seeded. *Cornfields and meadows on calcareous soil, occasional.*

XV. *VIC'IA*

Leaves paripinnate, the terminal leaflet being replaced by a tendril or point; stipules sagittate. Flowers axillary, solitary, or in clusters or racemes; stamens diadelphous; style cylindrical, hairy on lower side or both.

Leaflets 2 or 4, more than 1 inch long		2
Leaflets more than 4, or less than 1 inch long . . .		3
2	Tendrils present	V. bithynica
	Tendrils absent	Lathyrus montanus
3	Peduncles at least half as long as the leaves . . .	4
	Peduncles very short	8
4	Terminal leaflet replaced by a short point . .	V. Orobus
	Terminal leaflet replaced by a tendril . . .	5
5	Flowers ½ inch long or more	6
	Flowers very small	7
6	Flowers blue	V. Cracca
	Flowers white, with purple veins . . .	V. sylvatica
7	Hairy. Pod, short, 2-seeded . . .	V. hirsuta
	Glabrous or nearly so. Pod 4–6-seeded .	V. tetrasperma
8	Flowers yellow	V. lutea
	Flowers purple	9

9 Flowers in clusters of 3 or more . . . . V. sepium
  Flowers solitary or in pairs 10

10 Flowers large, seeds smooth . . . . . V. sativa
   Flowers small, seeds rough . . . . . V. lathyroides

V. hirsu'ta S. F. Gray. 110. Hairy Vetch, Tare. May–Aug. Leaflets small, linear or lanceolate, hairy. Flowers very small, pale blue or whitish, in long-stalked racemes. Pod flat, ovate, 2-seeded. *Hedgebanks and cornfields, common.*

V. tetrasper'ma Moench. 82. Slender Vetch, Smooth Tare. May–Aug. Leaflets about ¾ inch long, linear or lanceolate, glabrous or nearly so. Flowers small, pale purple, in long racemes. Pod flat, oblong, 4–6-seeded. *Hedgebanks and cornfields, frequent.*
  In *V. gra'cilis* (Lois.) the peduncles are much longer than the leaves.

V. Crac'ca L. 112. Tufted Vetch. June–Aug. Leaflets numerous, lanceolate, acute, about ¾ inch long. Flowers bright blue, in long racemes. Pod long, flat, several-seeded. *Hedges, common.*

V. Or'obus DC. 40. Upright Vetch. May–June. Leaflets numerous, oblong, about ½ inch long, the terminal one reduced to a point. Flowers large, purplish-white, in long-stalked many-flowered racemes. Pod flat, about 1 inch long, 3–4-seeded. *Mountain pastures and rocky woods, mostly in the north, rare.*

V. sylvat'ica L. 82. Wood Vetch. June–Aug. Stipules deeply divided. Leaflets ovate, glabrous. Flowers white, with purple veins, drooping, in long racemes, standard oblong. Pod broad, about 1 inch long, 4–6-seeded. *Hilly woods, occasional.*

V. se'pium L. 112. Bush Vetch. April–Sept. Leaflets ovate or oblong. Flowers reddish-purple, in sessile clusters or short racemes in the axils of the leaves. Pod glabrous, about 1 inch long. *Hedgebanks and woods, common.*

V. lu'tea L. 20. Yellow Vetch. May–Aug. Leaflets oblong or linear. Flowers yellow, solitary, axillary. Pod large, flat, ovate, hairy. *Dry waste places, rare.*

V. sati'va L. 112. Common Vetch. May–July. Leaflets 8–12, oblong. Flowers large, reddish-purple, solitary or in pairs in the leaf axils. Pod long (up to 2 inches), narrow, glabrous, containing 10–12 smooth seeds. *Fields and waysides, common.*

V. lathyroi'des L. 67. Spring Vetch. April–June. Small plant seldom exceeding 6 inches. Leaflet not more than ½ inch long, oblong or narrowly obovate. Flowers small, purple, solitary. Pod not exceeding 1 inch, seeds rough. *Dry pastures and open woods, occasional.*

V. bithyn'ica L. 19. Bithynian Vetch. June–July. Distinguished from all the others by its two pairs of large lanceolate leaflets. Flowers large, bluish-purple with pale wings, solitary or in pairs at the end of axillary peduncles shorter than the leaves. Pod hairy, 4–6-seeded. *Bushy seacliffs, rare.*

XVI. *LATH'YRUS*

Differs from *Vicia* chiefly in the larger and fewer leaflets and the style being flattened, and bearded only on its inner side. Flowers in a short few-flowered raceme at the end of a long axillary peduncle.

Flowers yellow . . . .
Flowers red or purple . . . .
2 Leaflets replaced by 2 large sagittate stipules . . L. Aphaca
  Leaflets 2 (excluding stipules) . . . . L. pratensis
3 Leaves simple, linear, grass-like . . . . L. Nissolia
  Leaflets 2 . . . . L. sylvestris
  Leaflets 4 or more . . . .
4 Leaf without tendril . . . . . . L. montanus
  Leaf with tendril . . . .
5 Stipules entire . . . . L. palustris
  Stipules toothed . . . . . . Vicia bithynica.

L. Aph'aca L. 30. Yellow Vetchling. May–Aug. Leaves (stipules) simple, opposite, entire, sagittate, with a tendril between. Flower small, yellow, solitary or in pairs. Pod long, flat, 4–8-seeded. *Corn fields, rare.*

L. Nisso'lia L. 45. Grass Vetchling. June–July. Leaves (flattened petioles) simple, entire, linear, stipules none. Flowers pink, solitary or in pairs. Pod long and narrow, many-seeded. *Meadows and road-sides in S. England, rare.*

L. praten'sis L. 112. Meadow Vetch. May–Sept. Stems straggling. Leaves with apparently 4 lanceolate leaflets, the lowest being stipules. Flowers yellow. Pod many-seeded. *Hedgebanks, very common.*

L. sylves'tris L. 68. Everlasting Pea. July–Sept. Stems winged, straggling, and climbing. Leaflets 2, lanceolate, parallel-veined, up to 4 inches long. Flowers reddish-purple, in a short few-flowered raceme at the end of a long axillary peduncle. Pod 2 or 3 inches long, seeds numerous. *Hedges, occasional.*

L. palus'tris L. 21. Marsh Pea. June–Aug. Stem winged. Leaflets 4–8, lanceolate, stipules entire. Flowers bluish-purple. Pod about an inch long. *Damp meadows and wet places, rare.*

L. monta'nus Bernh. (**L. macrorrhi'zus** Wimm.) 108. Tuberous Pea, Bitter Vetch. April–July. Root tuberous. Leaves without tendrils; leaflets 4–6, lanceolate or linear, up to 3 inches long. Flowers reddish-purple fading to pinkish or whitish, distant in the raceme. Pod about 1½ inches long. *Hedgebanks and woods, common.*

FAMILY 27. **ROSA'CEAE**

Leaves alternate, usually with conspicuous leafy stipules. Sepals 4–5, sometimes with a lower whorl of bracts (epicalyx). Petals usually 4–5, sometimes none. Stamens usually numerous, perigynous, or epigynous, inserted with the petals on the calyx or on an extension of the receptacle.

istil syncarpous or apocarpous, superior or inferior. Fruit a drupe,
ome, capsule, pod, or a number of achenes attached to an enlarged
eceptacle.

istil definitely superior 2
istil inferior or apparently so (carpels enclosed within the calyx
  tube) 7

2 Style 1 . . . . Prunus I
  Styles more than 1 3

3 Carpels fleshy in fruit, stem usually prickly . . Rubus III
  Carpels not fleshy, but borne on a swollen fleshy
    receptacle . . . . Fragaria VI
  Neither carpels nor receptacle fleshy 4

4 Carpels few . . . . Spiraea II
  Carpels numerous 5

5 Petals 8 . . . . Dryas IV
  Petals 5 or less 6

6 Carpels with long reddish appendages becoming hooks in
    fruit . . . . Geum V
  Carpels with yellow or white appendages not becoming hooks
    in fruit . . . . Potentilla VII

7 Petals absent 8
  Petals present 10

8 Leaves simple, palmately lobed or divided . Alchemilla VIII
  Leaves compound, pinnate 9

9 Stamens numerous . . . . . . Poterium X
  Stamens few . . . . . Sanguisorba XI

10 Herb with yellow flowers . . . . Agrimonia IX
  Tree or shrub 11

11 Carpels many, enclosed in a hollow flask-shaped re-
    ceptacle . . . . Rosa XII
  Carpels 1–5, completely embedded in the receptacle . 12

12 Stem with numerous spines . . . . Crataegus XV
  Stem with few or no spines 13

13 Flowers in compound corymbs . . . . Sorbus XIII
  Flowers solitary or in umbels . . . . Pyrus XIV

I. *PRU'NUS*

Shrubs or trees. Leaves alternate or in clusters, simple, toothed,
ith arching veins, stipules small and free; leaf scars broad. Flowers
hite, solitary or in umbels or racemes in the axils of the leaves or leaf
cars; sepals and petals 5; stamens numerous, attached with the petals
o the rim of a hollow cup at the bottom of which is a single 1-celled
vary with one style. Fruit a juicy drupe containing one hard 'stone'.

lowers in long racemes . . . . P. Padus
lowers in umbels or very short racemes 2

  Branches spiny . . . . P. spinosa
  Branches not spiny . . . . . . P. Avium

P. spino′sa L. (**P. commu′nis** Huds.) 108. Blackthorn, Slo‹
March–May. Branches dark brown or black, spiny. Leaves smal‹
ovate, finely toothed. Flowers small, white, short-stalked, solitary c
in pairs, appearing before the leaves. Drupe small, bluish black, semi
erect. *Hedges and open woods, common.*

    P. insiti′tia L., the Bullace, is a variant often met with growin‹
wild. The branches have few, if any, spines. The leaves are large‹
broader, and more hairy. The flowers are usually in pairs and appea‹
rather later, while the fruit is larger and more drooping.

P. A′vium L. 102. Wild Cherry, Gean, Mazzard. April–May. Leave‹
large, ovate, somewhat coarsely toothed, with glands at the base of th‹
blade, slender-stalked. Flowers white, long-stalked, in umbels. Drup‹
globular, red or black, without bloom. *Hedgerows and woods, occasiona‹*

P. Pa′dus L. 69. Bird Cherry. April–May. Leaves ovate or lanceolate
glabrous, somewhat stiff and glossy. Flowers small, white, in droopin‹
racemes. Drupe small, globular, black. *Hedgerows and woods, rare.*

II. *SPIRAE′A*

Flowers small, numerous, in terminal cymes or panicles. Sepals an‹
petals 5. Stamens numerous, with long thin filaments. Pistil superio‹
apocarpous; the carpels becoming pods in fruit.

S. Ulma′ria L. 112. Meadow Sweet. June–Sept. Stems erect. Leave‹
pinnate, with 5–9 leaflets; leaflets toothed, the terminal being th‹
largest and usually 3–5-lobed, all green above and whitish beneath
stipules broad and toothed. Flowers creamy white, sweet-scented
in large terminal corymbose cymes. Pods spreading, twisted. *Meadou‹
and roadsides, common.*

S. Filipen′dula L. 65. Dropwort. June–July. Stem erect. Leave‹
mostly radical, pinnate, with 15–20 pairs of small deeply toothe‹
leaflets, green below. Flowers white. Pods not twisted. *Meadows an‹
open woods, occasional.*

III. *RU′BUS*

Stems weak, rambling and, in the woody species, prickly. Leave‹
usually compound, leaflets toothed; stipules small, linear or lanceolate
Flowers white or pinkish; sepals and petals 5; stamens and carpel‹
numerous. Fruit a collection of small fleshy drupes attached to a conica‹
receptacle.

Stem woody . . . . ‹
Stem herbaceous . . . . ‹

2 Stem bristly, erect, lower leaves pinnate, fruit hollow and
    red . . . . R. Idaeu‹
  Stem thorny, arching; leaves ternate or digitate; fruit solid and
    black . . . . ‹

3 Flowers large, few; fruit of a few large drupelets covered with
    bluish bloom . . . . R. caesiu‹
  Flowers numerous; fruit of many drupelets without
    bloom . . . . R. fruticosu‹

4 Leaves ternate; flowers small, axillary   .   .   .   R. saxatilis
   Leaves simple; flowers large, terminal   .   .   R. Chamaemorus

R. Idae′us L. 109. Raspberry. June–Aug. Stems erect, bristly, sucker-
ing freely. Leaves pinnate or ternate, white beneath. Flowers white,
drooping; petals small and narrow. Fruit red, hollow when separated
from the receptacle. *Woods, frequent.*

R. frutico′sus L. 76. Blackberry, Bramble. July–Aug. Stems thorny,
arching. Leaves digitate or ternate, often whitish below. Flowers
white or pinkish, erect. Fruit black, solid (not separating from the
receptacle when picked). *Hedges, woods, and waste places, very common.*
     Has been divided into a very large number of species and sub-
species for which Babington's *Manual of British Botany* and the Rev.
W. Moyle Rogers's *Handbook of the British Rubi* may be consulted.

R. cae′sius L. 84. Dewberry. May–Aug. Stems prostrate or spreading, glaucous when young. Leaves ternate, green below. Flowers few,
large, white. Fruit usually of a few large drupelets covered with a
glaucous bloom. *Hedgebanks and waste places, common.*

R. saxat′ilis L. 70. Stone Bramble. June–Aug. Stem prostrate.
Flowering branches erect to 1 foot. Prickles few or none. Flowers
few, greenish white, petals narrow. Fruit of a few large red drupelets.
Open woods, occasional.

R. Chamaemo′rus L. 42. Cloudberry. June–July. Stems erect though
seldom above 6 inches, prickles none. Leaves simple, orbicular or
reniform, often lobed. Flowers solitary, large, white, on terminal
peduncles. Fruit large, orange-red. *Turfy bogs in the north.*

IV. *DRY′AS*

D. octopet′ala L. 18. Mountain Avens. June–Aug. Small tufted
plant with creeping stems. Leaves small, ovate, crenate, dark green
above, white below. Flowers large white, solitary on long stalks,
petals 8, carpels numerous. Fruit of numerous achenes with long
feathery tails. *Limestone hills in Scotland and N. England, locally
common.*

V. *GE′UM*

Leaves lobed or pinnate; stipules large and leafy. Sepals 5, with an
epicalyx of 5 smaller ones; petals 5; stamens numerous; carpels numerous,
each one ending in a long style. Fruit a dry head of numerous hooked
achenes.

G. urba′num L. 111. Wood Avens, Herb-Bennet. April–Nov. Leaves
pinnate, leaflets unequal, green on both sides. Flowers yellow, erect,
with spreading petals. *Hedgebanks, common.*

G. riva′le L. 103. Water Avens. May–July. Leaves mostly radical,
with a large orbicular terminal leaflet. Flowers purplish, drooping,
petals not spreading. *Wet places, frequent.*
     G. interme′dium (Ehrh.) is a cross between this and the preceding
species.

VI. *FRAGA'RIA*

F. ves'ca L. 112. Wild Strawberry. April–July. Stem with runners
Leaves mostly radical, ternate, long-stalked; leaflets ovate, toothed
with silvery hairs beneath. Flowers small, white; sepals 5, with ar
epicalyx; petals 5; carpels numerous, on a swollen fleshy receptacle
which enlarges and becomes the succulent part of the fruit, bearing the
achenes (so-called seeds) on its surface. *Hedgebanks and woods
common.*

VII. *POTENTIL'LA*

Leaves compound. Sepals 8–10. Petals 4–5. Stamens numerous
Carpels numerous on a receptacle which does not greatly enlarge o.
become fleshy. Fruit a dry head of small achenes.

Leaves ternate or digitate 2
Leaves pinnate 7
2 Flowers white . . . . P. sterili
Flowers purplish . . . . P. palustri
Flowers yellow 3
3 Petals mostly 4, leaves sessile . . . . . . P. erecta
Petals mostly 5, leaves stalked 4
4 Leaves white below . . . . . . P. argentea
Leaves green below 5
5 Stems creeping and rooting . . . . . P. reptans
Stems short and tufted 6
6 Leaflets 3, petals shorter than sepals . . . P. Sibbald
Leaflets 5 or more, petals longer than sepals . . . P. verna
7 Flowers purplish, in corymbs . . . . P. palustris
Flowers yellow, solitary . . . . . P. Anserina

P. ster'ilis Garcke. 109. Barren Strawberry. Feb.–May. Leaflets 3.
Flowers white. *Hedgebanks, common.*

P. ver'na L. 25. April–June. Stems short, tufted. Leaflets 5 or 7,
green or greenish on both sides. Flowers yellow. *Hilly fields and
waste places, rare.*

P. erect'a Hampe (P. Tormentil'la Neck.). 112. Tormentil. May–
Sept. Leaflet 3, rarely 5; leaves mostly sessile. Flowers yellow, mostly
with 4 petals. *Heaths, common.*

P. rep'tans L. Cinquefoil. May–Sept. Tap-root very long and thick.
Stems creeping and rooting. Leaves long-stalked; leaflets 5. Flowers
yellow, mostly with 5 petals. *Meadows and roadsides, common.*
    P. *procumbens* (Sibth.) is an intermediate between this and the
preceding species.

P. Anseri'na L. 112. Silverweed. May–Aug. Stem with runners.
Leaves pinnate; leaflets toothed, silvery. Flowers large, yellow, solitary
on long stalks. *Roadsides, common.*

P. argent'ea L. 61. Hoary Cinquefoil. June–July. Leaflets 5, white
beneath. Flowers small, yellow, in corymbs or panicles, petals 5.
Roadsides, occasional.

. palus'tris Scop. 105. Marsh Cinquefoil. May–June. Leaves pinnate or nearly digitate; leaflets 5, greyish-white beneath. Flowers dingy
purple, in corymbs. *Wet places, locally common.*

. Sibbal'di Haller f. 22. Sibbaldia. July–Aug. Leaflets 3, wedge-
shaped, 3-toothed at apex, glaucous. Flowers small, in cymes; petals
yellow, much smaller than the sepals. *Mountains, locally common.*

VIII. *ALCHEMIL'LA*

Herbs with palmately lobed or divided leaves and small greenish-
ellow flowers with no petals but with a double calyx which consists of
sepals with an epicalyx of 4 smaller ones outside. Stamens 4 or fewer.
istil inferior, of 1 or 2 carpels. Fruit of 1 or 2 achenes enclosed in the
alyx tube.

eaves trifid, deeply lobed, very small, flowers sessile .	A. arvensis	
eaves 5–7-lobed, flowers in panicles	2	
Leaves deeply lobed or digitate, silvery beneath	A. alpina	
Leaves shallowly lobed, green beneath . .	A. vulgaris	

. arven'sis Scop. 112. Parsley Piert. May–Aug. A small annual
with trifid deeply-cut leaves and minute flowers in sessile axillary
clusters half enclosed in the leafy stipules. *Fields and waste places,
common.*

. vulga'ris L. 106. Lady's Mantle. Aug.–Sept. Leaves orbicular or
reniform, sharply toothed, and divided into 5 or 7 shallow rounded
lobes. Radical leaves long-stalked; cauline leaves sessile. Flowers
numerous, in terminal panicles. *Meadows, frequent.*

. alpi'na Scop. 31. Alpine Lady's Mantle. June–Aug. Leaves deeply
divided into 5 or 7 narrow lobes or leaflets, which are toothed only in
the outer half, and are silvery beneath. Flowers in interrupted spikes
or small panicles. *Mountains of Scotland and N. England.*

IX. *AGRIMO'NIA*

. Eupato'ria L. 108. Agrimony. June–Oct. Erect plant with pinnate
leaves, leafy stipules and toothed leaflets. Flowers small, yellow, in
long spikes; sepals and petals 5; stamens 7–20; ovary inferior. Carpels
2, enclosed in the calyx tube, which develops long hooked bristles in
fruit. *Waysides and meadows, common.*

X. *POTE'RIUM*

. Sanguisor'ba L. 73. Salad Burnet. May–July. Leaves pinnate,
with 5–10 pairs small-toothed leaflets. Flowers small, unisexual, in a
globose head at the end of a long peduncle; sepals 4, petals 0; stamens
numerous, with long filaments; ovary inferior, carpels 2. Fruit 4-angled,
wrinkled and pitted, enclosing 1 or 2 achenes. *Waysides and dry pastures,
common.*

XI. *SANGUISOR'BA*

. officina'lis L. 69. Great Burnet. June–Aug. Very like *Poterium* but
the purple flowers are in ovoid or cylindrical heads and bisexual; while
the stamens are only 4, with short filaments. *Moist meadows, occasional.*

XII. *RO'SA*

Shrubs with prickly stems. Leaves pinnate, the lowest part of the petiole with 2-pointed stipules adhering to it. Flowers showy; sepals and petals 5; stamens numerous; carpels attached to the inside of a hollowed out receptacle which enlarges and becomes fleshy, enclosing the achenes

Styles united into a column projecting above the receptacle . . 2
Styles free and not or a little projecting above the receptacle . .

2 Stem trailing; column longer than the stamens . . R. arvensi
  Stem erect or arched; column shorter than the stamens   R. stylos:

3 Sepals all entire; fruit dark . . . . R. spinosissima
  Sepals some or all pinnatifid; fruit bright red . . . 4

4 Leaflets doubly serrate, with many glands on the lower surface . 5
  Leaflets doubly or simply serrate, with few or no glands on the lower
    surface 6

5 Prickles nearly straight, leaves very hairy . . . R. villosa
  Prickles hooked, leaves with few hairs . . . R. rubiginos:

6 Prickles nearly straight, sepals usually erect and persistent till
    the fruit ripens . . . . . . R. villosa
  Prickles usually hooked, sepals usually reflexed and falling off
    before the fruit ripens . . . . . R. canina

R. arven'sis Huds. 52. Trailing Rose. June–July. Stems trailing Prickles curved. Leaflets simply serrate. Flowers white, not scented usually in pairs or threes, styles forming a single capitate column longer than the stamens. Fruit dark red, smooth. *Hedges, frequent.*

R. stylo'sa Desv. 33. June–July. Stems erect or arched. Leaflets hairy below. Flowers white or pink, styles forming a conical head shorter than the stamens. *Hedges, occasional.*

R. spinosis'sima L. 93. Burnet Rose. May–Oct. Stems with very numerous short straight prickles. Leaflets small. Flowers small, white or pink, solitary, sepals entire and becoming erect. Fruit small, dark brown or black. *Hedges and dry banks, frequent.*

R. cani'na L. 110. Dog Rose. June–July. Prickles usually curved, with much dilated base. Flowers large, white or pink, scented; sepals deeply pinnatifid, reflexed, falling off before fruit ripens. Fruit scarlet, smooth *Hedges, common.*

R. villo'sa L. 74. Downy Rose. June–July. Prickles usually straight thin. Leaflets doubly serrate, usually very hairy on both sides. Flowers white or pale pink; sepals becoming erect, persistent till fruit ripens Fruit large, hispid. *Hedges and open woods, frequent*

R. rubigino'sa L. 86. Sweet Briar. May–July. Prickles curved, with much dilated base. Leaflets doubly serrate, glandular, aromatic Flowers pink. Fruit orange-scarlet, smooth or with a few glandular bristles. *Hedges and open woods, mostly in SE. England.*

XIII. *SOR'BUS*

Small deciduous trees with pinnate or simple leaves and small white flowers in showy compound corymbs. Sepals and petals 5; stamens 15–20; ovary inferior, with 2–5 carpels. Fruit a berry-like pome.

Leaves pinnately compound . . . . . S. Aucuparia
Leaves simple 2

Leaves lobed, green beneath . . . . . S. torminalis
Leaves not lobed, white beneath . . . . . S. Aria

. **Aucupa'ria** L. (**Pyrus Aucuparia** Gaertn.) 111. Rowan, Mountain Ash. May–June. Leaflets in 11–19 pairs, narrowly oblong or lanceolate, toothed. Flowers small, white, in showy corymbs at the end of short leafy branches. Fruit bright red. *Hilly woods, frequent.*

. **A'ria** Crantz. (**Py'rus Aria** Ehrh.) 80. White Beam. May–July. Leaves large, simple, toothed, dark green above, white below, lateral veins straight and parallel. Flowers larger and less numerous than in the preceding species. Fruit red. *Common in woods on chalk and limestone.*

. **tormina'lis** Crantz. (**Py'rus torminalis** Ehrh.) 49. Wild Service. May–June. Leaves simple, divided into pointed lobes. Flowers small, numerous. Fruit brown, spotted. *Woods, rare.*

XIV. *PY'RUS*

Small trees with simple finely toothed slender-stalked leaves. Leaf-ears narrow. Flowers large, white, in umbels or short racemes; sepals and petals 5; stamens numerous; ovary inferior, styles 5 or fewer. Fruit pome.

. **commu'nis** L. 51. Pear. May–June. Winter buds glabrous. Styles free to the base. Fruit an obovoid juicy pome with gritty flesh and leathery pips. *Hedges and woods, rare.*

. **Ma'lus** L. 99. Crab Apple. May–June. Winter buds hairy. Flowers pink in bud; styles united above the base. Fruit a globular pome indented at junction with stalk, flesh mealy. *Hedges and woods, frequent.*

XV. *CRATAE'GUS*

. **Oxyacan'tha** L. 112. Hawthorn, May. May–June. Shrub or small tree with spiny branches and small pinnatifid leaves. Flowers small, white, in conspicuous sessile umbels or corymbs; sepals and petals 5; stamens 20; ovary inferior, style usually 1. Fruit a small red berry-like pome containing 1 or 2 hard stones. *Hedges and woods, very common.*

FAMILY 28. **SAXIFRAGA'CEAE**

Leaves simple, exstipulate. Sepals and petals usually 5; stamens as many or twice as many as the petals (or sepals), perigynous. Ovary inferior or half superior, 2- or 4-celled, with as many styles or stigmas cells. Fruit a 2–4-valved capsule.

Petals none . . . . Chrysosplenium I
Petals 5 . . . .
2 Fertile stamens 10, styles 2 . . . . . Saxifraga
  Fertile stamens 5, stigmas 4 . . . . Parnassia II

I. *SAXIFRAGA*

Sepals and petals 5. Stamens 10, inserted on a fleshy growth surrounding the ovary. Ovary 2-celled, styles 2. Fruit a 2-valved capsule.

Flowers yellow . . . . S. aizoide
Flowers white, pink, or purple . . . . . .
2 Leaves opposite . . . . . . S. oppositifoli
  Leaves alternate . . . .
3 Calyx reflexed . . . .
  Calyx spreading or erect . . . . . .
4 Flowers white . . . . S. stellar
  Flowers pink . . . . S. umbros
5 Low moss-like plant with creeping barren stems and erect
    flowering stems . . . . . S. hypnoide
  Stems all erect or ascending . . . . . .
6 Leaves wedge-shaped, 3-lobed . . . S. tridactylite
  Radical leaves reniform . . . . . S. granula

S. oppositifo′lia L. 35. Purple Saxifrage. April–May. Low tufte
plant with creeping stems. Leaves small, crowded, opposite, obovat
ciliate. Flowers large, purple. *Mountains in the north, rare.*

S. stellar′is L. 44. Star Saxifrage. July–Aug. Leaves ovate, thin, wit
a few teeth. Flowers white, star-like, petals narrow, sepals reflexe
Mountains in the north, rare.

S. umbro′sa L. London Pride. June–July. Leaves ovate, toothe
thick and glabrous. Flowers small, pink, in loose panicles, sepa
reflexed. *Ireland. Common in English gardens.*

S. aizoi′des L. 33. Yellow Saxifrage. June–Sept. Leaves lanceolate c
linear, entire or with 2 teeth below the apex, thick, about ½ inch lon;
Flowers yellow, in a small loose panicle. *Mountains in Scotland ar
N. England, rare.*

S. tridactyli′tes L. 87. Rue-leaved Saxifrage. April–June. Leav
small, mostly wedge-shaped and 3-lobed. Flowers small, white, o
long thin stalks; sepals erect. *Walls and rocks, frequent.*

S. granula′ta L. 86. Meadow Saxifrage. May–June. Stems tall, erec
Radical leaves reniform, crenate, long-stalked. Flowers large, whit
in terminal cymes, sepals erect. *Meadows, locally common.*

S. hypnoi′des L. 50. Mossy Saxifrage. May–July. Grows in mos
green tufts. Leaves linear or trifid, about ½ inch long. Flowers rath
large, white, several at the end of a long erect peduncle, sepals ere
or spreading. *Hills in the north and west, rare.*

II. *CHRYSOSPLE'NIUM*

Creeping, moisture-loving herbs with orbicular crenate leaves and small yellow flowers in terminal leafy cymes. Sepals 4, petals o. Stamens 8, inserted on the edge of a disk. Ovary 2-celled, styles 2. Capsule 1-celled, opening in 2 valves.

C. oppositifo'lium L. 109. Golden Saxifrage. March–May. Leaves opposite, about ½ inch across, with scattered hairs. *Wet places, frequent.*

C. alternifo'lium L. 79. Alternate-leaved Golden Saxifrage. March–May. Like the preceding species but leaves alternate and more conspicuously toothed. *Wet places, occasional.*

II. *PARNAS'SIA*

P. palus'tris L. 91. Grass of Parnassus. July–Sept. Radical leaves cordate, glabrous, long-stalked. Flowers large, white, solitary at the end of a long erect peduncle which bears 1 sessile leaf below the middle; sepals and petals 5; fertile stamens 5, alternating with 5 tufts of capitate filaments; ovary superior, 4-celled, with 4 sessile stigmas. Capsule 1-celled, opening in 4 valves. *Wet places, mostly in the north.*

FAMILY 29. RIBESIA'CEAE

Shrubs. Leaves alternate, exstipulate, palmately veined or lobed. Flowers small; sepals and petals 4–5; stamens 5, inserted on the edge of a disk; ovary inferior, 1-celled, with parietal placentation. Fruit a juicy berry.

RI'BES

Stem spiny	R. Grossularia
Stem without spines	2
2 Flowers dioecious, racemes semi-erect . . .	R. alpinum
Flowers bisexual, racemes drooping	3
3 Calyx campanulate, berry black	R. nigrum
Calyx saucer-shaped, berry red	R. rubrum

R. Grossula'ria L. 101. Gooseberry. April–May. Stem with spines usually in twos or threes. Leaves small, orbicular, with 3–5 rounded lobed. Flowers green, solitary or in pairs. Berry yellowish-green, hairy. *Hedges and open woods, frequent.*

R. alpi'num L. 12. Mountain Currant. April–May. Leaves small, 3-lobed. Flowers dioecious, in semi-erect racemes. Fruit small, red, tasteless. *Woods in N. England and N. Wales, rare.*

R. ru'brum L. 86. Red Currant. April–May. Leaves as broad as long, 3–5-lobed. Flowers greenish-white, saucer-shaped, in drooping racemes on previous year's twigs. Fruit red. *Hedges and woods, frequent.*

R. ni'grum L. 86. Black Currant. April–May. Leaves large, as broad as long, with the characteristic smell of black currant. Flowers white, campanulate, in drooping racemes on young twigs. Fruit black when ripe. *Shady places, frequent.*

FAMILY 30. CRASSULA'CEAE

Herbs with fleshy leaves. Sepals 3 or more; petals as many, ofte
united. Stamens as many or twice as many petals. Pistil superio
apocarpous.

Petals united into a corolla-tube, leaves orbicular .   .   Cotyledon
Petals free, leaves not orbicular .   .   .   .

2 Petals 4–5 .   .   .   .   Sedum I
Petals 10–12   .   .   .   .   .   Sempervivum II

I. *COTYLE'DON*

C. Umbili'cus L. 58. Pennywort. June–Aug. Leaves fleshy, orbicula
long-stalked. Flowers pale greenish-yellow, tubular, in long erec
racemes; corolla cylindrical, 5-toothed; stamens 10, inserted at th
base of the corolla; carpels 5. *Walls and rocks, frequent*

II. *SE'DUM*

Petals 4–5, free. Stamens 8–10. Carpels 4–5.

Flowers purple   .   .   .   .   S. Telephiun
Flowers yellow, rarely purplish .   .   .   .
Flowers white or pale pink   .   .   .   .

2 Leaves flat, petals 4   .   .   .   .   S. rose
Leaves ovoid or cylindrical, petals 5   .   .   .   .   .

3 Leaves ovoid   .   .   .   .   S. acr
Leaves linear-cylindrical   .   .   .   .   .   S. rupestr

4 Leaves ovoid   .   .   .   .   S. anglicun
Leaves oblong   .   .   .   .

5 Glabrous   .   .   .   .   S. albun
Hairy .   .   .   .   S. villosun

S. ro'sea (L.) Scop. (S. Rhodi'ola DC.) 44. Roseroot, Midsummer
men. June–Aug. Leaves flat, crowded, sessile, about 1 inch long
toothed. Flowers yellow, rarely purplish, in dense terminal cymes
Mountains of Scotland and N. England, locally common.

S. Tele'phium L. 93. Orpine, Livelong. July–Sept. Leaves flat, dis
tant, about 2 inches long, coarsely toothed. Flowers purple, in termina
corymbs. *Hedgebanks, escape from gardens.*

S. ang'licum Huds. 65. English Stonecrop. June–Aug. Low plan
not exceeding 3 inches. Leaves ovoid, glabrous. Flowers white, tinge
with pink. *Rocks and waste places, occasional.*

S. al'bum L. 45. White Stonecrop. June–Aug. Leaves cylindrical o
oblong, glabrous. Flowers white. *Walls and rocks, rare.*

S. a'cre L. 100. Common Yellow Stonecrop, Wall-pepper. June–
July. Low plant not exceeding 3 inches. Leaves ovoid, flowers brigh
yellow. *Walls and roofs, common.*

S. rupes'tre L. 18. July–Aug. Leaves linear, flattened, slightly spurred at base. Flowers large, yellow, in terminal cymes at the end of tall, erect stems. *Stony places, rare.*

S. reflex'um (L.), a common escape from gardens, is similar but the leaves are rounded on both sides and the lower ones are recurved.

S. villo'sum L. 34. Hairy Stonecrop. June–July. Leaves oblong or linear, hairy. Flowers pale pink, few. *Damp rocks and stones in Scotland and N. England, frequent.*

III. *SEMPERVI'VUM*

S. tecto'rum L. Houseleek. July. Leaves ovate, fleshy, about 1 inch long, in rosettes on the barren shoots, alternate on the tall flowering stems. Flowers pink or purplish, in erect cymes, petals 10–12 or more. *Walls and roofs, introduced.*

FAMILY 31. DROSERA'CEAE

Herbs with long-stalked radical leaves covered with long glandular bristles. Flowers white, in terminal racemes on a long leafless stem; sepals and petals 5; stamens 5, hypogynous; ovary superior, 1-celled, styles 3–4. Fruit a capsule opening by longitudinal valves.

DRO'SERA

D. rotundifo'lia L. 108. Common Sundew. July–Sept. Leaves obovate or orbicular, as broad as long. *Bogs, common.*

D. longifo'lia L. 54. Long-leaved Sundew. July–Sept. Leaves longer than broad. Flowering stem short. *Bogs, occasional.*

D. ang'lica (Huds.) has linear leaves.

FAMILY 32. HALORAGA'CEAE

Aquatic herbs with opposite or whorled leaves and minute flowers.

Leaves opposite	Callitriche III
Leaves whorled	. 2
2 Leaves entire, stamens and stigma 1 . . .	Hippuris I
Leaves finely cut, stamens and stigmas several .	Myriophyllum II

I. *HIPPU'RIS*

H. vulga'ris L. 89. Marestail. June–July. Stem erect or floating, unbranched, crowded with whorls of linear strap-shaped leaves. Flowers minute, axillary, sessile, perianth none. Fruit a minute ovoid 1-seeded nut. *Ponds and ditches, occasional.*

II. *MYRIOPHYL'LUM*

Water plants with pinnately dissected whorled leaves and minute sessile flowers in terminal spikes. Flowers unisexual, male with 4 petals and 4–8 stamens, female with 4 sepals and 0 petals; ovary 4-celled, with 4 styles.

M. verticilla'tum L. 50. Water Milfoil. July–Aug. Floral leaves longer than the flowers, which are usually submerged. *Ditches and ponds, rare.*

M. spica'tum L. 102. Water Milfoil. June–Aug. Floral leaves shorter than the flowers, the spikes projecting above the water. *Ditches and ponds, frequent.*

III. *CALLIT'RICHE*

C. aquat'ica Sm. 108. Water Starwort. April–Sept. Stems long and slender, usually forming large tufts under or on the surface of the water. Lower leaves linear; upper obovate, forming floating rosettes. Flowers minute, solitary, axillary; the male consisting of a single stamen on a long slender filament; the female of a 4-lobed ovary with 2 long styles. Fruit minute, 4-lobed, the lobes sometimes keeled. *Ponds and shallow streams, common*

FAMILY 33. LYTHRA'CEAE

Herbs with opposite entire exstipulate leaves. Calyx 8–10-toothed. Petals 4–6 or 0. Stamens as many or twice as many as the petals, inserted on the calyx. Ovary superior, 2-celled, style 1. Fruit a capsule.

Petals minute or none . . . . Peplis
Petals large . . . . Lythrum I

I. *PEP'LIS*

P. Por'tula L. 103. Water Purslane. July–Sept. Small creeping plant. Leaves obovate, not exceeding ½ inch. Flowers minute, axillary; calyx campanulate, petals pink, stamens 6, style short. *Wet places, frequent*

II. *LY'THRUM*

L. Salica'ria L. 95. Purple Loosestrife. July–Sept. Tall erect plant. Leaves lanceolate, often in threes. Flowers reddish-purple, in terminal spikes; calyx tubular, ribbed, hairy; petals 4–6, stamens 8–12, style long *Marshy places and riverbanks, common*

FAMILY 34. ONAGRA'CEAE

Leaves exstipulate. Petals 2–4. Stamens as many or twice as many as the petals. Ovary inferior, 2–4-celled, style 1. Fruit a capsule.

Stamens 2 . . . . Circaea II
Stamens 8 2
2 Flowers red, seeds cottony . . . . . Epilobium
Flowers yellow, seeds not cottony . . . . Œnothera I

I. *EPILO'BIUM*

Flowers red or pink; petals 4, stamens 8, ovary long and narrow. Capsule with numerous seeds each with a tuft of white cottony hairs.

Flowers in terminal leafless racemes . . . E. angustifolium
Flowers axillary or in short leafy racemes 2

2 Stigma deeply 4-lobed 3
   Stigma entire 5

3 Leaves all opposite, very hairy, clasping the stem . E. hirsutum
   Leaves some alternate, slightly hairy or glabrous, not clasping the
   stem 4

4 Leaves sessile, lanceolate . . . . . E. parviflorum
   Leaves stalked, ovate . . . . . . E. montanum

5 Stem with conspicuous raised lines 6
   Stem without or with very faint raised lines . . . 7

6 Leaves narrow, strap-shaped, sessile . . E. tetragonum
   Leaves broadly lanceolate or ovate, shortly stalked . E. roseum

7 Leaves narrow-lanceolate or linear . . . . E. palustre
   Dwarf plant with ovate leaves . . . . E. alpinum

E. angustifo'lium L. 107. Rose-bay Willow-herb. French Willow.
July–Aug. A tall plant up to 5 feet high. Leaves alternate, lanceolate,
entire or nearly so. Flowers purplish red, in large leafless racemes;
petals entire or slightly notched, often unequal, stigma deeply 4-lobed.
Waste places in light soils, common.

E. hirsu'tum L. 96. Great Hairy Willow-herb, Codlins-and-Cream.
July–Aug. A tall stout plant up to 6 feet high. Leaves nearly all
opposite, lanceolate, clasping the stem, bright green, very hairy.
Flowers solitary in the leaf axils, large, rose-red; petals equal, notched;
stigma deeply 4-lobed. *Riverbanks and moist heavy soils, common.*

E. parviflo'rum Schreb. 110. Small-flowered Willow-herb. June–
Aug. Much shorter than the two preceding species. Leaves mostly
alternate, lanceolate, sessile, downy. Flowers small, pale, regular,
stigma deeply 4-lobed. *Riverbanks and ditches, frequent.*

E. monta'num L. 112. Broad-leaved Willow-herb. June–Aug. Not
exceeding 2 feet. Leaves ovate, finely but sharply toothed, shortly
stalked, glabrous or nearly so. Flowers small, regular, petals deeply
notched, stigma deeply 4-lobed. *Waysides and waste places very
common.*

E. ro'seum Schreb. 66. Pale-flowered Willow-herb. July–Aug. Very
like the preceding species but the leaves are narrower, the flowers
smaller and paler, and the stigma is entire or very shortly 4-lobed.
Damp places, occasional.

E. tetrago'num L. 110. Square-stalked Willow-herb. July–Aug.
Leaves narrowly lanceolate, sessile, with a prominent ridge running
down the stem from the base of each leaf. Flowers small, regular,
petals deeply notched, stigma entire. *Wet places, common.*

   E. obscu'rum (Schreb.) has broader leaves, shorter capsules, less
prominent ridges, and runners from the base of the stem.

E. palus'tre L. 112. Marsh Willow-herb. June–Aug. Like the preceding species but the leaves are even narrower, entire or nearly so,
and without the prominent lines running down the stem from the
leaves. *Wet places, frequent.*

E. alpi'num L. 25. Alpine Willow-herb. July–Aug. A small plant no
exceeding 6 inches in height, with creeping stems and ovate leaves
Wet places in the mountains of Scotland and N. England, locally common
     E. alsinefo'lium (Vill.) is more erect, with larger more prominently
toothed leaves.

II. ŒNOTHE'RA

Œ. Lamarckia'na Ser. 50. Evening Primrose. June–Sept. Leaves
alternate, ovate or lanceolate, entire or nearly so. Flowers large, yellow
opening in the evening; petals 4; stamens 8; styles 4, exceeding the
stamens. *Escape from gardens.*
     Œ. bien'nis L. has smaller flowers in which the styles equal the
stamens.

III. CIRCAE'A

Leaves opposite, ovate, stalked. Flowers small, white, or pink, in
terminal panicles; sepals, petals, and stamens 2; style 1.

C. lutetia'na L. 98. Enchanter's Nightshade. June–Aug. Leaves
hairy, finely toothed. Capsule pear-shaped and covered with hooked
hairs; seeds 2. *Woods and shady places, common.*

C. alpi'na L. 36. Alpine Enchanter's Nightshade. July–Aug. Leaves
glabrous, coarsely toothed. Capsule oblong, less hairy than in preceding species and containing only 1 seed. *Mountains in the north, locally
common.*

FAMILY 35. CUCURBITA'CEAE

Prostrate or climbing herbs with alternate palmately nerved or lobed
leaves opposite to tendrils. Flowers regular, unisexual; sepals and petals
5; stamens 5, inserted on the calyx or corolla; ovary inferior, 3–5-celled.
Fruit a juicy berry.

BRYO'NIA

B. dioi'ca Jacq. 58. White Bryony. May–July. Leaves palmately 5–7-
lobed. Flowers small, yellowish, dioecious. Berry red. *Hedges, frequent in the south.*

FAMILY 36. UMBELLIF'ERAE

Herbs with alternate and usually compound leaves. Flowers small,
in simple or compound umbels; sepals, petals, and stamens 5; ovary
inferior, 2-celled, styles 2. Fruit when ripe separating into 2 carpels
attached to a common axis and often bearing oil ducts (vittae) on their
surface.

Leaves spiny . . . . Eryngium II
All the leaves simple, not spiny 2
Lower leaves compound or very finely divided . . . 3
    2 Leaves palmately lobed . . . . . Sanicula III
      Leaves crenate, peltate . . . . . Hydrocotyle I
      Leaves entire . . . . . . Bupleurum VI
    3 Leaves thick and fleshy . . . . Crithmum XX
      Leaves not thick and fleshy 4

4 Fruit with a beak more than twice as long as itself   Scandix XVIII
   Fruit with a short or no beak 5
5 Fruit covered with prickles or bristles 6
   Fruit smooth or slightly hairy 8
6 Involucral bracts pinnatifid . . . . Daucus XXXI
   Involucral bracts entire or none 7
7 Fruit surmounted by a short smooth beak (*a*)   Chaerophyllum XVII
   Fruit covered to the top with hooked bristles (*b*)   Caucalis XXXII
8 Ribs of fruit with prominent wavy edge; stem spotted with
    purple (*c*) . . . . Conium IV
   Ribs of fruit entire, indistinct, or none . . . 9

(*a*)   (*b*)   (*c*)

(*d*)   (*e*)   (*f*)   (*g*)

9 Flowers yellow or greenish-yellow . . . 10
   Flowers white, greenish-white, or pink . . 13
10 All the leaflets with thread-like segments . Foeniculum XIX
   Lower leaflets lanceolate in general outline . Silaus XXIII
   Lower leaflets ovate in general outline . . . 11
11 Lower leaves 2- or 3-ternate, with large broad segments Smyrnium V
   Lower leaves pinnate or much divided . . . 12
12 Fruit flattened (*d*) . . . . Pastinaca XXVIII
   Fruit globular or ovoid (*e*) . . . . Carum X
13 Involucral bracts none 14
   Involucral bracts present under primary or secondary umbels or
    both 18
14 Flowers greenish-white, in lateral umbels . Apium VIII
   Flowers white, in terminal umbels . . . 15
15 Lower leaves 2- or 3-ternate, with broad segments Ægopodium XIII
   Lower leaves pinnate or finely divided . . . 16
16 Fruit narrow, aromatic (*f*) . . . . Carum X
   Fruit broad, not aromatic (*g*) 17
17 Stem short and stiff, leaves glaucous . . . Trinia VII
   Stem tall and slender, leaves green . . Pimpinella XIV
18 Leaflets whorled, linear . . . . Carum X
   Lower leaves 1-pinnate or 1-ternate . . 19
   Lower leaves more than 1-pinnate or 1-ternate . . 24

19 Ripe carpels flat, fruit dorsally compressed (*a*) . . . 20
   Ripe carpels not flat, fruit laterally compressed (*b*) . . . 21
20 Vittae short, not descending to base of carpel (*c*) Heracleum XXIX
   Vittae long, descending to base of carpel (*d*) . Peucedanum XXVII
21 Land plant 22
   Water or marsh plant 23
22 Lower leaves with 5–9 leaflets . . . . . Sison XI
   Lower leaves with 11 or more leaflets . . . . Carum X
23 Umbels terminal, long-stalked . . . . Sium XII
   Umbels lateral, short-stalked or sessile . . . Apium VIII

(*a*)   (*b*)   (*c*)   (*d*)

(*e*)   (*f*)   (*g*)   (*h*)   (*i*)

24 Fruit with broad wings (*e*) . . . . Angelica XXVI
   Fruit with narrow or no wings 25
25 Calyx teeth conspicuous in fruit, free at apex . . . 26
   Calyx teeth absent in fruit 28
26 Fruit longer than broad (*f*) . . . . Œnanthe XXI
   Fruit as broad as long 27
27 Umbels of 8 or fewer rays . . . . Coriandrum XXX
   Umbels of 10 or more rays . . . . Cicuta IX
28 Ripe carpels flat, narrowly winged (*g*) . . Peucedanum XXVII
   Ripe carpels not flat 29
29 Leaves 2- or 3-ternate, with large broad leaflets Ligusticum XXV
   Leaves pinnate or much dissected 30
30 Plant submerged in water . . . . . Apium VIII
   Plant not submerged in water 31
31 Umbels shorter than the long reflexed involucres . Æthusa XXII
   Umbels longer than the involucres 32
32 Lower leaves divided into linear segments, fruit oblong or ovoid 33
   Segments of lower leaves broad, fruit linear . . . 35
33 Leaf-segments very small and crowded, root not bul-
    bous . . . . Meum XXIV
   Leaf-segments few, not crowded, root bulbous . . 34
34 Styles erect in fruit (*h*) . . . . Conopodium XV
   Styles curved or reflexed in fruit (*i*) . . . Carum X

35 Fruit more than ½ inch long, whole plant very
    aromatic . . . . Myrrhis XVI
   Fruit not exceeding ½ inch, plant slightly or not
    aromatic . . . . . Chaerophyllum XVII

I. *HYDROCOT'YLE*

H. vulga'ris L. 112. White-rot, Marsh Pennywort. June–Aug.
Stems creeping, rooting at the nodes. Leaves orbicular, peltate, long-
stalked. Flowers minute, greenish-white, in small heads on peduncles
shorter than the petioles. Fruit small, flat, laterally compressed. *Bogs,
common.*

II. *ERYN'GIUM*

E. marit'imum L. 54. Sea Holly. July–Aug. Glabrous and glaucous.
Leaves stiff, broad, and prickly. Flowers blue, in globular heads in a
prickly involucre. *Sea-coasts, frequent.*

III. *SANIC'ULA*

S. europae'a L. 110. Wood Sanicle. May–June. Leaves mostly
radical, simple, palmately divided. Flowers minute, in small heads,
the heads usually in threes in umbels or panicles. Fruit prickly, burr-
like. *Woods on calcareous soils, common.*

IV. *CONI'UM*

C. macula'tum L. 107. Hemlock. May–Aug. Tall and erect, with
hollow spotted stems. Leaves pinnately compound, finely divided, and
fern-like. Flowers white, in smallish terminal umbels. Fruit nearly
globular, with prominent wavy ribs. *Damp hedges and banks of streams,
common.* Poisonous.

V. *SMYRN'IUM*

S. Olusa'trum L. 69. Alexanders. April–June. Lower leaves 2- or
3-ternate, with broad leaflets. Flowers greenish-yellow. Fruit ovoid,
angular, each carpel 3-ribbed. *Waste places near the sea, occasional.*

VI. *BUPLEU'RUM*

Leaves simple, entire. Flowers yellow. Fruit ovoid.

B. rotundifo'lium L. 49. Hare's-ear. June–Aug. Leaves broad and
clasping the stem. *Cornfields on calcareous soil in S. and E. England,
rare.*

B. tenuis'simum L. 31. Slender Hare's-ear. July–Sept. Leaves
linear and grass-like. *Pastures near the sea in S. and E. England, rare.*

VII. *TRIN'IA*

T. glauca Dumort. (**T. vulga'ris** DC.) 3. Honewort. May–June.
Stem 6–12 inches high, stiff, erect, much branched. Leaves twice
pinnate, leaflets trifid, glaucous. Flowers white. Fruit ovoid, each
carpel with 5 prominent ribs. *Dry limestone hills in S. Devon and
N. Somerset, rare.*

VIII. *A'PIUM*

Water or marsh plants with compound leaves and white flowers in lateral umbels which are usually short-stalked or sessile. Petals entire. Fruit ovoid, small.

Involucral bracts none	. . . . . . A. graveolens
Involucral bracts present	 2
2 Leaflets not lobed .	. . . . . . A. nodiflorum
Leaflets deeply lobed or divided	. . . A. inundatum

A. grave'olens L. 68. Celery. June–Sept. Stem up to 2 feet high, glabrous and furrowed. Leaflets short and broad, toothed or lobed. Flowers greenish-white, in sessile umbels along the stem. *Wet ditches near the sea, frequent.*

A. nodiflo'rum Reichb. (**Heloscia'dium nodiflorum** Koch.) 96. Marshwort. July–Oct. Stems spreading or creeping. Leaves pinnate, leaflets ovate or lanceolate, toothed. Flowers white, in sessile umbels. *Brooks and wet ditches, common.*

A. inunda'tum Reichb. (**Heloscia'dium inundatum** Koch.) 102. Fine-leaved Marshwort. July–Aug. Usually more or less submerged. Leaflets deeply or finely divided. Umbels stalked, with 2 or 3 rays only. *Shallow pools, frequent.*

IX. *CICU'TA*

C. viro'sa L. 38. Cowbane. July–Aug. Stem hollow. Leaflets lanceolate, acute, teeth few and unequal. Flowers small, white. Fruit globular, calyx teeth conspicuous. *Wet places, rare.* POISONOUS.

X. *CA'RUM*

Leaves finely divided into numerous segments. Flowers white or yellow, with involucral bracts. Fruit ovoid or oblong, laterally compressed.

Flowers yellowish-green	. . . . . C. Petroselinum
Flowers white	 2
2 Leaflets in whorls, linear, small	. . . C. verticillatum
Leaflets in pairs, ovate	. . . C. segetum
Leaflets finely divided	 3
3 Root globular, tuberous .	. . . . C. Bulbocastanum
Root elongated	. . . . C. Carvi

C. verticilla'tum Koch. 30. Whorled Caraway. July–Sept. Leaves mostly radical; leaflets very small, linear, apparently whorled. Flowers white. *Wet places in mountains of Wales and W. Scotland.*

C. Petroseli'num Benth. 34. Parsley. July–Aug. Upper leaves finely divided into linear segments, lower leaves into broad-toothed or lobed leaflets. Flowers yellowish-green. *Rocks and sea walls, rare (common in cultivation).*

2. **seg′etum** Benth. 46. Corn Parsley. July–Sept. Leaves mostly radical, pinnate, with 11 or more small ovate, toothed leaflets. Flowers small, white, umbels with few and unequal rays. *Damp calcareous fields, occasional.*

2. **Car′vi** L. 44. Caraway. June–July. Leaves finely divided, petioles sheathing. Carpels (caraway seeds) linear, curved, aromatic. *Meadows and waste places, rare.*

3. **Bulbocast′anum** Koch. 4. Great Earthnut. June–July. Root bulbous. Leaves finely divided into linear segments. Fruit oblong, with reflexed styles. *Dry pastures, rare.*

XI. *SI′SON*

5. **Amo′mum** L. 57. Bastard Stone Parsley. July–Oct. Tall, erect, and glabrous. Lower leaves pinnate, with 5–9 ovate or lanceolate, toothed leaflets. Flowers few, small, white, in small umbels of 3–6 unequal rays. Fruit very small, broad, laterally compressed. *Hedgebanks, common in the south.*

XII. *SI′UM*

Marsh plants with pinnate leaves and long-stalked umbels of white flowers. Fruit broadly ovoid, laterally compressed.

5. **latifo′lium** L. 36. Water Parsnip. July–Aug. Umbels all terminal. Leaflets large, evenly toothed. *Wet places, occasional.*

5. **erect′um** Huds. 87. Lesser Water Parsnip. July–Aug. Umbels mostly lateral. Leaflets small, unevenly toothed. *Wet places, frequent.*

XIII. *ÆGOPO′DIUM*

E. **Podagra′ria** L. 112. Goutweed, Ground Elder. June–Aug. Lower leaves 2- or 3-ternate, with large broad leaflets. Flowers white, in large terminal umbels without involucres. Fruit small, laterally compressed, styles reflexed. *Waysides and waste places, locally abundant.*

XIV. *PIMPINEL′LA*

Lower leaves pinnate or pinnately dissected. Flowers white; umbels without involucres. Fruit ovoid, ribs faint.

P. **Saxif′raga** L. 106. Burnet Saxifrage. July–Sept. About 1–2 feet high, branches few. Radical leaves usually pinnate with 7–9 pairs broadly ovate, toothed leaflets, but sometimes dissected into linear segments; upper leaves linear or with linear segments. *Meadows and roadsides, common.*

P. **ma′jor** Huds. (P. **mag′na** L.) 54. Greater Burnet Saxifrage. July–Sept. Very like the preceding species but much larger. *Rich meadows, occasional.*

XV. *CONOPO′DIUM*

C. **denuda′tum** Koch. (Bu′nium flexuo′sum With.) 110. Pignut, Earthnut. May–June. Very like *Carum Bulbocastanum* from which it differs in having the styles erect in fruit. Involucral bracts few or none. *Meadows and woods, common.*

XVI. *MYR'RHIS*

M. Odora'ta Scop. 67. Sweet Cicely. May–June. Stems hairy. Leaves large, fern-like, 2- or 3-pinnate; leaflets lanceolate, deeply toothed or pinnatifid. Flowers white. Fruit narrow, about 1 inch long. Whole plant very aromatic. *Hilly districts in Scotland, Wales, and N. England occasional.*

XVII. *CHAEROPHYL'LUM*

Leaves 2- or 3-pinnate, divided into numerous small broad leaflets Flowers white. Fruit narrow and glabrous or broad and hispid.

Umbels lateral, fruit broad and hispid . . . C. Anthriscus
Umbels terminal, fruit narrow and glabrous . . . 2
2 Leaflets with fine points . . . . C. sylvestre
Leaflets blunt , ... C. temulum

C. tem'ulum L. 102. Rough Chervil. June–Aug. Stem spotted, rough with short reflexed hairs, swollen at joints. Leaflets small, blunt, with rounded lobes. Fruit narrow, ribbed. *Hedgebanks, common.* POISONOUS

C. Anthris'cus Crantz. (**Anthriscus vulgaris** Pers.) 86. Beaked Parsley. May–June. Leaves small. Umbels lateral, short-stalked Fruit hispid, with a smooth beak. *Waste places, frequent.*

C. sylves'tre L. (**Anthriscus sylvestris** Hoffm.) 112. Wild Beaked Parsley. May–June. Leaves large, fern-like, with numerous finely pointed leaflets. Flowers white, in numerous terminal umbels. Fruit narrow, glabrous, not ribbed when fresh. *Hedgebanks, very common.* POISONOUS.

XVIII. *SCAN'DIX*

S. Pec'ten-Ve'neris L. 102. Venus's Comb, Shepherd's Needle May–Aug. Leaves finely divided into numerous linear segments Flowers small, white, in 2-rayed umbels. Fruit narrow, about $\frac{1}{2}$ inch long, with a beak much longer than itself, the whole extending to 2 inches or more. *Cornfields and waste places, frequent.*

XIX. *FOENIC'ULUM*

F. vulga're Mill. 21. Fennel. July–Sept. A tall, dark green, glabrous plant with yellow flowers. Leaves all finely divided into linear segments. Fruit ovoid, ribbed, laterally compressed. *Waste places especially near the sea, occasional.*

XX. *CRITH'MUM*

C. marit'imum L. 33. Samphire. June–Aug. Leaves thick and fleshy glabrous, divided into narrow cylindrical segments. Flowers very small in small umbels. Fruit ovoid, ribbed. *Rocks by the sea, occasional.*

XXI. *ŒNAN'THE*

Leaves finely divided into linear or fern-like segments. Flowers white or greenish-white, sepals conspicuous. Fruit narrow, crowned by the persistent sepals.

Segments of upper leaves few, linear 2
Segments of upper leaves numerous, broad 4

2 Stem very hollow, upper leaves shorter than stalks . Œ. fistulosa
  Stem nearly solid, upper leaves longer than stalks . . . 3

3 Root-fibres swollen near end . . . Œ. pimpinelloides
  Root-fibres not swollen near end . . . Œ. Lachenalii

4 Umbels terminal . . . . . . Œ. crocata
  Umbels lateral . . . . . Œ. Phellandrium

E. fistulo′sa L. 74. Water Dropwort. July–Sept. Stems thick and very hollow. Lower leaves pale green and fern-like. Flowers white, in small 3–5-rayed umbels at the end of long peduncles. Fruit with long rigid styles, in burr-like heads. *Wet ditches, frequent.* POISONOUS.

E. pimpinelloi′des L. 17. June–Aug. Fibrous roots swelling at the ends into ovoid tubers. Stems solid. Upper leaves with linear segments; radical leaves divided into numerous small pinnatifid segments. Flowers greenish. Fruit oblong by the thickening of its base. *Damp meadows, rare.*

E. Lachena′lii Gmel. 77. Parsley Water Dropwort. July–Sept. Like the preceding species but fibrous roots without tubers and fruit narrowly ovoid. *Wet and often brackish places, frequent.*

E. croca′ta L. 95. Hemlock Water Dropwort. June–Aug. Root tuberous. Leaves large, all with numerous broad fern-like leaflets. Flowers white, in long-stalked terminal umbels. *Ditches, common.* POISONOUS.

E. Phelland′rium Lam. 55. Fine-leaved Water Dropwort. June–Aug. Much-branched and spreading. Leaves finely divided into numerous small leaflets. Flowers small, white, in numerous lateral umbels. Fruit cylindrical, stalked. *Wet ditches, frequent.* POISONOUS.

XXII. *AETHU′SA*

E. Cyna′pium L. 106. Fool's Parsley. July–Sept. Leaves finely divided into lanceolate segments. Flowers white, in long-stalked umbels with long reflexed involucres. Fruit globular, furrowed. *Cornfields, common.*

XXIII. *SILA′US*

S. flaves′cens Bernh. (**S. praten′sis** Bess.) 69. Pepper Saxifrage. July–Sept. Tall and erect. Leaves divided into narrow lanceolate segments. Flowers yellowish-green, in small few-rayed umbels on long peduncles. Fruit ovoid. *Meadows and hedgebanks, frequent.*

XXIV. *ME′UM*

M. athaman′ticum Jacq. 30. Spignel, Baldmoney. June–July. Radical leaves in tufts, pinnately compound, finely divided into numerous short linear segments, aromatic. Flowers white or pink. Fruit oblong, ribbed. *Mountain pastures in the north.*

XXV. *LIGUS'TICUM*

L. scot'icum L. 29. Lovage. July–Aug. Stem thick and hollow. Leaves once or twice ternate; leaflets broad. Flowers white, with numerous involucral bracts. Fruit ovoid, ribbed. *Rocky coasts in the north.*

XXVI. *ANGEL'ICA*

A. sylves'tris L. 112. Wild Angelica. July–Sept. Tall plant with thick hollow stems. Leaves 2-pinnate, with broad ovate leaflets. Flowers white or pink, in large terminal umbels. Fruit dorsally compressed; carpels with broad wings. *Damp woods and moist hedgebanks, common.*

XXVII. *PEUCED'ANUM*

Leaves ternate or finely divided. Flowers white or pinkish. Fruit dorsally compressed; ripe carpels flat, winged.

P. palus'tre Moench. 12. Hog's Fennel, Milk Parsley. July–Aug. Tall plant with milky juice. Leaves finely divided into numerous narrow segments. Ripe carpels ovate, narrowly winged. *Marshes, rare.*

P. Ostru'thium Koch. 23. Masterwort. July–Aug. Tall erect plant. Leaves ternate; leaflets broad, toothed and lobed. Ripe carpels orbicular, broadly winged. *Moist meadows in the north, rare.*

XXVIII. *PASTINA'CA*

P. sati'va L. 62. Wild Parsnip. June–Sept. Leaves pinnate, with large broad leaflets. Flowers yellow. Fruit dorsally compressed; ripe carpels flat, ovate. *Waste places, common in S. England.*

XXIX. *HERAC'LEUM*

H. Sphondyl'ium L. 112. Cow Parsnip. April–Oct. A coarse rough plant with stout hairy stems and large pinnate leaflets. Flowers white, the outer ones very irregular, in large terminal umbels. Fruit large and flat, dorsally compressed, distinguished by the conspicuous dark brown vittae which end abruptly before reaching the base of the carpel. *Meadows and roadsides, very common.*

XXX. *CORIAN'DRUM*

C. sati'vum L. Coriander. June–July. Upper leaves divided into linear segments, lower leaves with broad leaflets, all giving a disagreeable smell when rubbed. Flowers white, in terminal umbels with 8 or fewer rays. Fruit broadly ovoid, calyx teeth conspicuous, vittae none. *Escape from cultivation.*

XXXI. *DAU'CUS*

D. Caro'ta L. 110. Wild Carrot. June–Sept. Stems hairy. Leaves pinnately divided into numerous fine segments. Flowers white, in terminal umbels with long pinnatifid involucral bracts. Fruit with long prickles on the ribs. *Fields and roadsides, very common.*

XXXII. *CAU'CALIS*

Fruit prickly. Involucral bracts small, entire.

Flowers in small short-stalked heads . . . C. nodosa
Flowers in terminal long-stalked umbels 2

2 Primary involucre of 1 bract or none . . . C. arvensis
  Primary involucre of several bracts 3

3 Terminal leaflet much the longest; fruit with hooked
    prickles . . . . . . C. Anthriscus

  Terminal leaflet not longer than the lateral ones; fruit with straight
    prickles . . . . C. daucoides

C. daucoi'des L. 42. Bur Parsley. June–July. Leaves finely divided
into small narrow pinnatifid segments. Flowers pinkish, in terminal
umbels. Fruit large, with long prickles. *Cornfields in S. and E. England, rare.*

C. arven'sis Huds. (Tori'lis arvensis Link.) 58. Spreading Hedge
Parsley. June–Aug. A small and spreading plant with narrow leaflets.
Flowers white, in small terminal umbels, each primary umbel without
or with only 1 involucral bract. Fruit small, with short prickles.
Cornfields and waste places, frequent.

C. Anthris'cus Huds. (Tori'lis Anthriscus Gmel.) 109. Hedge
Parsley. July–Sept. A tall erect plant with coarsely toothed leaflets,
the terminal one much longer than the others and usually continued
into a long fine point. Flowers white or pinkish, in long-stalked
terminal umbels. Fruit small, burr-like. *Hedgebanks, common.*

C. nodo'sa Scop. (Tori'lis nodosa Gaertn.) 81. Knotted Hedge
Parsley. June–Aug. Distinguished from all the others by the flowers
being in small almost sessile heads along the trailing stems. Leaves finely
divided into small pinnatifid leaflets. Fruit with long stiff prickles.
Roadsides and waste places, frequent.

Family 37. **ARALIA'CEAE**

Trees, shrubs, or shrubby climbers with alternate and usually lobed.
or compound leaves. Flowers small, 5-partite, in terminal umbels; ovary
inferior. Fruit a berry-like drupe.

HED'ERA

I. He'lix L. 112. Ivy. Sept.–Nov. Evergreen shrub climbing by small
roots on the stem. Leaves leathery and glossy, long-stalked; those on
the flowering shoots entire or nearly so, the others palmately 3–5-lobed.
Flowers small, yellowish-green, in small terminal umbels or umbel-like
racemes; calyx with 5 minute teeth; petals 5; stamens 5; ovary inferior, 5-celled, style apparently single but really consisting of several
styles joined together into a column. Fruit black. *Walls, hedgebanks,
and woods, common.*

Family 38. CORNA'CEAE

Trees or shrubs (rarely herbs) with entire and usually opposite leaves.
Flowers small; ovary inferior, 2-celled, style 1. Fruit a small drupe.

COR'NUS

Calyx with 4 minute teeth. Petals 4. Stamens 4, alternating with the
petals.

C. sue'cica L. 18. Dwarf Cornel. Aug.–Sept. Low herb. Leaves
opposite, entire, sessile, about 1 inch long, with 1–2 pairs of parallel
veins. Flowers very small, in a terminal head surrounded by an involucre of 4 white petal-like bracts. Fruit red. *Mountains of Scotland
and N. England, rare.*

C. sanguin'ea L. 67. Dogwood. June–July. Shrub. Leaves opposite,
entire, stalked, with about 4 pairs of parallel veins. Flowers small,
white, in terminal cymes, without bracts, petals narrow. Fruit black.
In autumn and winter the twigs are reddish. *Hedges and open woods,
common in S. England.*

Family 39. ADOXA'CEAE

Contains only 1 genus and species formerly included in *Araliaceae*
and then in *Caprifoliaceae*, from both of which, however, it differs in
being a herb and in possessing 8 or more stamens. The corolla is
gamopetalous, with the stamens attached to it.

Adox'a Moschatelli'na L. 101. Moschatel, Town Clock. March–
April. A small glabrous herb. Leaves radical or opposite, ternate,
leaflets broad, obtuse, lobed or ternate. Flowers small, green, in a
globular head at the end of a long peduncle bearing two opposite leaves;
sepals 2–3; petals 4–5; stamens 8–10, inserted on a ring at the base
of the corolla with which they can be pulled off as one piece; ovary
inferior, 3–5-celled. Fruit a small green berry. *Woods and shady
places, common.*

Family 40. CAPRIFOLIA'CEAE

Woody plants with opposite leaves. Calyx and corolla 5-lobed;
stamens usually 5, epipetalous. Ovary inferior, 3–5-celled. Fruit a
berry-like drupe.

Leaves compound, pinnate	.	.	.	.	Sambucus I
Leaves simple .	.	.	.	.	. 2
2 Low creeping plant, stamens 4	.	.	.	Linnaea III
Erect or climbing shrub, stamens 5	.	.	.	. 3
3 Corolla regular; stigmas 3, sessile	.	.	.	Viburnum II
Corolla irregular; stigma one, on a long style	.	.	Lonicera IV

I SAMBU'CUS

Leaves opposite, pinnately compound. Flowers small, white, in large
flat-topped cymes; calyx and corolla 5-lobed; stamens 5; stigma 3–5-
lobed, sessile.

. ni′gra L. 112. Common Elder. June–July. Tall shrub with warted pithy stems and opposite pinnate leaves. Leaflets usually 5, ovate or lanceolate, toothed. Flowers creamy-white. Fruit black. *Hedges and woods, common.*

. Eb′ulus L. 87. Dwarf Elder, Danewort. July–Aug. Semi-herbaceous, not exceeding 3 feet. Leaflets 7–11, lanceolate, with a pair of smaller ones at the base of the petiole. Flowers white tipped with purple. Fruit black. *Hedges, roadsides, and waste places, occasional*

II. *VIBUR′NUM*

Shrubs with opposite simple leaves. Flowers white, in terminal ymes; calyx and corolla 5-lobed; stamens 5; stigmas 2–3, sessile.

. Op′ulus L. 103. Guelder Rose. May–July. Leaves opposite, palmately lobed; petiole glandular, with a pair of linear stipule-like appendages at the base. Flowers white, of two kinds, the outer large and sterile, the inner small and perfect. Fruit large, red, usually drooping. *Hedges and open woods, frequent.*

. Lanta′na L. 49. Wayfaring Tree. May–June. Young branchlets covered with a white or rusty felt. Leaves ovate, cordate at base, velvety above, white- or rusty-felted below, toothed but not lobed. Flowers white, in dense terminal cymes. Fruit small, black when ripe, erect. *Hedges and open woods, common in S. England, rare in the north.*

III. *LINNAE′A*

. borea′lis L. 18. Twin-flower. July–Aug. Creeping plant with woody base. Leaves small, opposite, ovate, rounded and coarsely toothed at apex, hairy. Flowers pink or white, drooping, in pairs at the top of a slender peduncle; corolla 5-lobed, funnel-shaped; stamens 4. Fruit dry, yellow, ovoid, 1-seeded. *Coniferous woods in Scotland and N. England, rare.*

IV. *LONIC′ERA*

Shrubs or woody climbers with opposite entire leaves. Corolla 5-lobed, ubular at the base and usually 2-lipped; stamens 5; style long. Fruit a uicy berry-like drupe.

Erect shrub, flowers short, in axillary pairs . . . L. Xylosteum	
Climber; flowers long, in terminal heads 2	
Upper leaf-pairs connate . . . . L. Caprifolium	
Leaves all distinct . . . . . L. Periclymenum	

. Caprifo′lium L. 28. May–June. Woody climber. Flowers yellowish-white, tubular, 2-lipped, in one or two terminal whorls in a large leafy cup. Fruit orange-coloured. *Escape from gardens, rare.*

. Pericly′menum L. 112. Common Honeysuckle, Woodbine. June–Sept. Woody climber. Leaves ovate or oblong, the pairs never united at the base. Flowers white, yellow, or reddish, tubular, 2-lipped, in a single terminal whorl. Fruit red. *Hedges and woods, common.*

L. Xylos'teum L. 25. Fly Honeysuckle. May–June. Erect shrub. Leaves ovate or orbicular, obtuse, downy. Flowers small, in pairs in the leaf axila, yellowish-white, with a short tube and two spreading lips. Fruit red. *Hedges and woods, rare; common in shrubberies.*

Family 41. RUBIA'CEAE

The British members of the family are herbs with entire whorled leaves (two opposite leaves with several stipules of equal size). Flowers small, in heads or panicles; calyx very small; corolla 4–5-lobed; stamens as many as corolla lobes, epipetalous; ovary inferior, style bifid, stigma capitate. Fruit separating into two 1-seeded carpels.

Corolla rotate . . . .
Corolla with a tubular or funnel-shaped base . . . .

2 Corolla 5-lobed, fruit fleshy . . . . . . Rubia
  Corolla 4-lobed, fruit dry . . . . . Galium

3 Calyx teeth distinct, flowers in involucrate heads . Sherardia I
  Calyx teeth indistinct, flowers in panicles . . Asperula I

I. *RU'BIA*

R. peregri'na L. 25. Wild Madder. June–Aug. Stems straggling, with rough angles. Leaves usually 4 in a whorl, ovate or lanceolate, dark green, rather thick and stiff, rough on the edges and midrib. Flowers small, greenish, in axillary or terminal panicles, corolla usually 5-lobed. Fruit a black berry. *Hedgebanks in SW. England and S. Wales, rare.*

II. *GA'LIUM*

Stems weak, 4-angled; either smooth, or rough with reflexed hairs or prickles. Calyx indistinct. Corolla rotate, 4-lobed. Fruit dry, 2-lobed.

Flowers yellow . . . .
Flowers white . . . .

2 Leaves ovate, 4 in a whorl . . G. Cruciata
  Leaves linear, 6–8 in a whorl . . . . . G. verum

3 Leaves mostly 4 (sometimes 5 or 6) in a whorl . .
  6–8 leaves in a whorl . . . . .

4 Stem smooth, fruit hairy or rough . . G. boreale
  Stem rough, fruit smooth . . . G. palustre

5 Angles of stem smooth . . . . .
  Angles of stem rough . . . . .

6 Stem exceeding 1 foot, fruit smooth . . G. Mollugo
  Stem less than 1 foot, fruit with granulated surface . G. saxatile

7 Fruit with hooked bristles . . . G. Aparine
  Fruit without hooked bristles . . . .

8 Panicles shorter than the leaves . . G. tricorne
  Panicles longer than the leaves . . .

9 Stem not exceeding 6 inches, leaves about ¼ inch . G. anglicum
  Stem exceeding 1 foot, leaves about ½ inch . G. uliginosum

G. **borea′le** L. 47. Northern Bedstraw. June–Aug. Stem firm and erect, smooth. Leaves in fours, 3-nerved. Flowers white, in compact terminal panicles. Fruit covered with hooked bristles. *Mountain pastures in the north.*

G. **Crucia′ta** Scop. 95. Crosswort. May–Aug. Leaves broadly ovate, in fours. Flowers minute, yellow, in small axillary clusters shorter than the leaves. Fruit smooth. *Meadows and hedgebanks, frequent.*

G. **ve′rum** L. 112. Yellow Bedstraw, Ladies' Bedstraw. July–Sept. Leaves linear, 6–8 in a whorl. Flowers yellow, in large panicles. Fruit smooth. *Meadows and hedgebanks, common.*

G. **Mollu′go** L. 94. Hedge Bedstraw. June–Sept. Stems long, smooth and dark green. Leaves 6–8 in a whorl, mucronate. Flowers white, numerous, in large panicles. Fruit smooth. *Shady hedgebanks and open woods, common.*

    G. erect′um (Huds.), less straggling, with narrower leaves and more compact panicles, occurs in drier and more open situations.

G. **saxat′ile** L. 111. Heath Bedstraw. June–Aug. Stems procumbent, smooth, seldom exceeding 6 inches. Leaves 6–8 in a whorl, small, obovate or oblanceolate. Flowers white, numerous, in terminal panicles. Fruit with granulated surface. *Heaths and poor pastures, common.*

    G. sylves′tre (Poll.) with stiffer stems and longer and narrower leaves occurs occasionally on calcareous hills.

G. **palus′tre** L. 112. Water Bedstraw. June–Aug. Stems weak, slender, and rough. Leaves mostly in fours but often up to 6, obtuse and not mucronate. Flowers few, white. Fruit smooth. *Wet places, common.*

G. **uligino′sum** L. 96. Rough Water Bedstraw. July–Aug. Stems weak, slender, and rough. Leaves 6–8 in a whorl, mucronate. Flowers few, white. Fruit granulated. *Wet places, occasional.*

G. **ang′licum** Huds. 12. Wall Bedstraw. June–July. Stems very slender, rough, not exceeding 6 inches. Leaves 6–8 in a whorl, very small. Flowers minute, white. Fruit very small, with granulated surface. *Walls and stony places in S. England, rare.*

G. **Apari′ne** L. 112. Cleavers, Goosegrass. May–Aug. Stems straggling or climbing, very rough. Leaves 6–8 in a whorl, lanceolate, hairy. Flowers few, small, greenish-white. Fruit covered with hooked bristles. *Hedgebanks and open woods, very common.*

G. **tricor′ne** Stokes. 53. Corn Bedstraw. June–Oct. Like the preceding species but much smaller, with panicles shorter than the leaves and large granulated fruits in threes on recurved stalks. *Cornfields, occasional.*

III. *ASPER′ULA*

Calyx indistinct. Corolla tubular or funnel-shaped, 4-lobed. Fruit rough or hispid.

A. **odora′ta** L. 108. Woodruff. April–June. Stems erect, smooth. Leaves ovate or lanceolate, 6–8 in a whorl. Flowers few, small, white.

Fruit hispid. The whole plant smells of new-mown hay. *Woods, common.*

A. cynan'chica L. 39. Squinancy Wort. June–Aug. A small plant with thin wiry stems and opposite or whorled linear leaves not exceeding ½ inch. Flowers very small, white or lilac. Fruit slightly granulated. *Calcareous downs and dry pastures, occasional.*

IV. *SHERAR'DIA*

S. arven'sis L. 112. Field Madder. May–Sept. A small spreading plant with whorls of sharply pointed leaves rough on the edges. Flowers lilac, tubular, in terminal involucrate heads, calyx teeth distinct, persistent in fruit. *Cornfields and roadsides, common.*

FAMILY 42. **VALERIANA'CEAE**

Herbs with opposite exstipulate leaves. Flowers small, in terminal corymbs or panicles; corolla somewhat irregular, 5-lobed; stamens 3 or 1, epipetalous; ovary inferior, 1-celled and containing 1 ovule, style long and simple. Fruit an achene.

Corolla spurred, stamen 1 . . . . Kentranthus II
Corolla not spurred, stamens 3 2

2 Fruit with pappus of feathery hairs . . . Valeriana I
Fruit without pappus . . . . . Valerianella III

I. *VALERIA'NA*

Cauline leaves compound or deeply divided. Calyx very small at first, afterwards developing into a feathery pappus. Stamens 3.

V. dioi'ca L. 80. Small Marsh Valerian. May–June. Not higher than 1 foot. Radical leaves entire, ovate, long-stalked, cauline leaves pinnatifid. Flowers pink, unisexual. *Marshy places, frequent.*

V. officina'lis L. 111. Great Wild Valerian. All-heal. June–Aug. Leaves all pinnately compound, leaflets lanceolate, toothed. Flowers white or pinkish. *Riverbanks and damp shady places, common.*

II. *KENTRAN'THUS*

K. ru'ber DC. 43. Red Valerian. May–Sept. Leaves ovate or lanceolate, glabrous and glaucous, entire or with a few coarse teeth. Flowers red, rarely white, in a dense terminal cyme; corolla spurred, stamen 1. Fruit with a feathery pappus. *Walls and banks, an escape from gardens.*

III. *VALERIANEL'LA*

Stems forked. Flowers small, in small heads or cymes at the end of the branches; corolla regular, 5-lobed; stamens 3. Fruit without a pappus.

Fruit surmounted by a conspicuous oblique hollow tooth . . 2
Fruit without or with a very small tooth at the top . . . 3

Fruit broadly ovoid, with 2 large empty cells in addition to the
  seed (*a*)   .   .   .   .   V. rimosa
Fruit narrow, with very small empty cells (*b*)   .   .   V. dentata
Fruit oblong, deeply hollowed on the same side as the 2 empty
  cells (*c*)   .   .   .   .   V. carinata
Fruit broadly ovoid, with a corky swelling on the same side as the
  seed (*d*)   .   .   .   .   V. olitoria

  (*a*)   (*b*)   (*c*)   (*d*)

V. olito′ria Poll. 108. Cornsalad, Lamb's Lettuce. May–July. A
small plant with slender repeatedly forked branches terminated by
small heads of pale blue flowers. Leaves oblong or oblanceolate,
sessile, teeth few or none. Fruit small, broadly ovoid, without a conspicuous projection on the top. *Hedgebanks and cornfields, common.*

V. carina′ta Lois. 25. Keeled Cornsalad. May–July. Like the preceding species but flowers lilac and fruit narrower, with a deep hollow
on the side next the empty cells. *Walls and banks, rare.*

V. rimo′sa Bast. (V. Auric′ula DC.) 45. Sharp-fruited Cornsalad.
June–July. Leaves linear. Flowers pale blue. Fruit broadly ovoid,
with a sharp hollow tooth on the top, and with two large empty cells
as well as the seed. *Cornfields, rare.*

V. denta′ta Poll. 84. Narrow-fruited Cornsalad. June–Aug. Flowers
lilac or pinkish, in rather lax cymes. Fruit narrowly pear-shaped,
surmounted by a conspicuous hollow tooth, and containing 2 very
small empty cells in addition to the seed. *Cornfields, common.*

Family 43. DIPSA′CEAE

Herbs with opposite exstipulate leaves. Flowers in heads or spikes
surrounded by an involucre of bracts; calyx very small; corolla 4–5-lobed,
often irregular; stamens 4, epipetalous, anthers free; ovary inferior,
1-celled and containing 1 pendulous ovule, style 1. Fruit an achene.

Stem and scales of the receptacle prickly   .   .   .   Dipsacus I
Stem and scales of the receptacle not prickly   .   .   Scabiosa II

I. DIP′SACUS

Stem tall, erect, and prickly. Flowers in composite heads with a prickly
involucre and prickly scales between the flowers (florets); corolla 4-lobed.

D. sylves′tris Huds. 76. Teasel. July–Sept. Stem very prickly.
Leaves lanceolate, sessile, fine-pointed, midrib prickly on the underside.

Flower-heads large, ovoid; the involucral bracts long, linear, an
curved upwards; florets pale lilac. *Hedges, riverbanks, and open wood*
common.

D. pilo'sus L. 53. Small Teasel. July–Sept. Stem slightly prickly c
bristly. Leaves ovate, short-pointed, stalked. Flower-heads smal
globular, with short involucral bracts; florets white. *Hedges, riverbank.*
and open woods, occasional.

II. *SCABIO'SA*

Herbs with hairy but not prickly stems. Flowers blue or lilac, in com
posite heads with a green hairy involucre.

Leaves entire or nearly so . . . . . . S. Succis
Leaves toothed or lobed . . . .
2 Corolla 5-lobed . . . . . . S. Columbari
Corolla 4-lobed . . . . S. arvensi

S. Succi'sa L. 112. Devil's-bit Scabious. Aug.–Oct. Leaves ovate o
lanceolate, entire or with a few teeth. Flower-heads deep blue, on lon
peduncles; florets all equal or nearly so, corolla 4-lobed, receptacle witl
scales between the florets. *Meadows and heaths, common.*

S. Columba'ria L. 72. Small Scabious. July–Sept. Stem nearl
glabrous. Radical leaves pinnatifid, with broad segments; caulin
leaves finely divided into linear segments. Flower-heads pale purplish
blue, outer florets irregular and much larger than the inner, coroll
5-lobed, receptacle with scales between the florets. *Meadows an*
heaths, frequent.

S. arven'sis L. (**Knau'tia arvensis** Coult.) 108. Field Scabious
June–Sept. Tall very hairy plant with lanceolate, coarsely toothed o
deeply pinnatifid leaves. Flower-heads pale purplish-blue, the oute
florets irregular and much larger than the inner, corolla 4-lobed
receptacle with hairs between the florets. *Meadows and waysides*
common.

Family 44. COMPOS'ITAE

Flowers in an involucrate capitulum, i.e. in a compact head having th
appearance of a single flower surrounded by a false calyx (involucre
composed of bracts, the true calyx being reduced to hairs or bristle
(pappus) or to a mere border; corolla tubular and 5-toothed, or ligulate
i.e. flat, with a short tube at the base. The flowers (florets) in one hea
may be all tubular or all ligulate, but in many species the tubular floret
are compressed into a central *disk*, while the ligulate florets appear o
the circumference of the head, forming a *ray*; stamens 5, epipetalous, th
anthers united into a tube round the style; ovary inferior, 1-celled an
containing 1 erect ovule; style 1, with a bifid stigma. Fruit an achene
often crowned by the persistent pappus.

Florets all tubular . . . . :
Both tubular and ligulate florets in the same head . . . 1
Florets all ligulate 3

2 Flower-heads pink, purple, blue, or white 3
  Flower-heads yellow or greenish . . . 13

3 Leaves prickly 4
  Leaves not prickly 6

SUBFAMILY. CYNAROI'DEAE

4 Outer bracts of involucre resemble the leaves . Carlina XXI
  Outer bracts of involucre quite different from the leaves . 5

5 Receptacle with long chaffy bristles* (a) . Carduus XXIII
  Receptacle without long bristles (b) . . Onopordon XXIV

(a)   (b)   (c)   (d)

6 Outer bracts of involucre hooked . . . . Arctium XXII
  Outer bracts of involucre not hooked . . . 7

7 Bracts of involucre toothed, fringed, or prickly-
    pointed . . . . . . Centaurea XXVII
  Bracts of involucre entire or not prickly pointed . . 8

8 Some or all of the pappus hairs branched (c) . . . 9
  All the pappus hairs simple (unbranched) (d) . . . 10

9 Flower-heads solitary . . . . Carduus XXIII
  Flower-heads in a cluster . . . . Saussurea XXV

10 Leaves compound or pinnatifid, alternate . Serratula XXVI
  Leaves simple or opposite 11

SUBFAMILY. CORYMBIF'ERAE

1 Leaves opposite . . . . . . Eupatorium I
  Leaves alternate or radical 12

2 Radical leaves large, orbicular . . . Petasites XVIII
  Leaves not orbicular, entire . . . Antennaria VII

3 Leaves opposite . . . . . . Bidens X
  Leaves alternate or radical 14

4 Pappus none 15
  Pappus present 17

5 Flower-heads very small, in racemes or panicles Artemisia XVI
  Flower-heads at least ¼ inch across . . . 16

6 Leaves finely divided into linear segments, plant not exceeding
    1 foot . . . . . . Matricaria XIV
  Leaves pinnately divided into flat-toothed segments, plant
    tall . . . . Tanacetum XV

* Do not confuse the pappus with the bristles on the receptacle.

17 Involucral bracts equal, in 1 row, with scales at base (*a*)   Senecio X
     Involucral bracts unequal, irregularly arranged, plant covered with white cottony down 1

18 Receptacle conical, with a few scales between the florets   Filago V
     Receptacle flat, without scales . . . Gnaphalium VII

19 Pappus none or replaced by a few bristles . . . 2
     Pappus of hairs 2

(*a*)   (*b*)   (*c*)

(*d*)   (*e*)   (*f*)   (*g*)

20 Leaves opposite . . . . . . Bidens
     Leaves alternate or radical 2

21 Receptacle with scales (s) between the florets (*b*) . . 2
     Receptacle without scales (*c*) 2

22 Receptacle small, flat; disk florets white or whitish . Achillea X
     Receptacle large, conical; disk florets bright yellow   Anthemis XI

23 Involucral bracts in 1 or 2 rows, with scales at base (*d*)   Bellis II
     Involucral bracts in several rows (*e*) 2

24 Receptacle flat or convex; leaves entire, toothed, or broadly lobed . . . . . . Chrysanthemum XII
     Receptacle conical; leaves divided into linear segments . . . . . . Matricaria XIV

25 Ray florets blue, purple, or white 2
     Ray florets yellow 2

26 Ray florets few, in 1 row (sometimes absent) . . Aster I
     Ray florets numerous, in several rows . . Erigeron

27 Involucral bracts in a single row, with scales at base (*f*) . 2
     Involucral bracts in several rows (*g*) . . . 3

28 Flowering stems leafless except for small bracts, appearing before the leaves . . . . . Tussilago XVI
     Flowering stems leafy, appearing with or after the leaves . 2

29 Ray florets without a pappus . . . Doronicum XI
     Ray florets with pappus . . . . Senecio X

30 Ray florets 5–10 . . . . . Solidago
     Ray florets numerous . . . . . . Inula IX

SUBFAMILY. LIGULA'TAE

1 Pappus none or reduced to scales 32
  Pappus present, composed of hairs 34

2 Flowers blue . . . . . . Cichorium XXVIII
  Flowers yellow 33

3 Leaves all radical . . . . . Arnoseris XXIX
  Cauline leaves present . . . . . Lapsana XXX

4 Hairs of pappus all simple (unbranched) (*a*) . . . 35
  Some or all of the pappus hairs branched (*b*) . . . 40

  (*a*)   (*b*)   (*c*)   (*d*)   (*e*)   (*f*)

5 Flowering stems unbranched and hollow throughout . . . . Taraxacum XXXVII
  Flowering stems branched or partly solid . . . 36

6 Achenes broad at the top (*c*) 37
  Achenes much narrowed at the top or continued into a slender
  beak (*d*) 39

7 Ripe achenes flat, leaves large and glabrous . Sonchus XXXIX
  Ripe achenes cylindrical or angular, leaves usually not large and
  with hairs 38

8 Cauline leaves usually auricled and sheathing, pappus usually
  white and silky . . . . . Crepis XXXIII
  Cauline leaves, if present, usually with tapering base, pappus short,
  brownish, and brittle . . . . . Hieracium XXXIV

9 Florets few in each head, achenes flat . . Lactuca XXXVIII
  Florets numerous, ripe achenes cylindrical or
  angular . . . . Crepis XXXIII

10 Involucral bracts all equal and at least as long as the flowers,
  leaves linear . . . . . . Tragopogon XL
  Involucral bracts unequal, shorter than the flowers, leaves not
  linear 41

11 Outer bracts of involucre much larger than the
  inner . . . . Helminthia XXXII
  Outer bracts of involucre smaller than the inner . . 42

12 Receptacle with scales (s) between the florets (*e*) Hypochoeris XXXV
  Receptacle without scales (*f*) 43

13 Leaves mostly radical . . . . . Leontodon XXXVI
  Stem leafy . . . . Picris XXXI

Subfamily I. CORYMBIF'ERAE

Florets of the disk tubular and usually bisexual; outer florets ligulate or absent, unisexual or sterile. Style not swollen.

I. *EUPATOR'IUM*

E. cannabi'num L. 101. Hemp Agrimony. July–Aug. Tall plant with opposite ternate leaves. Flower-heads pink, in terminal corymbs; florets all tubular. *Riverbanks and damp woods, common.*

II. *SOLIDA'GO*

S. Virgau'rea L. 111. Golden Rod. July–Sept. Leaves ovate or lanceolate, with few teeth. Flower-heads yellow, in a narrow terminal panicle; ray florets few. *Woods, common.*

III. *BEL'LIS*

B. peren'nis L. 112. Common Daisy. Jan.–Dec. Leaves mostly radical, spathulate, slightly toothed or entire. Flower-heads small, solitary on leafless peduncles, involucral bracts in 1 or 2 rows; disk florets yellow, ray white; pappus none. *Meadows, lawns, &c., very common.*

IV. *AS'TER*

A. Tripo'lium L. 83. Sea Aster. Aug.–Oct. Leaves linear, entire, thick and somewhat fleshy. Flower-heads in a terminal corymb, disk yellow; ray florets purple, few or none. *Salt marshes and tidal mud banks, common.*

V. *ERIG'ERON*

E. canaden'sis L. 39. Aug.–Sept. Stiff, erect, and much branched, glabrous or nearly so. Leaves linear-lanceolate, entire. Flower-heads small, numerous; outer florets white or pinkish, not longer than the involucre. *Waste places, an occasional alien.*

E. a'cris L. 71. Purple Fleabane. Aug.–Sept. Small erect plant with hairy stems and lanceolate entire leaves. Flower-heads small, few, in terminal panicles, disk yellow; ray florets pale purple, numerous, very narrow. *Walls and waysides, occasional.*

VI. *FILA'GO*

Small plants covered with white cottony down. Leaves narrow, lanceolate or linear, entire. Flower-heads small, with brown or pale yellow involucres, in globular clusters; florets all tubular; receptacle conical, with a few scales.

F. germa'nica L. 97. Upright Cudweed. July–Sept. Leaves ½–1 inch long. Ten or more flower-heads in each cluster. *Dry places, frequent.*

F. min'ima Pers. 99. Field Cudweed. June–Sept. Leaves about ¼ inch long. Six or fewer flower-heads in each cluster. *Heaths and dry pastures, frequent.*

VII. *ANTENNA'RIA*

, **dioi'ca** Gaertn. 92. Mountain Everlasting. June–July. A small plant covered with white cottony down. Leaves oblanceolate or linear, entire. Flower-heads dioecious, with white or pinkish petal-like involucres, in terminal corymbs. *Mountain pastures in the north.*

VIII. *GNAPHA'LIUM*

Cottony plants with linear or narrow leaves. Flower-heads small, often ustered, with yellowish-brown scarious involucres; receptacle flat, thout scales.

. **uligino'sum** L. 112. Marsh Cudweed. July–Sept. Flower-heads very small, in corymbs. *Damp places, common.*

. **sylvat'icum** L. 106. Wood Cudweed. July–Sept. Flower-heads larger than in the preceding species, in elongated racemes. *Open woods and heaths, frequent.*

IX. *IN'ULA*

Stiff, erect herbs with simple alternate leaves and yellow flowers. Inlucral bracts in several rows. Ray florets numerous.

ay florets scarcely longer than the involucre 2
ay florets much longer than the involucre 3
Flower-heads ovoid in dense corymbs . . . I. Conyza
Flowers-heads flat, small, and few . . . . I. Pulicaria
Flower-heads 2 inches or more across, solitary . . I. Helenium
Flower-heads 1 inch or less, in corymbs or panicles . . . 4
Leaves linear, thick and fleshy . . . I. crithmoides
Leaves flat . . . . I. dysenterica

Hele'nium L. 65. Elecampane. July–Aug. A tall plant with large oblong leaves. Flower-heads very large, solitary, yellow. *Moist pastures, rare.*

Cony'za DC. 64. Ploughman's Spikenard. Aug.–Oct. Stems stiff, erect, and hairy. Leaves ovate or lanceolate, faintly toothed. Flower-heads numerous, in dense corymbs; inner bracts of involucre reddish; ray florets very short. *Dry stony places on calcareous soils, frequent.*

crithmoi'des L. 19. Golden Samphire. July–Oct. Stem erect and glabrous. Leaves linear, fleshy, entire or 3-toothed at apex. Flowerheads few, yellow, in a short leafy panicle; ray spreading. *Rocky coasts and salt marshes, rare.*

dysenter'ica L. 82. Common Fleabane. July–Sept. Stems and leaves woolly. Leaves ovate or lanceolate, clasping the stem. Flowerheads numerous, yellow, in a terminal corymb; ray florets numerous and spreading; pappus inserted in a cup. *Damp places, common.*

Pulica'ria L. 26. Small Fleabane. Aug.–Sept. A small hairy plant seldom exceeding 1 foot. Leaves small, narrow, and wavy. Flowerheads few, small; ray florets very short; pappus inserted in a cup. *Damp places, rare.*

X. *BI'DENS*

Leaves opposite, glabrous. Flower-heads greenish-yellow, surrounde by long leafy bracts; ray florets none or very few. Achenes flattened, wi two or more barbed points on the top.

B. cer'nua L. 88. Bur-marigold. Aug.–Sept. Leaves opposite, lar ceolate, toothed, long-pointed. Flower-heads drooping. *Wet place frequent.*

B. triparti'ta L. 89. Bur-marigold. Aug.–Sept. Leaves opposit deeply divided into three lanceolate segments. *Wet places, frequent.*

XI. *ACHILLE'A*

Flowers white; ray spreading; receptacle flat, with scales between th florets. Pappus none.

A. Millefo'lium L. 112. Yarrow, Milfoil. June–Nov. Leaves pi nately divided into numerous small segments. Flower-heads smal white, numerous, in flat-topped terminal corymbs; ray florets 5– *Roadsides and meadows, very common.*

A. Ptar'mica L. 112. Sneezewort. July–Sept. Leaves linear, serrat Flower-heads few; ray florets 10–15. *Shady places, occasional.*

XII. *AN'THEMIS*

Leaves finely divided into linear segments. Flower-heads with yellow disk and white ray; receptacle conical, with scales between th florets. Pappus none.

Plant with a very disagreeable smell	A. Cotul
Plant with a pleasant aromatic smell	A. nobil
Plant odourless or nearly so	A. arvens

A. Cot'ula L. 74. Stinking Mayweed. July–Sept. Stem and leave nearly glabrous, evil-smelling. Scales between the florets linear, acute ray florets without a style. *Cornfields and waste places, common i S. England.*

A. arven'sis L. 85. Corn Chamomile. July–Sept. Stem and leave downy, odourless. Scales between the florets lanceolate, acute; ra florets with a style. *Cornfields, frequent.*

A. no'bilis L. 57. Chamomile. July–Sept. Stem and leaves glabrou or downy, aromatic. Scales between the florets obtuse; ray floret with a style. *Gravelly and sandy places, occasional.*

XIII. *CHRYSAN'THEMUM*

Ray florets spreading. Receptacle flat or convex, without scales. In volucral bracts in several rows. Pappus none.

Ray yellow	C. segetur
Ray white	
2 Leaves pinnate, flower-heads small, in corymbs	C. Partheniun
Leaves toothed, flower-heads large, solitary .	C. Leucanthemun

C. seg'etum L. 111. Corn Marigold. July–Sept. Flower-heads large, yellow, solitary. Leaves glaucous. *Cornfields, locally common.*

C. Leucan'themum L. 112. Ox-eye Daisy. June–Aug. Flower-heads large, solitary, white, with yellow disk; involucral bracts with narrow reddish-brown margins. *Meadows and waysides, common.*

C. Parthe'nium Pers. 106. Feverfew. July–Sept. Leaves pinnate. Flower-heads small, white, with yellow disk, in terminal corymbs. *Hedgebanks and waste places, occasional.*

XIV. *MATRICA'RIA*

Similar to *Anthemis* but without any scales between the florets.

Ray none . . . . M. discoidea
Ray present 2

Involucral bracts with brown scarious edges . . M. inodora
Involucral bracts without brown scarious edges M. Chamomilla

M. inodo'ra L. 112. Corn Feverfew, Scentless Mayweed. July–Sept. Odourless. Leaves finely divided into linear segments. Flower-heads white, with a yellow conical and usually solid centre, on long peduncles. *Cornfields and waste places, common.*

M. Chamomil'la L. 68. Wild Chamomile. June–Oct. Like the preceding species, but aromatic and the receptacle usually hollow. *Cornfields and waste places, frequent.*

M. discoi'dea DC. (M. suaveo'lens Buchenau.) 77. June–Sept. Aromatic. Leaves finely divided into linear segments. Flower-heads yellow, hemispherical, without a ray. *Waste places, common.*

XV. *TANACE'TUM*

T. vulga're L. 110. Tansy. July–Sept. Tall plant with deeply pinnatifid or pinnate aromatic leaves; leaf segments linear, flat, and coarsely toothed. Flower-heads small, yellow, hemispherical, without a ray, in a large terminal corymb; pappus none. *Waste places, frequent.*

XVI. *ARTEMIS'IA*

Aromatic herbs or shrubs with divided leaves usually white or grey on one or both sides. Flower-heads small, yellow or greenish, without ray florets or pappus, in terminal racemes or panicles.

Leaves green above, segments acute . . . . A. vulgaris
Leaves white or grey on both sides, segments obtuse . . 2

Leaf segments oblong, silky . . . . A. Absinthium
Leaf segments narrow-linear, small, cottony . . A. maritima

A. Absin'thium L. 80. Wormwood. Aug.–Sept. Leaves grey-green, silky, pinnately dissected into blunt oblong lobes. Flower-heads numerous, drooping. *Waste places near the sea, occasional.*

4565

H

A. vulga′ris L. 112. Mugwort. Aug.–Sept. Tall and erect. Leaves pinnately dissected into lanceolate acute lobes, green above and white below. Flower-heads numerous, erect, in spikes in the upper leaf axils. *Waste places, common.*

A. marit′ima L. 53. Sea Wormwood. Aug.–Oct. A low much-branched woody plant covered with close white cottony down. Leaves small, pinnately dissected into narrow-linear segments. Flower-heads small, numerous, in terminal panicles. *Salt marshes, locally common.*

XVII. *TUSSILA′GO*

T. Far′fara L. 112. Coltsfoot. March–April. A herb with a creeping rootstock and large orbicular, deeply cordate, radical leaves. Flower-heads yellow, solitary, appearing before the leaves, on long cottony peduncles with narrow alternate bracts; involucral bracts equal, in one row, with scales at base. Achenes cylindrical. *Waste ground on stiff soil, common.*

XVIII. *PETASI′TES*

P. ova′tus Hill. (**P. vulga′ris** Desf.) 110. Butterbur. March–April. Leaves large, cordate, unevenly toothed, downy beneath. Flower-heads in a raceme, pinkish purple, dioecious. *Riverbanks, common.*

XIX. *DORONI′CUM*

D. Pardalian′ches L. 40. Leopard's Bane. May–July. Radical leaves cordate, cauline ovate. Flower-heads large, yellow, on long slender peduncles; ray florets without a pappus; involucral bracts all equal, in a single row. *Escape from gardens.*

XX. *SENE′CIO*

Flower-heads yellow, with or without a ray, in terminal corymbs; involucral bracts equal, in a single row, with scales at base; ray florets with a pappus.

Achenes all glabrous	. . . .	
Some or all of achenes hairy	. . . .	
2 Ray spreading	. . . . .	S. aquaticu
Ray revolute or wanting	. . . . .	S. viscosu
3 Achenes of ray glabrous	. . . . .	S. Jacobae
Achenes all hairy	. . . . . .	
4 Ray absent	. . . . . .	S. vulgar
Ray small, revolute	. . . . .	S. sylvaticu
Ray conspicuous, spreading	. . . . .	
5 Leaves entire or finely toothed	. . . .	
Leaves divided or coarsely toothed	. . .	
6 Leaves glabrous or nearly so	. . .	S. sarracenicu
Leaves hairy	. . . . .	S. campestr
7 Glabrous	. . . . .	S. squalid
Hairy	. . . . . .	S. erucifoli

vulga'ris L. 112. Common Groundsel. Jan.–Dec. Seldom exceeding 18 inches. Leaves narrow-oblong, coarsely toothed or pinnatifid.
Flower-heads cylindrical, without ray florets. *A very common weed
everywhere.*

sylvat'icus L. 110. Wood Groundsel. July–Aug. A hairy, somewhat
viscid, plant up to 3 feet high. Flower-heads in large spreading corymbs,
usually with a few rolled-back ray florets; outer bracts minute. *Woods
and waste places, frequent.*

visco'sus L. 69. Stinking Groundsel. Aug.–Sept. Whole plant
covered with sticky hairs and strong-smelling. Flower-heads cylindrical, in loose corymbs, usually with a few rolled-back ray florets,
outer bracts ⅓ as long as inner. Achenes glabrous. *Waste places, rare.*

squal'idus L. 33. May–Oct. Leaves glabrous, narrow and sharply
toothed, the lower ones with narrow acute lobes. Flower-heads large,
with a bright yellow spreading ray. Achenes silky. *Waste places,
locally common.*

erucifo'lius L. 69. Hoary Ragwort. June–Sept. Stem and leaves
downy. Leaves with narrow distant lobes. Flower-heads large, pale
yellow, in a loose corymb; ray spreading; outer bracts long. Achenes
all hairy. *Waysides, &c., common.*

Jacobae'a L. 112. Common Ragwort. July–Sept. Lower leaves
lyrate, with pinnatifid terminal lobe. Flower-heads large, bright yellow,
in a dense corymb; outer bracts short. Achenes of the ray glabrous.
Waysides and poor pastures, a very common and troublesome weed.

aquat'icus Huds. 111. Water Ragwort. June–Sept. Lower leaves
lyrate, with a large ovate terminal lobe. Flower-heads large, in a loose
corymb; ray spreading; outer bracts short. Achenes all glabrous. *Damp
meadows and wet places, common.*

sarracen'icus L. 40. Broad-leaved Ragwort. Aug.–Sept. A tall
plant up to 6 feet with large ovate or lanceolate, toothed, undivided
leaves. Flower-heads comparatively small, numerous, in dense corymbs;
ray spreading; outer bracts of involucre long. *Riverbanks and damp
places, rare.*

campes'tris DC. 23. May–June. A small plant with hairy undivided
leaves, the radical ones in a rosette. Flower-heads yellow, in a dense
terminal corymb; ray spreading; no outer bracts to the involucre. *Calcareous downs, rare.*

Subfamily II. CYNAROI'DEAE

Florets all tubular, usually pink, blue, or purple, the outer ones often
regular and spreading into a kind of ray. Style swollen or with a collar
f hairs below its branches.

XXI. *CARLI'NA*

vulga'ris L. 85. Carline Thistle. July–Aug. 6–12 inches high. Stem
not winged. Leaves lanceolate, prickly, gradually merging into the
outer bracts of the involucre which resemble them. Flower-heads
large, surrounded when open by a horizontal ray of whitish linear
bracts. Achenes silky; pappus hairs branched. *Dry pastures, common.*

XXII. *ARC'TIUM*

A. Lap'pa L. 104. Burdock. July–Aug. A tall erect plant with spreading
branches and large broad leaves. Flower-heads globular, covered
with stiff hooked bracts; florets purple; pappus short and stiff. *Waste
places, common.*

The commonest kind is *A. mi'nus* (Bernh.) with small almost sessile
heads with a webby involucre and projecting florets. *A. ma'jus* (Bernh.)
has large long-stalked heads 1 inch or more in diameter and a glabrous
involucre with the florets scarcely projecting.

XXIII. *CAR'DUUS*

Thistles with bristly receptacle and compressed glabrous achenes.

Pappus hairs simple (unbranched) (*a*) . . . . . .
Pappus hairs branched (*b*) . . . .

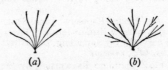

(*a*)   (*b*)

2 Leaves variegated with white veins . . . C. Marianus
  Leaves not variegated . . . . . .

3 Involucre cylindrical, bracts broad. . . C. pycnocephalus
  Involucre ovoid or globular, bracts linear . .

4 Flower-heads large, globular, drooping, solitary on the end of
    long peduncles . . . . . C. nutans
  Flower-heads small, ovoid, erect, in clusters . . C. crispus

5 Stem winged . . . .
  Stem not winged . . . .

6 Flower-heads small, stem winged along its whole length C. palustris
  Flower-heads large, stem partly winged . . C. lanceolatus

7 Flower-heads sessile or very shortly stalked . . .
  Flower-heads long-stalked . . . . .

8 Stem very short or none, leaves all radical . . C. acaulis
  Stem erect, leafy . . . . . . C. eriophorus

9 Leaves very prickly, flower-heads not solitary . C. arvensis
  Leaves slightly or not prickly, flower-heads solitary. . . 1

10 Leaves not prickly, white below . . . C. heterophyllus
   Leaves with small prickly teeth, greyish-green below C. pratensis

C. pycnoceph'alus L. (**C. tenuiflo'rus** Curtis.) 77. Slender Thistle.
May–Aug. Tall and slender, covered with white cottony hairs. Stem
winged. Flower-heads small, cylindrical or campanulate, involucral
bracts broad at base; pappus of simple hairs; florets pale pink or
whitish. *Dry waste places near the sea, occasional.*

C. nu'tans L. 83. Musk Thistle. June–Sept. Tall and stout, with
winged stem. Flower-heads large, deep purple, solitary and drooping.

at the end of long peduncles; pappus of simple hairs. *Pastures on cal-careous soil, frequent.*

. cris'pus L. **(C. acanthoi'des** L.) 95. Welted Thistle. May–Sept. Tall and narrow with very prickly winged stems. Flower-heads small, deep crimson, in erect clusters; pappus of simple hairs. *Fields and waysides, frequent.*

. lanceola'tus L. 112. Spear Thistle. July–Oct. Tall and stout, with partly winged stems. Flower-heads few, large, ovoid, bright rosy purple, with an involucre of long spreading spines; pappus of branched hairs. *Fields, common.*

. erioph'orus L. 49. Woolly Thistle. July–Aug. Stout and much branched. Stem without wings. Flower-heads few, large, globular, the involucre and underside of leaves covered with white cottony hairs; florets deep crimson; pappus of branched hairs. *Dry pastures on cal-careous soils, occasional.*

. palus'tris L. 112. Marsh Thistle. June–Aug. Tall and slender with winged and very prickly stems. Leaves long and narrow. Flower-heads rather numerous, small, crimson or white; pappus of branched hairs. *Damp meadows and woods, common.*

. praten'sis Huds. 50. Meadow Thistle. June–July. Leaves lan-ceolate, undivided, edged with small prickles. Flower-heads crimson, not large, usually solitary on long peduncles. *Damp meadows, occa-sional.*

. heterophyl'lus L. 56. Melancholy Thistle. July–Aug. Leaves large, lanceolate, not prickly, white below and clasping the stem. Flower-heads large, solitary, on long peduncles. *Mountain pastures in the north.*

. acau'lis L. 46. Dwarf Thistle. July–Aug. Flower-heads crimson, sessile in a tuft of radical spreading leaves. *Common in the south.*

. arven'sis L. 112. Common Field Thistle. July–Aug. Rootstock creeping. Stems tall, slender and erect, not winged. Flower-heads small, pinkish-purple, dioecious, in terminal corymbs, the males small and globular, the females larger and cylindrical; pappus of branched hairs. *Poor pastures and waste places, very common.*

. Maria'nus L. 41. Milk Thistle. June–Aug. Leaves smooth and glossy above and variegated with white veins. Flower-heads large, solitary at the end of branches, drooping, with broad leafy involucral bracts. *Waste places, rare.*

XXIV. *ONOPOR'DON*

). Acan'thium L. 70. Scotch or Cotton Thistle. July–Sept. A tall stout cottony plant with branched and very broadly winged stems. Flower-heads large, dull purple, globular, with an involucre of spread-ing spines; receptacle honeycombed, without long bristles. Achenes ovoid, 4-sided, transversely wrinkled. *Waste places, occasional.*

XXV. *SAUSSU'REA*

S. alpi'na DC. 30. Alpine Saw-wort. July–Sept. Stem erect, un
branched, not exceeding 1 foot. Leaves lanceolate, minutely toothed
Flower-heads purple, in a dense terminal corymb; pappus of branched
hairs. *Mountains in the north, rare.*

XXVI. *SERRAT'ULA*

S. tincto'ria L. 68. Saw-wort. July–Aug. Rather like a knapweed but
the involucral bracts are neither fringed nor prickly pointed. Leave
pinnately divided into sharply-toothed lanceolate segments. Flower
heads pinkish-purple, slender-stalked; receptacle with chaffy scale
between the florets; pappus of simple hairs. *Meadows and open woods
occasional.*

XXVII. *CENTAURE'A*

Leaves not prickly. Flower-heads usually purple or blue, with har
ovoid or globular involucres with fringed or prickly pointed bracts
receptacle with bristles between the florets; outer florets often spreadin
and forming a kind of ray.

Involucral bracts ending in a long spine	. . .	C. Calcitrap
Involucral bracts not ending in a spine	. . . .	. 2
2 Leaves deeply pinnatifid	. . . .	C. Scabios
Leaves entire or toothed	. . . .	.
3 Outer florets bright blue	. . . .	C. Cyanu
Outer florets reddish-purple or white	. . .	. C. nigr

C. ni'gra L. 111. Black Knapweed. June–Sept. Upper leaves entire
lower ones toothed or shallowly lobed. Flower-heads reddish-purple
with dark brown deeply fringed involucral bracts. *Meadows and way
sides, very common.*

C. Scabio'sa L. 84. Great Knapweed. July–Sept. All the leaves deeply
pinnatifid. Flower-heads reddish-purple; involucral bracts green
with dark fringed borders. *Meadows and waysides, common.*

C. Cy'anus L. 100. Cornflower, Bluebottle. June–Aug. All the leave
entire, narrow-lanceolate or linear, covered with grey cottony down
Outer florets bright blue. *Cornfields, locally common.*

C. Calcitra'pa L. 17. Star Thistle. July–Sept. Leaves pinnatifid
Flower-heads purple (sometimes white), sessile, involucres spiny
Waste places near the sea in S. England, rare.

SUBFAMILY III. **LIGULA'TAE**

Florets all ligulate, usually yellow, rarely blue.

XXVIII. *CICHOR'IUM*

C. In'tybus L. 67. Chicory. July–Sept. Leaves pinnatifid, hairy, clasp
ing the stem. Flower-heads sessile or nearly so, bright blue; pappu
replaced by a ring of small scales. *Fields and waysides, occasional.*

XXIX. *ARNOS'ERIS*

A. min'ima Schw. & Koerte. (**A. pusil'la** Gaertn.) 26. Lamb's or Swine's Succory. July–Sept. Leaves all radical, obovate or oblanceolate, coarsely toothed. Flower-heads small, yellow, on long leafless peduncles swollen and hollow in the upper part. *Dry waste places in E. England and E. Scotland, rare.*

XXX. *LAP'SANA*

L. commu'nis L. 112. Nipplewort. June–Oct. Upper leaves lanceolate; lower leaves lyrate, with a large ovate terminal lobe. Flower-heads small, yellow, slender-stalked, in open corymbs; pappus none. *Hedgebanks and waste places, very common.*

XXXI. *PIC'RIS*

P. hieracioi'des L. 62. Hawkweed Ox-tongue. July–Oct. Tall, erect, and hispid. Leaves lanceolate, covered with rough hairs. Flower-heads yellow, on long stiff peduncles, receptacle without scales between the florets; pappus of branched hairs except on a few of the outer achenes. Achenes transversely ribbed, narrowed at the top. *Waste places on calcareous soil, frequent.*

XXXII. *HELMINTH'IA*

H. echioi'des Gaertn. 66. Ox-tongue. July–Sept. Tall, erect, and hispid. Leaves lanceolate, warted and covered with rough hairs. Flower-heads yellow, several at the end of a long peduncle; outer bracts of the involucre cordate and leaf-like, edged with stiff bristles; pappus of branched hairs, stalked. *Waste ground on stiff soil, frequent.*

XXXIII. *CRE'PIS*

Cauline leaves usually clasping the stem. Flowering stems branched forming an open corymb. Flower-heads small, yellow; pappus of simple hairs, usually white and silky.

All or inner achenes with a slender beak	. . . .	2
Achenes all without a beak	. . . .	3
2 Bracts along the peduncles	. . . .	C. foetida
Bracts only at junctions	.	C. taraxacifolia
3 Upper leaves broadly sagittate, pappus dirty white or yellowish-brown	. . . . . .	C. paludosa
Upper leaves lanceolate or oblong, pappus white and silky .	.	4
4 Leaves nearly entire, without lobes or coarse teeth	.	C. mollis
Lower leaves pinnatifid or coarsely toothed	. .	5
5 Upper leaves sagittate, glabrous, or slightly hairy	.	C. capillaris
Upper leaves not sagittate, hispid	. . .	C. biennis

C. foe'tida L. 12. Stinking Hawk's-beard. June–July. A small, hairy, strong-smelling plant seldom exceeding 1 foot. Lower leaves deeply pinnatifid. Flower-heads few, with a few small bracts along each separate peduncle. Outer achenes almost without a beak. *Dry pastures in SE. England, rare.*

C. taraxacifo′lia Thuill. 64. Beaked Hawk′s-beard. May–July. A tall plant with compound or deeply pinnatifid leaves and corymbs of numerous yellow flower-heads; peduncles naked. Ripe achenes all with a slender beak. *Waste ground, locally common.*

C. capilla′ris Wallr. (**C. vi′rens** L.) 112. Smooth Hawk′s-beard. June–Nov. Glabrous or nearly so. Upper leaves narrow-sagittate, lower coarsely toothed or shortly pinnatifid. Flower-heads few. Achenes without a beak. *Fields and waysides, very common.*

C. bien′nis L. 54. Rough Hawk′s-beard. June–July. Tall and erect. Leaves rough with short hairs, the upper ones clasping the stem but not sagittate, lower leaves deeply runcinate. Achenes not beaked. *Waste places, rare.*

C. mol′lis Aschers. (**C. succisaefo′lia** Tausch.) 21. July–Aug. Seldom exceeding 1 foot. Leaves oblanceolate or obovate, entire or nearly so. Flower-heads few, rather large. Achenes not beaked. *Shady places in the north, rare.*

C. paludo′sa Moench. 65. Marsh Hawk′s-beard. July–Sept. Lower leaves runcinate, upper broadly sagittate, toothed. Flower-heads rather large; pappus dirty white or yellowish-brown. *Shady places in the north, frequent.*

XXXIV. *HIERA′CIUM*

Differs from *Crepis* chiefly in the achenes, which are usually shorter and broader, without much, if any, narrowing at the top, and crowned by a dirty white or yellowish-brown pappus of simple hairs. Upper leaves rarely sagittate or clasping the stem.

Flower-heads solitary	
Flower-heads not solitary	
2 Leaves white below, stem with runners . . .	H. Pilosella
Leaves green below, stem without runners . .	H. alpinum
3 Radical leaves present at the time of flowering . . .	
Radical leaves absent at the time of flowering . .	
4 Stem leafy	H. vulgatum
Stem with few or no leaves	H. murorum
5 Upper leaves auricled	
Upper leaves not auricled	
6 Auricles short and rounded	H. prenanthoides
Auricles long and pointed	Crepis paludosa
7 Upper leaves narrow, with a tapering base .	H. umbellatum
Upper leaves broad, with a rounded base . .	H. sabaudum

H. muro′rum L. 24. Wall Hawkweed. June–Aug. Radical leaves ovate, stalked, present at the time of flowering, cauline leaves few or none. Flower-heads yellow, in a loose terminal corymb. *Walls and banks, occasional.*

H. vulga′tum Fr. (**H. sylvat′icum** Sm.) 55. Wood Hawkweed. June–Aug. Radical leaves ovate, stalked, present at the time of flowering, cauline leaves numerous, not or scarcely clasping the stem. Flower-heads yellow, in a loose terminal corymb. *Woods and banks, frequent.*

. alpi′num L. 16. Alpine Hawkweed. July–Aug. Leaves mostly radical, green below. Flower-head large, solitary, bright yellow, involucre covered with long rusty hairs. *Mountains in the north, rare.*

. prenanthoi′des Vill. 18. July–Sept. Radical leaves withered at the time of flowering; upper leaves clasping the stem with rounded auricles. Flower-heads yellow, in a terminal corymb. *Scottish Highlands, rare.*

. umbella′tum L. 71. Umbellate Hawkweed. Aug.–Sept. Tall and erect. Radical leaves withered at the time of flowering; upper leaves narrow, with a tapering base. Flower-heads rather large, bright yellow, in an umbel-like terminal corymb. *Hedgebanks and open woods, frequent.*

. sabau′dum L. 87. Savoy Hawkweed. Aug.–Sept. Tall and erect. Radical leaves withered at the time of flowering; upper leaves broad, with rounded base. Flower-heads in a loose terminal corymb not resembling an umbel. *Hedgebanks and open woods, occasional.*

. Pilosel′la L. 111. Mouse-ear Hawkweed. June–Aug. Plant with runners. Leaves small, entire, white below, fringed with long hairs. Flower-head solitary, pale lemon-yellow, on a leafless peduncle covered with white down. *Dry places, common.*

XXXV. *HYPOCHOE′RIS*

Leaves all radical. Flowering stems leafless. Flower-heads yellow, with a few chaffy scales between the florets; pappus of branched hairs. Achenes mostly with a slender beak.

. gla′bra L. 55. Smooth Cat's-ear. June–Aug. Leaves glabrous. Flower-heads small, the florets scarcely exceeding the involucre. Outer achenes without a beak. *Sandy places, occasional.*

. radica′ta L. 112. Common Cat's-ear. June–Aug. Leaves hispid, coarsely toothed. Flower-heads large, the florets much longer than the involucre. All the achenes beaked. *Meadows, very common.*

XXXVI. *LEON′TODON*

Leaves all radical. Flowering stems leafless. Flower-heads yellow, without scales between the florets; pappus of branched hairs. Achenes narrowed at top but not beaked.

Flowering stem branched . . . . . L. autumnalis
Flowering stem unbranched 2

Leaves very hairy, all the achenes with a pappus of hairs L. hispidus
Leaves with few hairs, outer achenes with a pappus of
scales . . . . L. hirtus

. hir′tus L. 82. Lesser Hawkbit. June–Aug. A small plant with a rosette of narrow sinuate radical leaves, glabrous or with a few stiff hairs. Flower-heads small, bright yellow, solitary, involucre usually glabrous. Outer achenes with a pappus of scales. *Dry pastures, common.*

L. his′pidus L. 95. Rough Hawkbit. June–Aug. Leaves all radica
long and narrow, coarsely toothed or pinnatifid, very hairy. Flowe
heads large, solitary on the end of a long hairy peduncle; involucr
usually hairy. Outer achenes with a short pappus of simple hairs, inn
achenes with pappus of branched hairs. *Meadows, common.*

L. autumna′lis L. 112. Autumnal Hawkbit. July–Oct. Leaves a
radical, long and narrow, coarsely toothed or pinnatifid, glabrous o
nearly so. Flowering stems very long and branched at the top in
2 or more heads. All the achenes with branched pappus. *Meadow
common.*

XXXVII. *TARAX′ACUM*

T. officina′le Weber. 112. Dandelion. March–Oct. Tap root lon
with milky juice. Leaves all radical, runcinate, glabrous. Flower-head
large, solitary at the end of a long hollow peduncle, the outer bracts o
the involucre reflexed; pappus of simple hairs, long-stalked. Achene
with a long slender beak (the stalk of the pappus). *Meadows and was
places, very common.*

    T. erythrosper′mum (Bab.) has slender crimson fruits with roug
tips. *T. palus′tre* (DC.) is a variety with very narrow and scarcel
lobed leaves and erect or spreading outer bracts, inhabiting marshe
and bogs.

XXXVIII. *LACTU′CA*

    Flower-heads small, yellow, with narrow involucre and few florets
pappus of simple hairs. Achenes narrowed at the top and usually flat.

L. viro′sa L. 60. Prickly Lettuce. July–Sept. A tall stiff plant. Leave
lanceolate or oblong, twisted, glabrous, midrib prickly below. Flower
heads small, numerous, in an open leafy panicle; florets 6–12; involucra
bracts unequal. *Walls and stony places, occasional.*

L. mura′lis Gaertn. 75. Wall Lettuce. June–Sept. Not so tall as th
preceding species. Leaves fewer, lyrate, with a broad ivy-shape
terminal lobe. Flower-heads numerous, in a terminal and almost lea
less panicle; florets 4–5; involucre of five linear equal bracts with a fe
scales at the base. *Walls, hedgebanks, and open woods, frequent.*

XXXIX. *SON′CHUS*

    Erect plants with large glabrous pinnatifid leaves and yellow flower
heads in small terminal panicles. Pappus of simple hairs. Achene
flattened, not beaked or much narrowed at the top.

Flower-heads large, with a hairy involucre . . S. arvensi
Flower-heads small, with a nearly glabrous involucre . . .
2 Leaves somewhat prickly, auricles rounded . . . S. aspe
   Leaves not prickly, auricles pointed . . . S. oleraceu

S. olera′ceus L. 112. Common Sowthistle. May–Oct. Stem hollo
and rather thick. Lower leaves large, pinnatifid, clasping the stem wit
pointed auricles. Flower-heads small, involucre glabrous or nearly s
becoming conical after flowering. Achenes with a granulated surface
Waste ground, very common.

, as'per Hill. 112. Rough Sowthistle. May–Sept. Leaves oblong or shallowly lobed, with numerous sharp, almost prickly, teeth, clasping the stem with rounded auricles. Flower-heads like those of the preceding species. Achenes smooth. *Waste ground, common.*

. arven'sis L. 112. Corn Sowthistle. July–Aug. A tall plant with large pinnatifid leaves clasping the stem with rounded auricles. Flower-heads large, with hairy involucres. Achenes with a granulated surface. *Cornfields and waste ground, less common than the previous two.*

XL. *TRAGOPO′GON*

. praten'sis L. 92. Goat's-beard. June–July. Leaves long, linear, and grass-like. Flower-heads yellow, solitary at the end of long peduncles; involucral bracts all equal, with long points; pappus of branched hairs. Achenes narrowed at the top into a long slender beak forming a stalk to the pappus. *Meadows, common.*

FAMILY 45. **CAMPANULA′CEAE**

Leaves alternate, exstipulate. Calyx and corolla 5-lobed. Stamens 5, tached to the base of the corolla. Ovary inferior, 2–5-celled, style 1. ruit a several-seeded capsule.

orolla very irregular	Lobelia I
orolla regular	2
Flowers in involucrate heads, corolla divided to base into linear segments	3
Flowers not in involucrate heads, corolla campanulate or rotate, with broad lobes	Campanula IV
Anthers united at base	Jasione II
Anthers free	Phyteuma III

I. *LOBE′LIA*

. Dortman'na L. 44. Water Lobelia. July–Aug. Leaves all radical, linear, cylindrical, growing in tufts under water. Flower pale blue, irregular, 2-lipped, in a raceme above the water, anthers united into a tube. *Mountain lakes, occasional.*

II. *JASI′ONE*

. monta'na L. 85. Sheep's-bit, Sheep's Scabious. June–Sept. Leaves lanceolate or linear, entire, with wavy margins. Flower-heads blue, solitary at the end of long peduncles; corolla lobes linear, anthers united at the base. *Heaths and dry banks, frequent.*

III. *PHYTEU′MA*

. orbicula're L. 10. Rampion. July–Aug. Leaves lanceolate, toothed. Flower-heads large, deep blue, the flower buds long and curved, anthers free, stigmas 2–3. *Chalk downs in S. England, rare.*

IV. *CAMPAN'ULA*

Corolla campanulate or rotate, 5-lobed. Anthers free. Stigmas 2–5.

Calyx tube long and narrow, sepals longer than the petals   C. hybric
Calyx tube short and broad, sepals shorter than the petals   .

2 Stem prostrate, leaves as broad as long and palmately
    lobed   .   .   .   .   C. hederace
    Stem erect or ascending, upper leaves longer than broad   .

3 Flowers sessile, in terminal clusters .   .   .   .   C. glomerat
    Flowers stalked, in racemes or panicles   .   .   .   .

4 Calyx with hairs   .   .   .   .
    Calyx glabrous   .   .   .   .

5 Sepals reflexed after flowering   .   .   .   C. rapunculoid
    Sepals always erect or spreading   .   .   .   C. Tracheliu

6 Upper leaves broad, with numerous teeth   ,   .   C. latifol
    Upper leaves narrow, entire, or with very few teeth   .   .

7 Lobes of corolla much shorter than the tube   .   C. rotundifol
    Lobes of corolla as long as, or nearly as long as, the tube   .

8 Pedicels much longer than the flowers   .   .   .   C. patul
    Pedicels scarcely longer than the flowers   .   ,   C. Rapunculu

C. hedera'cea L. (**Wahlenber'gia hederacea** Reichb.) 48. Ivy
leaved Bellflower. July–Sept. A small prostrate plant with ivy-shape
leaves and small pale blue flowers on long stalks. *Damp pastures an
woods, occasional.*

C. glomera'ta L. 52. Clustered Bellflower. July–Sept. Stem firm an
erect. Leaves ovate or lanceolate, toothed, upper ones sessile and clasp
ing the stem. Flowers deep purplish-blue, sessile, in terminal clusters
Dry pastures on calcareous soils, frequent.

C. Trache'lium L. 59. Nettle-leaved Bellflower. July–Sept. Leave
deeply and irregularly toothed, lower ones cordate. Flowers large
blue, short-stalked, solitary, or in clusters of 2 or 3 in the leaf axils
Hedgebanks and woods, frequent.

C. latifo'lia L. 80. Giant Bellflower. July–Aug. A tall plant wit
furrowed stems and large ovate or lanceolate finely-toothed leaves
Flowers large, blue or white, short-stalked, solitary in the upper lea
axils forming a leafy raceme; sepals erect. *Woods, mostly in the north
occasional.*

C. rapunculoi'des L. 55. Creeping Bellflower. June–Aug. Rootstoc
creeping. Stem cylindrical. Upper leaves ovate or lanceolate, toothed
lower leaves cordate. Flowers large, blue, in a long one-sided raceme
sepals reflexed after flowering. *Waysides and open woods, rare.*

C. rotundifo'lia L. 111. Harebell. July–Sept. Upper leaves linea
entire, lower ovate or cordate but usually absent at the time of flower
ing. Flowers small, pale blue, drooping, long-stalked. *Heaths, commor*

C. Rapun'culus L. 22. Rampion, Ramps. July–Aug. Upper leave
linear, entire or nearly so. Flowers small, pale blue, in a long raceme o
narrow panicle, fruits erect. *Hedgebanks, rare.*

C. pat'ula L. 29. Spreading Bellflower. July–Sept. Stems rough. Leaves oblong or lanceolate, entire or nearly so. Flowers large, few, purplish-blue, long-stalked, in a spreading panicle, corolla lobes spreading or reflexed when fully open. *Shady places, rare.*

C. hy'brida L. (Specula'ria hybrida DC.) 52. Corn Bellflower, Venus's Looking-glass. June–Sept. Leaves oblong, with wavy margins. Flowers blue, sessile, calyx lobes longer than the corolla. *Cornfields, occasional.*

FAMILY 46. VACCINIA'CEAE

Low shrubs or woody plants with alternate exstipulate leaves. Flowers small, campanulate or urceolate, nodding, solitary or in twos or threes; calyx and corolla 4–5-lobed; stamens twice as many as corolla lobes; ovary inferior, 4–5-celled. Fruit a berry.

VACCIN'IUM

Corolla deeply 4-cleft, with reflexed lobes	.	.	V. Oxycoccus
Corolla campanulate or urceolate, with short lobes		.	. 2
2 Anthers without awns, berry red	.	.	V. vitis-Idaea
Anthers awned, berry bluish-black	.	.	. 3
3 Stem angled, leaves toothed	.	.	V. Myrtillus
Stem cylindrical, leaves entire	.	.	V. uliginosum

V. vitis-Idae'a L. 71. Cowberry. June–Sept. Stem procumbent. Leaves small, evergreen, obovate, entire or faintly toothed near apex. Flowers pink, anthers without awns. Berry red. *Moors, mostly in the north, common.*

V. uligino'sum L. 23. Bog Bilberry. May–June. Leaves small, deciduous, obovate, obtuse. Flowers very small, pink, anthers awned. Berry black, with glaucous bloom. *Moors and bogs in the north.*

V. Myrtil'lus L. 102. Whortleberry, Bilberry. April–June. Branchlets angled. Leaves ovate, toothed. Flowers white, tinged with red, anthers awned. Berry blue-black, glaucous. *Moors and open woods, locally common.*

V. Oxycoc'cus L. 75. Cranberry. July–Aug. Stem thin, wiry, prostrate and creeping. Leaves small, evergreen, ovate or lanceolate, margins recurved, glaucous beneath. Flowers pink, with four spreading or reflexed petals exposing the stamens. Berry red. *Moors, mostly in the north, occasional.*

FAMILY 47. ERICA'CEAE

Shrubs or low woody plants (rarely herbs). Calyx and corolla 4–5-lobed; stamens usually twice as many as corolla lobes, hypogynous; ovary superior, 4–5-celled. Fruit a capsule or berry.

Herbs, petals free or nearly so	.	.	. 2
Woody plants, petals united		.	. 3
2 Leaves brown, reduced to scales	.	.	Monotropa VII
Leaves green, not reduced to scales	.	.	Pyrola VI

3 Leaves alternate . . . .
  Leaves opposite or whorled . . . . . .
4 Leaves obovate, obtuse, fruit a berry . . Arctostaphylos
  Leaves lanceolate, acute, fruit a capsule . . Andromeda
5 Stamens 5 . . . . Loiseleuria
  Stamens 8 . . . .
6 Calyx coloured, longer than the corolla . . . Calluna II
  Calyx green, shorter than the corolla . . . . Erica I

I. *ARCTOSTAPH'YLOS*

A. Uva-ur'si Spreng. 36. Bearberry. May–July. Stem procumben
Leaves small, evergreen, obovate and obtuse. Flowers pink, globula
drooping in terminal racemes; calyx and corolla 5-toothed; stamens 1
Berry red. *Dry moors in the north, rare.*

II. *ANDROM'EDA*

A. polifo'lia L. 35. Marsh Andromeda, Bog Rosemary. June–July. .
low glabrous woody plant with alternate lanceolate leaves white unde
neath and with the margins rolled back. Flowers small, pink, urceolat
drooping in terminal racemes; calyx and corolla 5-toothed; stamens 1
Fruit a dry capsule. *Bogs, mostly in the north, rare.*

III. *CALLU'NA*

C. vulga'ris L. 112. Ling. July–Sept. A low shrub with minut
opposite leaves spurred at the base. Flowers very small, pale pink o
white, in long, terminal, spike-like racemes; sepals 4, coloured an
longer than the 4 petals, both persistent in fruit; stamens 8. Fruit
capsule. *Heaths, common.*

IV. *ERI'CA*

Leaves small and narrow, with margins much recurved, opposite o
in whorls. Flowers small; sepals 4, small and green; corolla campanulat
or urceolate, 4-toothed at the mouth, persistent in fruit; stamens 8. Frui
a capsule.

Anthers exserted . . . . E. vagan
Anthers included within the corolla . . . . .
2 Anthers without awns, leaves ovate . . . E. ciliari
  Anthers awned, leaves linear . . . . .
3 Leaves 4 in a whorl . . . . . . E. Tetrali
  Leaves 3 in a whorl . . . . . . E. cinere

E. cilia'ris L. 4. Fringed Heather. June–Sept. Low woody plant wit
minute ovate ciliate leaves and large pink flowers in terminal 1-side
racemes, anthers without awns. *SW. England, rare.*

E. Tet'ralix L. 112. Cross-leaved Heather. June–Sept. Low wood
plant with linear leaves in fours and large pink flowers in termina
clusters. *Heaths, common.*

. **cine′rea** L. 108. Bell Heather. June–Sept. Low woody plant with linear leaves in threes and reddish-purple flowers in terminal racemes. *Heaths, common.*

. **va′gans** L. 1. Cornish Heather. July–Aug. Low woody plant with 4–5 linear leaves in a whorl and pale pink axillary flowers with exserted anthers. *Cornish heaths.*

V. *LOISELEU′RIA*

. **procum′bens** Desv. (**Aza′lea procumbens** L.) 19. Alpine Azalea. May–July. Low trailing shrub with small, opposite, ovate leaves and pink flowers in terminal clusters. Corolla broadly campanulate, 5-lobed; stamens 5. *Moors in N. Scotland, rare.*

VI. *PY′ROLA*

Small herbs with mostly radical ovate leaves and pink, white, or greenish-white drooping flowers on a leafless scape. Sepals and petals 5, free or nearly so; stamens 10. Fruit a 5-celled capsule.

lower solitary	P. uniflora
lowers in a raceme	2
Leaves acute, flowers in a compact 1-sided raceme .	P. secunda
Leaves obtuse, flowers in a loose raceme . . .	3
Style shorter than petals	P. minor
Style longer than petals	4
Style curved	P. rotundifolia
Style straight	P. media

. **rotundifo′lia** L. 34. Large Wintergreen. July–Sept. Flowers white, with a long, protruding, much curved style. *Woods and heaths, rare.*

. **me′dia** L. 47. Medium Wintergreen. June–July. Like the preceding species but style straight or nearly so. *Woods and heaths in the north, rare.*

. **mi′nor** L. 78. Common Wintergreen. June–July. Leaves ovate or orbicular, long-stalked. Flowers pale pink, drooping, style short. *Woods, occasional.*

. **secun′da** L. 33. Toothed Wintergreen. July–Aug. Leaves ovate, acute, sharply toothed. Flowers greenish-white, in a crowded 1-sided raceme, style long and straight. *Mountain woods and heaths, rare.*

. **uniflo′ra** L. (**Mone′ses uniflora** A. Gray.) 11. July–Aug. Flowers white, solitary, drooping, fragrant. *Pine woods in N. Scotland, rare.*

VII. *MONOT′ROPA*

I. **Hypop′ithys** L. 50. Bird's-nest. July–Aug. A saprophytic plant with erect stems bearing light brown or yellowish scales instead of leaves, and yellow flowers in a terminal raceme. Sepals and petals 4–5, free or nearly so; stamens 8–10. Fruit a 4–5-celled capsule. *Woods, occasional.*

Family 48. PLUMBAGINA'CEAE

Herbs with mostly radical leaves. Flowers in terminal heads, spike
or panicles; calyx and corolla 5-lobed; stamens 5, hypogynous; ovar
superior, 1-celled and containing 1 ovule; styles 5. Fruit a 1-seede
nut.

Flowers in panicles .   .   .   .   Statice
Flowers in heads .   .   .   .   Armeria

I. *STAT'ICE*

Leaves ovate or lanceolate, entire, mucronate. Flowers pale purpl
in 1-sided spikes arranged in panicles.

S. Limo'nium L. 42. Common Sea Lavender. July–Aug. Leave
usually more than 2 inches long, pinnately nerved. Flowers in a spread
ing, more or less flat-topped panicle. *Salt marshes, frequent.*

S. binervo'sa G. E. Sm. 28. Rock Sea Lavender. July–Aug. Leave
about an inch long, 3-nerved. Flowers in elongated panicles. *Rock
sea-shores, occasional.*

II. *ARME'RIA*

A. marit'ima Wild. 82. Thrift, Sea Pink. April–Sept. Leaves linea
in dense tufts. Flowers pink, in a globular involucrate head on the en
of a leafless peduncle; calyx and involucral bracts papery and sem
transparent, the lowest forming a sheath to the upper part of th
peduncle. *Muddy sea-shores and mountains, common.*

Family 49. PRIMULA'CEAE

Calyx and corolla usually 5-lobed. Stamens as many as corolla lobe
and inserted on the corolla tube opposite the lobes; ovary 1-celled, wit
free central placentation; style 1, with capitate stigma.

Leaves submerged in water and dissected into linear segments Hottonia
Leaves terrestrial, not dissected .   .   .   .   .   .

2 Leaves all radical .   .   .   .   Primula
  Stem leafy .   .   .   .

3 Leaves mostly opposite .   .   .   .
  Leaves, at least the lower ones, alternate .   .   .   .

4 Flowers yellow .   .   .   .   .   .   Lysimachia I
  Flowers not yellow .   .   .   .

5 Corolla absent, calyx pink .   .   .   .   .   .   Glaux
  Corolla present, calyx green .   .   .   .   .   Anagallis V

6 Leaves minute .   .   .   .   .   .   Centunculus V
  Leaves not minute .   .   .   .

7 Upper leaves in 1 whorl, lower alternate .   .   Trientalis I
  Upper leaves not in a whorl .   .   .   .   .   Samolus VI

I. *HOTTO'NIA*

. palus'tris L. 53. Water Violet. May–June. The leaves and lower part of the plant grow under water but send up an erect leafless stem bearing whorls of pale lilac flowers. Leaves pinnately dissected into linear segments. Calyx and corolla 5-lobed; stamens 5. *Water-channels, locally common.*

II. *PRIM'ULA*

Herbs with radical leaves. Flowers solitary or in an umbel at the end f a leafless peduncle; calyx 5-toothed, tubular or campanulate; corolla ibular at base with 5 spreading lobes at the top; stamens 5, inserted at e top of the corolla tube in the short-styled flowers and half-way down the long-styled.

lowers purple, leaves not or slightly wrinkled . .	P. farinosa
lowers yellow, leaves much wrinkled. . . .	. 2
Flowers solitary on each peduncle	P. vulgaris
Flowers in an umbel	. 3
Calyx inflated, with prominent ridges and broad open teeth	P. veris
Calyx cylindrical, scarcely ridged, teeth narrow . .	P. elatior

. vulga'ris Huds. 112. Primrose. March–May. Flowers large, pale greenish-yellow, solitary on each peduncle. *Hedgebanks and woods, common.*

. ve'ris L. 100. Cowslip, Paigle. April–June. Flowers small, yellow, in a long-stalked terminal umbel, calyx inflated, prominently ridged. *Meadows, common.*

The false Oxlip, with large flowers, is a hybrid between this and the preceding species.

. ela'tior Jacq. 8. Oxlip. April–May. Leaves abruptly narrowed into a long stalk. Flowers small, pale yellow, in a 1-sided umbel; throat of corolla open (not wrinkled or folded). *Woods in E. England, locally common.*

. farino'sa L. 14. Bird's-eye Primrose. May–July. Leaves not wrinkled. Flowers small, purple with a yellow eye, erect in a terminal umbel. *Mountain pastures in the north, rare.*

III. *LYSIMA'CHIA*

Leaves opposite or in whorls, entire. Flowers yellow; calyx and corolla eeply 5-lobed; stamens 5.

tem erect	L. vulgaris
tem prostrate	. 2
Flowers small, sepals very narrow . . .	L. nemorum
Flowers large, sepals broad	L. Nummularia

. vulga'ris L. 89. Yellow Loosestrife. July–Sept. A tall plant with broadly lanceolate entire leaves usually in whorls of 3 or 4. Flowers large, yellow, in a terminal leafy panicle. *Riverbanks and wet places, frequent.*

L. Nummula′ria L. 79. Moneywort, Creeping Jenny. July–Aug. Stems prostrate, trailing. Leaves opposite, ovate, obtuse. Flowers large, yellow, solitary in the leaf axils, sepals broad. *Damp places, frequent.*

L. nem′orum L. 109. Yellow Pimpernel. May–July. Stems prostrate. Leaves opposite, ovate. Flowers small, yellow, solitary in the leaf axils, sepals very narrow. *Woods, frequent.*

IV. *TRIENTA′LIS*

T. europae′a L. 42. June–July. Stem erect, about 3–6 inches high, with a whorl of obovate or oblanceolate leaves at the top, the lower leaves being smaller and alternate. Flowers white or pale pink, on slender stalks arising from the whorl of leaves; sepals and petals 6–7. *Woods in the north, rare.*

V. *GLAUX*

G. marit′ima L. 83. Sea Milkwort. June–July. A low, spreading plant with small, opposite, entire leaves and small pale pink flowers solitary or sessile in the leaf axils. Calyx pink, 5-lobed; corolla none; stamens 5. *Salt marshes, frequent.*

VI. *ANAGAL′LIS*

Stem procumbent or prostrate. Leaves opposite, entire. Flowers solitary, axillary, long-stalked; sepals 5, narrow; petals 5; stamens 5. Capsule opening by a transverse lid.

A. arven′sis L. 111. Scarlet Pimpernel, Poor Man's Weather-glass. May–Sept. Stem 4-angled. Leaves opposite, ovate, sessile. Flowers usually red, sometimes pink, white, or blue, with broad overlapping petals. *A common weed in cornfields and gardens.*

    A. caerulea (Schreb.) has blue flowers with narrower and not overlapping petals.

A. tenel′la L. 103. Bog Pimpernel. July–Aug. A very small plant with slender creeping stems and minute orbicular leaves. Flowers pale pink, on long, slender peduncles. *Bogs and wet places, frequent.*

VII. *CENTUN′CULUS*

C. min′imus L. 73. Chaffweed. June–Aug. A very small plant with minute alternate leaves and very small axillary and almost sessile flowers. Sepals 4, linear; petals 4, pink, very minute. Capsule opening by a transverse lid. *Wet sandy places, occasional.*

VIII. *SAM′OLUS*

S. Valeran′di L. 85. Brookweed. June–Sept. A pale green erect herb with alternate obovate leaves and small white flowers in racemes forming a terminal panicle. Calyx campanulate, 5-lobed; petals 5; stamens 5; ovary inferior. *Wet places near the sea, frequent.*

FAMILY 50. OLEA'CEAE

Trees, shrubs, or woody climbers with opposite leaves. Flowers regular;
alyx and corolla usually 4-lobed, or absent; stamens 2; ovary superior,
-celled; style 1.

'ree with pinnate leaves and winged fruits . . . Fraxinus I
hrub with simple leaves and black berries . . . Ligustrum II

I. *FRAX'INUS*

'. **excel'sior** L. 111. Common Ash. April–May. A tree with black
winter buds and opposite pinnately compound leaves. Leaflets lanceolate, toothed. Flowers small, unisexual or bisexual, in short
panicles on the previous year's twigs; appearing before the leaves;
calyx and corolla absent. Fruit a dry 1-winged samara consisting of
a nut with an elongated wing attached to the end. *Hedgerows and woods,
common.*

II. *LIGUS'TRUM*

'. **vulga're** L. 99. Privet. June–July. A nearly evergreen shrub.
Leaves opposite, lanceolate, entire. Flowers small, white, in panicle-
like terminal cymes, calyx and corolla 4-lobed; stamens 2. Fruit a black
berry. *Hedges and woods, common.*

FAMILY 51. APOCYNA'CEAE

Trailing or climbing plants with opposite entire leaves. Flowers
egular, solitary in the leaf axils, twisted in bud; sepals 5, free; corolla
ubular, with 5 spreading lobes; stamens 5, inserted on the corolla tube;
vary superior, 2-celled or divided into 2 carpels with a common style.
'ruit of 2 follicles.

VIN'CA

'. **major** L. Greater Periwinkle. April–June. A trailing plant with
broadly ovate glossy leaves and large bright blue flowers with ciliate
sepals. *Escape from gardens.*

'. **minor** L. 90. Lesser Periwinkle. March–June. Like the preceding
species but leaves smaller and narrower and sepals glabrous. *Woods
and shady places, occasional.*

FAMILY 52. GENTIANA'CEAE

Herbs with usually opposite entire exstipulate leaves. Flowers regular;
alyx and corolla 4–5-lobed; stamens equal in number to the corolla lobes
nd alternating with them, epipetalous; ovary superior, 1-celled. Fruit
capsule splitting longitudinally into 2 valves.

Leaves alternate 2
Leaves opposite 3
Flowers yellow, leaves simple . . . . Limnanthemum V
Flowers white, leaves ternate . . . . Menyanthes IV
Flowers yellow . . . . Blackstonia I
Flowers pink . . . . Erythraea II
Flowers blue or white . . . . . . Gentiana III

I. *BLACKSTO'NIA*

B. perfolia'ta Huds. (**Chlo'ra perfoliata** L.) 64. Yellow-wort. June–
Sept. An erect glaucous plant. Cauline leaves opposite, united at base
glaucous. Flowers yellow, in terminal dichotomous cymes; sepal
petals, and stamens 8. *Dry pastures on limestone, frequent.*

II. *ERYTHRAE'A*

E. Centau'rium Pers. 102. Centaury. June–Sept. Leaves opposite
Flowers small, pink, in terminal dichotomous cymes or heads; coroll
tubular, with 5 spreading lobes; stamens 5; style persistent in fruit. *Dr*
pastures, common.

III. *GENTIA'NA*

Leaves opposite. Flowers blue (rarely white), tubular or funnel
shaped, with 4–5 spreading lobes; stamens 4–5; style persistent in frui

Calyx 4-lobed, lobes very unequal . . . . G. campestri
Calyx 5- (rarely 4-) lobed, lobes nearly equal . . . .
2 Plant of boggy places, with large blue flowers . G. Pneumonanth
 Plant of dry places, with small purplish flowers . G. Amarell

G. Pneumonan'the L. 29. Marsh Gentian. Aug.–Sept. Leaves linear
Flowers large, corolla 5-lobed, deep blue with greenish lines, no
fringed at throat. *Bogs, occasional.*

G. campes'tris L. 101. Field Gentian. Aug.–Sept. Flowers purplish
blue, fringed at throat, corolla 4-lobed, calyx lobes unequal. *Dr*
pastures, frequent.

G. Amarel'la L. 89. Autumn Gentian, Felwort. Aug.–Oct. Flower
purplish-blue, fringed at throat, corolla 4–5-lobed; calyx lobes a
narrow, equal or nearly so. *Chalk downs and pastures on calcareo*
soils, frequent.

IV. *MENYAN'THES*

M. trifolia'ta L. 111. Buckbean, Bogbean. May–July. Water plan
with creeping rootstock and large, compound, ternate leaves with ovat
leaflets. Flowers white, in a raceme on a leafless peduncle; coroll
5-lobed, fringed on the inside. *Ponds and bogs, frequent.*

V. *LIMNAN'THEMUM*

L. nymphaeoi'des Link. 20. Fringed Water-lily. July–Aug. Leave
orbicular or cordate, floating. Flowers large, yellow, solitary, on lon
peduncles; calyx and corolla 5-lobed. *Ponds and still waters in SI*
England, rare.

Family 53. **POLEMONIA'CEAE**

Flowers regular; calyx and corolla 5-lobed, corolla twisted in bud
stamens 5, epipetalous, alternating with the corolla lobes; ovary superio
3-celled; style 1, with 3 stigmas. Fruit a 3-celled capsule.

POLEMO'NIUM

P. caeru'leum L. 6. Jacob's Ladder, Greek Valerian. June–July. A tall, erect herb with alternate pinnately compound leaves. Leaflets numerous, lanceolate, entire. Flowers large, blue or white, in terminal corymbs or panicles. *Copses in N. England, rare.*

FAMILY 54. **BORAGINA'CEAE**

Usually hairy and rough herbs with alternate entire leaves. Flowers usually in scorpioid 1-sided cymes; calyx and corolla 5-lobed; stamens 5, epipetalous; ovary superior, 4-cleft, with a simple basilar style. Fruit of four 1-seeded nutlets surrounded by a persistent calyx.

Throat of corolla closed by scales	2
Throat of corolla open	8

2 Corolla tubular, straight, with small erect or reflexed
   lobes . . . . . . Symphytum III
  Corolla rotate, or tubular with relatively large spreading lobes . 3

3 Upper leaves opposite or nearly so . . . Asperugo II
  Leaves all alternate 4

4 Anthers emerging to form a prominent cone . . Borago IV
  Anthers included or not forming a cone . . . 5

5 Corolla tube long and curved . . . . Lycopsis VI
  Corolla tube short and straight 6

6 Nutlets prickly, burr-like . . . . Cynoglossum I
  Nutlets not prickly 7

7 Flowers bracteate, nutlets wrinkled . . . Anchusa V
  Flowers not bracteate, nutlets smooth . . . Myosotis IX

8 Stamens protruding beyond the tube of the corolla . 9
  Stamens included in the corolla tube . . . 10

9 Corolla irregular . . . . . Echium XI
  Corolla regular . . . . . Mertensia VIII

10 Calyx tubular, lobed at the top . . . Pulmonaria VII
  Calyx divided to the base . . . . Lithospermum X

I. *CYNOGLOS'SUM*

Flowers regular, with spreading petals; corolla tube short, throat closed by prominent scales. Nutlets prickly, burr-like.

C. officina'le L. 77. Common Hound's-tongue. June–Aug. A tall, erect plant covered with soft hairs. Leaves lanceolate, large. Flowers reddish-purple, in numerous terminal 1-sided cymes. Nutlets flattened and burr-like. *Sand-dunes and waste places, occasional.*

C. monta'num L. 19. Green Hound's-tongue. June–July. Greener and with fewer and stiffer hairs than the preceding species. Flowers bluish-purple. *Woods and shady places in S. and E. England, rare.*

II. *ASPERU'GO*

A. procum'bens L. Madwort. June–Aug. Stems procumbent, with prickly hooked hairs. Leaves lanceolate, rough with short stiff hairs opposite or nearly so. Flowers small, blue, axillary, drooping, calyx lobes unequal. *Waste places, a rare alien.*

III. *SYM'PHYTUM*

Flowers tubular, drooping, in scorpioid cymes; corolla tube long, with short lobes and a ring of scales at the throat; stamens shorter than the corolla tube.

S. officina'le L. 99. Common Comfrey. May–July. A stout, large plant with branching stems and large decurrent leaves. Flowers purple yellowish, or white. *Moist shady waysides, common.*

S. tubero'sum L. 54. Tuberous Comfrey. May–Aug. Smaller than the preceding species, with an unbranched stem and leaves not or scarcely decurrent. Flowers yellowish white. *Shady places, mostly in the north.*

IV. *BORA'GO*

B. officina'lis L. Borage. May–Aug. A rough, hairy plant about a foot high. Leaves ovate or lanceolate, the lower ones long-stalked. Flowers blue, drooping on long stalks; corolla rotate, the anthers forming conspicuous cone in the centre. *Waste ground, escape from gardens.*

V. *ANCHU'SA*

A. sempervi'rens L. 67. Alkanet. May–July. Stem and leaves covered with stiff hairs. Leaves broadly ovate. Flowers vivid blue, regular with short scales in the throat; in short curved axillary spikes. Nutlet wrinkled. *Waysides, rare.*

VI. *LYCOP'SIS*

L. arven'sis L. 109. Bugloss. May–Aug. Stem and leaves covered with very stiff hairs. Leaves lanceolate, with wavy margins. Flowers blue, corolla tube curved and closed by scales at the throat. Nutlets wrinkled. *Sand-dunes and waste places, common.*

VII. *PULMONA'RIA*

P. angustifo'lia L. 4. Narrow-leaved Lungwort. March–June. Root stock creeping. Leaves lanceolate. Flowers blue, with a ring of hairs but no scales at the throat, calyx divided about half-way to the base. Nutlets smooth. *Woods in SW. England, rare.*

P. officina'lis (L.), the Common Lungwort, an escape from gardens, has ovate spotted leaves and pinkish-purple flowers.

VIII. *MERTEN'SIA*

M. marit'ima S. F. Gray. 33. Sea Lungwort, Oyster Plant. June–Aug. A procumbent glaucous plant with numerous thick ovate leaves and small purplish-blue flowers without scales in the throat. Stamens shorter than the corolla lobes though protruding beyond the throat. *Sea-shores in the north.*

IX. *MYOSO'TIS*

Leaves oblong or linear, entire. Flowers in bractless raceme-like cymes, small, blue, purplish, pinkish, or yellowish, corolla with small scales in the throat. Nutlets smooth.

Hairs on calyx adpressed	M. scorpioides
Hairs on calyx spreading or hooked	2
Pedicels as long as or longer than the calyx . . .	3
Pedicels shorter than the calyx	4
Corolla more than ¼ inch across	M. sylvatica
Corolla very small	M. arvensis
Corolla tube longer than the calyx	M. versicolor
Corolla tube shorter than the calyx	M. collina

M. scorpioi'des L. (*M. palus'tris* Hill.) 112. Water Forget-me-not. June–Aug. Stem long, decumbent, rooting at the base. Leaves rather large, oblong or lanceolate. Flowers comparatively large, bright blue with a yellow eye, petals slightly notched; calyx covered with straight or adpressed hairs. *Wet shady places, common.*

M. caespito'sa (Schultz), Tufted Scorpion-grass, with smaller flowers and narrow calyx teeth, and *M. re'pens* (Don), Creeping Scorpion-grass, with runners, are common varieties of the above.

M. sylvat'ica Hoffm. 60. Wood Forget-me-not. June–July. Distinguished from the preceding species by the deeply cleft calyx covered with spreading hairs and the larger bright blue flowers with horizontal petals. *Woods, occasional.*

M. arven'sis Hill. 112. Field Scorpion-grass. May–Sept. Stem and leaves hairy. Flowers very small, on stalks as long as or longer than the calyx, which has spreading or hooked hairs. *Hedgebanks, very common.*

M. colli'na Hoffm. 91. Early Scorpion-grass. April–June. A small hairy plant not exceeding 6 inches. Leaves mostly radical. Flowers very small, bright blue on stalks shorter than the calyx, corolla tube not longer than the calyx. *Walls and dry banks, common in S. England.*

M. versic'olor Sm. 112. Yellow-and-blue Scorpion-grass. April–July. Like the preceding species but stems more leafy and the flowers are yellow at first changing to dull blue, corolla tube longer than the calyx. *Meadows and hedgebanks, common.*

X. *LITHOSPER'MUM*

Corolla without scales in the throat. Stamens not protruding. Calyx divided to the base.

Flowers blue, barren stems procumbent .	L. purpureo-caeruleum
Flowers white, stem erect	2
Leaf with conspicuous lateral veins, nutlets smooth and shining	L. officinale
Leaf without lateral veins, nutlets rough . . .	L. arvense

L. purpureo-caeru′leum L. 8. Creeping Gromwell. June–July. Barren stems long and straggling. Leaves narrowly lanceolate, hair Flowers large, bright blue. Nutlets white, smooth, and shinin *Woods in Wales and S. England, rare.*

L. officina′le L. 83. Common Gromwell. June–Aug. Stem stiff an erect. Leaves broadly lanceolate, downy, with conspicuous later veins. Flowers small, yellowish-white, in leafy terminal cymes. Nutle smooth and shining. *Waste places, occasional.*

L. arven′se L. 89. Corn Gromwell. May–July. Stem erect but rathe weak, hairy. Leaves hairy, narrowly lanceolate or linear, with a prom nent midrib but without visible lateral veins. Flowers small, white, i leafy terminal cymes. Nuts rough and wrinkled. *Cornfields, occasiona*

XI. *E′CHIUM*

E. vulga′re L. 98. Viper's Bugloss. June–Aug. A tall erect plan covered with stiff hairs. Leaves lanceolate or linear. Flowers larg irregular, bright blue, in a long terminal panicle of 1-sided cyme stamens long and protruding. Nutlets wrinkled. *Dry waste place frequent in S. England, rare in the north.*

FAMILY 55. CONVOLVULA′CEAE

Twining or prostrate herbs with alternate leaves, or leafless. Flower regular; sepals 4–5; corolla 4–5-lobed; stamens 4–5, epipetalous ovary superior, 2–4-celled, styles 1–2. Fruit a capsule.

Stem leafy, flowers large . . . . . Convolvulus
Leafless parasite, flowers very small . . . . Cuscuta

I. *CONVOL′VULUS*

Flowers large, funnel-shaped, sepals 5, corolla 5-lobed, style 1.

Bracts small, linear, placed low on the peduncle . . C. arvens
Bracts large, enclosing the calyx . . . . .
2 Stem twining, leaves sagittate . . . . . C. sepiu
Stem prostrate, leaves reniform . . . . C. Soldanell

C. se′pium L. 101. Great Bindweed. June–Oct. Flowers large, white with a pair of leafy bracts enclosing the calyx. *Hedges, common.*

C. Soldanel′la L. 47. Sea Bindweed. July–Aug. Stem prostrate scarcely twining. Leaves small, thick, reniform. Flowers large, pal pink, with bracts enclosing the calyx. *Sandy coasts, occasional.*

C. arven′sis L. 108. Small Bindweed. June–Sept. Leaves hastate Flowers small, white or pink, with a pair of small linear bracts on th peduncle some distance below the flower. *Cornfields and wayside. occasional.*

II. *CUS′CUTA*

Leafless parasitic climbers. Flowers small, in clusters along the stem corolla white or flesh-coloured, 4–5-lobed; stamens as many as coroll lobes, with a ring of scales below them; styles 2.

. **europae′a** L. 37. Great Dodder. July–Sept. Corolla-scales minute, stamens not protruding. *Hedges in the south, especially on nettles, rare.*

. **Epithy′mum** L. 59. Small Dodder. July–Oct. Corolla-scales prominent, stamens protruding. *Heaths, parasitic on gorse and heather, occasional.*

C. *Trifo′lii* (Bab.), growing on clover, has smaller and distant corolla-scales.

FAMILY 56. SOLANA′CEAE

Leaves alternate, exstipulate. Flowers regular or nearly so; calyx and corolla 5-lobed; stamens 5, epipetalous; ovary superior, 2-celled, style 1. Fruit a berry or capsule.

Corolla rotate . . . . Solanum I
Corolla campanulate 2

Flowers purple, fruit a berry . . . . Atropa II
Flowers yellow, fruit a capsule . . . Hyoscyamus III

I. *SOLA′NUM*

Corolla rotate, with an erect cone of anthers in the centre.

. **Dulcama′ra** L. 100. Woody Nightshade, Bittersweet. June–Aug. Stem woody at base, long and straggling. Leaves ovate, entire, often with two small lobes at the base. Flowers small, rich purple, with conspicuous yellow anthers; in drooping cymes. Berry red. *Hedges, common.* POISONOUS.

. **ni′grum** L. 66. Black Nightshade. July–Oct. Erect herb with ovate leaves and white flowers. Berry black. *Waste places, frequent in the south.* POISONOUS.

II. *AT′ROPA*

. **Belladon′na** L. 40. Deadly Nightshade. June–Aug. Erect herb up to 3 feet. Leaves large, ovate, entire. Flowers large, solitary campanulate, pale purple. Berry large, black. *Woods and waste places on calcareous soils, occasional.* VERY POISONOUS.

III. *HYOSCY′AMUS*

. **ni′ger** L. 85. Henbane. May–Aug. A coarse, hairy plant up to 2 feet high. Leaves large, pinnately lobed, upper ones clasping the stem. Flowers large, yellow with a network of purple veins, slightly irregular. Fruit a large capsule enclosed in the hairy calyx. *Waste ground, occasional.* POISONOUS.

FAMILY 57. SCROPHULARIA′CEAE

Herbs with exstipulate leaves. Flowers usually irregular and 2-lipped; calyx 4–5-toothed, persisting in fruit; corolla 4–5-lobed; stamens typically ., didynamous (rarely 5 or 2), epipetalous; ovary superior, 2-celled, style 1. Fruit a capsule.

Stamens 2 . . . . Veronica IX
Stamens 5 . . . . Verbascum I
Stamens 4 2

2 Corolla rotate, tube very short or none . . . .
  Corolla tubular, 2-lipped . . . .

3 Leaves narrow, entire . . . . . Limosella V
  Leaves orbicular, crenate . . . . . Sibthorpia VI

4 Corolla tube spurred at base . . . . Linaria I
  Corolla tube saccate at base . . . Antirrhinum II
  Corolla tube neither spurred nor saccate . . .

5 Calyx inflated after flowering . . . . .
  Calyx not inflated . . . .

6 Flowers yellow . . . . . . Rhinanthus XII
  Flowers red . . . . . . Pedicularis XI

7 Calyx with 4 teeth . . . .
  Calyx with 5 teeth 1

8 Upper lip of corolla 2-lobed . . . Euphrasia X
  Upper lip of corolla entire or nearly so . . .

9 Upper lip of corolla much compressed . Melampyrum XIV
  Upper lip of corolla not compressed . . Bartsia X

10 Flowers small, nearly globular . . Scrophularia IV
   Flowers large 1

11 Flowers purple . . . . . Digitalis VII
   Flowers yellow . . . . . . Mimulus V

I. *VERBAS'CUM*

Tall stiff herbs with elongated spikes, racemes or panicles of yellow flowers. Corolla rotate, 5-lobed, stamens 5.

Leaves strongly decurrent, staminal filaments with white hairs . . . . V. Thapsus
Leaves not or slightly decurrent, filaments with purple hairs .

2 Flowers small, leaves woolly beneath . . . V. nigrum
  Flowers large, leaves glabrous or nearly so . . V. virgatum

V. Thap'sus L. 100. Great Mullein. June–Aug. A tall erect plant covered with soft woolly hairs. Leaves large, ovate or lanceolate, faintly toothed, decurrent. Flowers yellow, in a long erect spike, filaments of stamens with white hairs. *Waysides and fields, frequent.*

V. ni'grum L. 51. Dark Mullein. June–Sept. Leaves lanceolate, crenate, rounded or cordate at base, slightly woolly on the under side. Flowers small, yellow, in erect racemes, filaments of stamens with purple hairs. *Waysides, occasional.*

V. virga'tum Stokes. 34. Large-flowered Mullein. June–Aug. Leaves glabrous or nearly so, upper ones clasping the stem. Flowers large, yellow (sometimes white), in a long narrow raceme, filaments of stamens with purple hairs. *Waste places, rare.*

II. *LINA'RIA*

Corolla 2-lipped, spurred, stamens 4.

Stem erect or ascending 2
Stem trailing 4

Flowers large, wholly yellow	L. vulgaris
Flowers small, purple or variegated	. 3
Flowers in a terminal panicle	L. repens
Flowers solitary, axillary	L. minor
Leaves palmately veined and lobed . . .	L. Cymbalaria
Leaves pinnately veined	5
Leaves hastate, pedicels glabrous	L. Elatine
Leaves ovate, pedicels hairy	L. spuria

Cymbala′ria Mill. 98. Ivy-leaved Toadflax. May–Sept. Stems trailing, glabrous. Leaves small, broad, palmately veined and lobed. Flowers small, lilac, solitary in the leaf axils. *Walls, common.*

Elat′ine Mill. 59. Sharp-leaved Fluellen. July–Oct. Stems trailing on the ground, hairy. Leaves hastate, hairy. Flowers small, yellow, with a purple upper lip, solitary in the leaf axils, spur of corolla straight, pedicels glabrous. *Cornfields in S. England, frequent.*

spu′ria Mill. 44. Fluellen. July–Oct. Like the preceding species but the leaves are broadly ovate and not hastate, the pedicels hairy, and the spur of the corolla curved. *Cornfields in S. England, occasional.*

re′pens Mill. 32. Creeping Toadflax. July–Sept. Rootstock creeping. Stems erect or ascending. Leaves linear, lower ones whorled. Flowers small, white, with purple veins, in a terminal panicle. *Waste places on calcareous soil, rare.*

vulga′ris Mill. 98. Yellow Toadflax. July–Oct. Stem erect or ascending. Leaves linear, crowded. Flowers large, yellow, in a terminal raceme or panicle. *Hedgebanks and cornfields, common.*

mi′nor Desf. 76. Small Toadflax. June–Sept. A small plant seldom exceeding six inches. Leaves lanceolate or linear. Flowers very small, purple, long-stalked, axillary. *Waste places in S. England, frequent.*

III. *ANTIRRHI′NUM*

Like *Linaria* from which it differs chiefly in the corolla, which is not spurred but bulged at the base.

ma′jus L. Snapdragon. June–Sept. Leaves lanceolate or linear. Flowers large, crimson or yellow, in erect racemes. *Walls, an escape from gardens.*

Oron′tium L. 51. Lesser Snapdragon. Weasel's-snout. July–Sept. Flowers small, reddish purple, solitary in the leaf axils. *Cornfields, occasional.*

IV. *SCROPHULA′RIA*

Tall plants with 4-angled stems and opposite leaves. Flowers small, greenish-brown, globular, 2-lipped, in terminal panicles, calyx 5-toothed.

aquat′ica L. 78. Water Figwort. June–Sept. Stem winged. Leaves oblong, crenate, obtuse. *Damp shady hedgebanks and wet places, common.*

S. nodo'sa L. 111. Knotted Figwort. June–Aug. Root tuberous.
Stem not winged. Leaves ovate, serrate, acute. *Woods and shady
hedgebanks, common.*

V. *MIM'ULUS*

M. ǵutta'tus DC. (**M. lu'teus** L.) 89. Monkey-flower, Monkey Musk.
June–Aug. Leaves opposite, ovate, coarsely and irregularly toothed,
glabrous. Flowers large, yellow, 2-lipped, solitary in the leaf axils;
calyx 5-toothed. *Wet places, occasional.*

VI. *LIMOSEL'LA*

L. aquat'ica L. 53. Mudwort. July–Sept. A small tufted plant growing
in mud. Leaves all radical, oblong, entire, long-stalked. Flowers small,
regular, pink, corolla rotate or campanulate, 5-lobed, stamens 4.
Wet mud, rare.

VII. *SIBTHORP'IA*

S. europae'a L. 9. Cornish Moneywort. June–Aug. Stem creeping
and rooting at the nodes. Leaves small, orbicular or reniform, crenate,
hairy. Flowers minute, pink, solitary in the leaf axils; corolla 5-lobed,
stamens 4. *Damp and shady places in SW. England and S. Wales, rare.*

VIII. *DIGITA'LIS*

D. purpu'rea L. 110. Foxglove. June–Sept. A tall plant with large
alternate leaves and long erect 1-sided racemes of large reddish-purple
flowers. Calyx 5-toothed; corolla tubular, spotted inside; stamens 4,
didynamous. *Woods and dry hill-sides, common except on calcareous
soils.*

IX. *VERON'ICA*

Leaves opposite except on the flowering shoots. Flowers small, blue,
lilac or whitish; corolla rotate, 4-lobed; stamens 2. Capsule 2-lobed.

Flowers solitary in the leaf axils	.	.
Flowers in spikes or racemes	.	.
2 Leaves lobed, sepals cordate	.	V. hederaefolia
Leaves toothed but not lobed, sepals ovate	.	
3 Lobes of capsule inflated and close together	.	V. agrestis
Lobes of capsule flat and diverging	.	V. persica
4 Spikes or racemes terminal	.	.
Spikes or racemes axillary	.	.
5 Stem erect, flowers in a long dense spike	.	V. spicata
Stems spreading, flowers in short lax spikes	.	
6 Leaves dentate, hairy	.	V. arvensis
Leaves crenate, glabrous, 3-nerved	.	V. serpyllifolia
7 Pedicels shorter than the calyx	.	V. officinalis
Pedicels longer than the calyx	.	
8 Leaves linear-lanceolate, entire	.	V. scutellata
Leaves ovate or lanceolate, toothed	.	9
9 Leaves hairy	.	10
Leaves glabrous	.	11

0 Leaves sessile, stem with hairs on alternate sides   V. Chamaedrys
  Leaves stalked, stem with hairs all round   .   V. montana

1 Leaves lanceolate, sessile .   .   .   V. Anagallis-aquatica
  Leaves oblong or ovate, mostly stalked .   . V. Beccabunga

V. hederaefo'lia L. 106. Ivy-leaved Speedwell. Feb.–May. Stem prostrate. Leaves palmately 3–5-lobed, with scattered hairs. Flowers pale lilac or white, solitary, sepals cordate. *Hedgebanks, common.*

V. agres'tis L. 112. Field Speedwell. March–Sept. Leaves ovate, coarsely toothed, hairy. Flowers blue-and-white, solitary, sepals ovate, Fruit not much broader than long, the lobes inflated. *Hedgebanks and cultivated ground, very common.*
    V. poli'ta (Fries) is a common variety with all-blue flowers and acute sepals.

V. per'sica Poir. **(V. Buxbau'mii** Ten.) 110. Large Field Speedwell. Feb.–Oct. Like the preceding species but with larger flowers on longer pedicels and the fruit with compressed and widely diverging lobes. *Hedgebanks and cultivated ground, common.*

V. arven'sis L. 112. Wall Speedwell. April–Aug. A small spreading plant with ovate, coarsely toothed hairy leaves. Flowers small, pale blue, in narrow terminal leafy racemes. *Walls and dry sandy places, common.*

V. serpyllifo'lia L. 112. Thyme-leaved Speedwell. May–Aug. Stems tufted and creeping. Leaves ovate, crenate, 3-nerved, glabrous or nearly so, rather thick. Flowers pale blue or whitish, sessile, in short erect or ascending spikes. *Cornfields and waste places, common.*

V. spica'ta L. 14. Spiked Speedwell. July–Aug. Stem erect or ascending. Leaves ovate or oblong, crenate. Flowers blue or pink, densely crowded in a long erect spike. *Dry calcareous pastures, rare.*

V. officina'lis L. 112. Common Speedwell. May–July. Stem creeping and rooting. Leaves obovate or oblong, toothed, hairy. Flowers small, pale blue, in axillary spikes. *Heaths, common.*

V. Chamae'drys L. 112. Germander Speedwell. April–June. Stem weak and ascending, with hairs on alternate sides. Leaves ovate, coarsely toothed, sessile or very shortly stalked. Flowers blue, in axillary racemes. *Hedgebanks, common.*

V. monta'na L. 90. Mountain Speedwell. May–July. Stem trailing, rooting at the nodes, hairy on all sides. Leaves ovate, coarsely toothed, stalked. Flowers blue, in few-flowered axillary racemes. *Woods, common.*

V. scutella'ta L. 110. Marsh Speedwell. June–Aug. Leaves narrowly lanceolate or linear, entire or with a very few small teeth. Flowers white or pink, in alternate axillary racemes. *Wet places, occasional.*

V. Anagal'lis-aquat'ica L. 105. Water Speedwell. June–Aug. Stem erect, thick and succulent. Leaves lanceolate, toothed, clasping the stem. Flowers blue, in opposite axillary racemes. *Wet places, frequent.*

V. Beccabun'ga L. 112. Brooklime. May–Aug. Stem procumbent
rooting, thick and succulent. Leaves oblong or ovate, slightly crenate
rather thick and mostly stalked. Flowers blue, in opposite axillar
racemes. *Ponds and streams, common.*

X. *EUPHRA'SIA*

E. officina'lis L. 112. Eyebright. June–Sept. A small plant seldom
exceeding 6 inches. Leaves sessile, deeply toothed or lobed. Flower
small, sessile in the upper leaf axils; white, with yellow in the throa
and streaked with purple, 2-lipped, upper lip 2-lobed, calyx with
teeth. Capsule oblong. *Heaths and dry pastures, common.*

XI. *BART'SIA*

Lower leaves opposite. Flowers 2-lipped; upper lip arched, not com
pressed; calyx with 4 teeth.

Flowers yellow	B. viscos
Flowers pink or purple	.
2 Flowers pink, in panicles	B. Odontite
Flowers dull purple, in simple spikes . .	B. alpin

B. Odonti'tes L. 112. Red Bartsia. June–Sept. Stiff and erect up to a
foot. Leaves lanceolate, toothed. Flowers purplish-pink, numerous
in 1-sided spikes forming a panicle. *Fields and roadsides, common.*

B. visco'sa L. 24. Yellow Bartsia. June–Oct. Stiff and erect up to 1
inches, sticky. Leaves lanceolate, toothed. Flowers yellow, in a ter
minal spike. *Damp pastures near the sea in S. England, rare.*

B. alpi'na L. 6. Alpine Bartsia. June–Aug. A small plant seldom ex
ceeding 6 inches. Leaves ovate, crenate, sessile. Flowers purple, in
short leafy spike. *Mountain pastures in the north, rare.*

XII. *PEDICULA'RIS*

Leaves pinnately divided. Flowers red or pink, tubular, the upper li
of the corolla arching and flattened vertically, the calyx jagged and leafy
and inflated after flowering.

P. palus'tris L. 112. Marsh Lousewort, Red Rattle. June–Aug. Stem
erect or ascending, 1–2 feet high. Flowers crimson, calyx hairy. *We*
places, occasional.

P. sylvat'ica L. 112. Lousewort. May–July. Stems procumbent
spreading, seldom above 6 inches high. Flowers pink, calyx glabrous
Moist pastures and heaths, frequent.

XIII. *RHINAN'THUS*

R. Crista-gal'li L. 112. Yellow Rattle. May–July. An erect stiff plan
with opposite lanceolate, coarsely toothed leaves; floral leaves ovate
Flowers large, yellow, 2-lipped, the upper lip vertically compressed
calyx orbicular, with 4 small teeth. Seeds large, flat, winged. *Meadows*
frequent.

XIV. *MELAMPY'RUM*

Leaves opposite, lanceolate. Flowers tubular, yellow, upper lip of
rolla vertically compressed, calyx with four teeth.

eaves and bracts all entire	.	.	.	.	M. sylvaticum
pper bracts usually toothed	.	.	.	.	. 2

Flowers variegated with purple	.	.	.	. M. cristatum
Flowers all yellow .	.	.	.	.	. M. pratense

. crista'tum L. 14. Crested Cow-wheat. July. Flowers yellow
variegated with purple, in a short dense spike with toothed bracts.
Woods in E. England, rare.

. praten'se L. 109. Common Cow-wheat. June–Sept. Flowers
yellow, with a paler or white tube, in distant axillary pairs, upper bracts
usually toothed at base. *Woods, frequent.*

. sylvat'icum L. 20. Alpine Cow-wheat. July–Aug. Flowers small,
deep pure yellow, upper bracts entire. *Mountain woods in the north, rare.*

FAMILY 58. **OROBANCHA'CEAE**

Brownish herbs parasitic on the roots of other species. Leaves reduced
scales. Flowers in terminal spikes; calyx 2–4-lobed; corolla irregular,
ore or less 2-lipped; stamens 4, didynamous, epipetalous; ovary
perior, 1-celled, style 1. Fruit a 2-valved capsule.

lowers sessile, calyx teeth long and narrow	.	.	Orobanche I
lowers stalked, calyx teeth short and broad	.	.	Lathraea II

I. *OROBAN'CHE*

Parasitic herbs with irregular sessile flowers in long terminal spikes.

hree bracts to each flower	.	.	.	.	O. purpurea
ne bract to each flower .	.	.	.	.	. 2

Stem stout, 1–3 feet	.	.	.	.	. 3
Stem slender, usually less than 1 foot	.	.	.	. 4

On broom and gorse, staminal filaments glabrous in the lower part .	. . .	O. major
On knapweeds, staminal filaments hairy in the lower part		O. elatior

Flowers purplish-brown on yellowish stems	.	.	O. minor
Flowers reddish-yellow, on brown stems .	.	.	O. rubra

. purpu'rea Jacq. 8. Blue Broomrape. June–July. 4–12 inches high.
Flowers deep purplish-blue, with 3 bracts, one underneath and a small
one on each side, calyx divided about half-way. *On yarrow, near the
sea in S. and E. England, rare.*

. ma'jor L. (O. Ra'pum-genis'tae Thuill.) 68. Great Broomrape.
June–Aug. A stout plant 1–3 feet high, stem swollen at base. Flowers
brown; the filaments of the stamens glabrous in the lower part; stigmas
yellow. *On broom and gorse, occasional.*

O. ru′bra Sm. 16. Red Broomrape. June–Aug. 4–9 inches high. Flowers dull red, scented, stamens inserted near the base of the corolla tube. *On thyme in W. England and W. Scotland, rare.*

O. ela′tior Sutt. 38. Tall Broomrape. June–Aug. 1–2 feet high. Like *O. major* but flowers dull yellow and the filaments of the stamens hairy in the lower part. *On knapweeds in S. and E. England, occasional.*

O. mi′nor Sm. 49. Lesser Broomrape. June–Oct. Stem slender, 6–18 inches high. Flowers purplish-brown, stigmas purplish-red. *On clover, occasional.*

    O. pic′ridis (F. Schultz) and *O. hed′erae* (Duby) grow on *Picris* and ivy respectively.

II. *LATHRAE′A*

L. squama′ria L. 70. Toothwort. April–May. A brown parasitic herb with a creeping fleshy rootstock covered with thick scales. Flowers whitish, shortly stalked; calyx teeth broadly triangular. *Damp shady places on roots of trees, occasional.*

FAMILY 59. LENTIBULARIA′CEAE

Water or marsh plants. Flowers irregular, on a long leafless peduncle; corolla 2-lipped, spurred at base; stamens 2, epipetalous; ovary superior, 1-celled. Fruit a capsule, seeds attached to central placenta.

Leaves floating, finely divided .   .   .   .   . Utricularia
Leaves terrestrial, entire .   .   .   .   . Pinguicula I

I. *UTRICULA′RIA*

Floating plants with finely divided leaves to which little bladders are attached. Flowers yellow, in a few-flowered terminal raceme; calyx 2-lobed.

U. vulga′ris L. 92. Common Bladderwort. July–Aug. Flowers rich yellow, ½ inch long or more, spur conspicuous. *Water-channels, frequent.*

U. mi′nor L. 83. Lesser Bladderwort. July–Sept. Like the preceding species but smaller. Flowers pale yellow; spur of corolla reduced to mere bulge. *Water-channels, occasional.*

II. *PINGUI′CULA*

Marsh plants. Leaves all radical, entire, fleshy, with incurved margins. Flowers purple or yellow, solitary; calyx 4–5-lobed.

P. vulga′ris L. 98. Common Butterwort. May–July. Flowers bluish purple, spur long, slender and straight. *Bogs, frequent.*

P. lusitan′ica L. 31. Western Butterwort. June–Sept. Flowers pale lilac or yellow; spur short, stout, and curved. *Bogs in W. England and W. Scotland, rare.*

FAMILY 60. VERBENA'CEAE

Leaves opposite. Calyx 5-toothed. Corolla tubular, with 4 spreading
obes. Stamens 4, didynamous (rarely 2), inserted on the corolla tube.
Ovary superior, 2–4-celled, style 1.

VERBE'NA

. officina'lis L. 72. Vervain. July–Sept. Stems wiry and spreading,
1–2 feet high. Leaves ovate or lanceolate, coarsely toothed or lobed.
Flowers very small, lilac, in terminal spikes. Fruit of four 1-seeded nuts
enclosed in the calyx. *Waste places, occasional.*

FAMILY 61. LABIA'TAE

Stem usually quadrangular. Leaves opposite. Flowers usually irregular
nd 2-lipped, in the axils of the upper leaves forming whorls, spikes, or
anicles; stamens typically 4, didynamous, rarely 2, inserted on the
orolla tube; ovary superior, 4-cleft, with a single basilar style with bifid
tigma. Fruit of 4 nutlets enclosed in the persistent calyx.

tamens 2		2
tamens 4		3
2 Calyx and corolla 2-lipped (*a*)	Salvia VII
Calyx 5-cleft; corolla 4-cleft, almost regular (*b*)	Lycopus II

(*a*)	(*b*)	(*c*)	(*d*)	(*e*)

3 Corolla regular or nearly so, stamens longer than the corolla (*c*)	Mentha I
Corolla irregular, 2-lipped	4
4 Upper lip of corolla well developed	5
Upper lip of corolla very small or none	16
5 Calyx 2-lobed, with a protuberance on the back of the upper lobe (*d*)	Scutellaria IX
Calyx with 3 or more teeth	6
6 Calyx unequally 5-toothed, 3 above and 2 below	7
Calyx teeth equal or nearly so	10
7 Upper lip of corolla not longer than the stamens (*e*)	Thymus IV
Upper lip of corolla longer than the stamens	8
8 Flowers in a dense terminal head	Prunella X
Flowers in axillary whorls or spikes	9

4565 K

9 Corolla tube straight, upper lip flat (*a*) .   .   .   Calamintha V
   Corolla tube curved, upper lip concave (*b*)   .   .   Melissa V
10 Calyx with 3-4 teeth (*c*)   .   .   .   .   .   Melittis X
   Calyx with 10 recurved teeth (*d*)   .   .   .   Marrubium XII
   Calyx with 5 teeth   1

(*a*)   (*b*)   (*c*)   (*d*)

(*e*)   (*f*)   (*g*)   (*h*)   (*i*)

(*j*)   (*k*)   (*l*)   (*m*)   (*n*)   (*o*)

11 Stamens diverging, almost equal, leaves entire or nearly
   so (*e*) .   .   .   .   Origanum II
   Stamens parallel or converging, unequal, leaves usually with
   numerous teeth   1
12 Ovary and nutlets flat-topped or concave (*f*)   .   .   Lamium X
   Ovary and nutlets convex (*g*)   1
13 Inner stamens longer than the outer (*h*)   .   .   Nepeta VII
   Outer stamens as long as or longer than the inner (*i*)   .   .   1
14 Anthers hairy, at right angles to axis of flower (*j*) .   Galeopsis XI
   Anthers glabrous, parallel or at an acute angle to axis of flower (*k*)   1
15 Calyx teeth longer than broad (*l*) .   .   .   .   Stachys XI
   Calyx teeth as broad as long (*m*)   .   .   .   .   Ballota XV
16 Lip of corolla 5-lobed (*n*)   .   .   .   .   Teucrium XVI
   Lip of corolla 3-lobed (*o*)   .   .   .   .   Ajuga XVII

I. *MEN'THA*

Aromatic herbs. Calyx 5-toothed. Corolla 4-lobed, nearly regular. Stamens 4, exserted.

Flower-whorls in a terminal spike or head	2
Flower-whorls scattered along the stem, which usually ends in a pair of leaves	6
Upper leaves sessile	3
Leaves all stalked	5
Leaves broadly ovate	M. rotundifolia
Leaves lanceolate or oblong-lanceolate	4
Leaves lanceolate, glabrous or nearly so . . .	M. spicata
Leaves oblong-lanceolate, hairy	M. longifolia
Flowers in elongated spikes	M. piperita
Flowers in globular or ovoid heads . . .	M. aquatica
Throat of calyx hairy, leaves small . .	M. Pulegium
Throat of calyx without hairs, leaves large . . .	7
Calyx tubular, with lanceolate teeth (*a*) . .	M. sativa
Calyx campanulate, with broad teeth (*b*) . .	M. arvensis

(*a*)   (*b*)

M. rotundifo'lia Huds. 51. Round-leaved Mint. Aug.–Sept. An erect hairy plant with roundish wrinkled leaves whitish below. Flowers pale pink, in slender terminal spikes forming a panicle. *Waste places, occasional.*

M. longifo'lia Huds. (**M. sylves'tris** L.) 81. Horse Mint. Aug.–Sept. An erect hairy plant with narrowly ovate or lanceolate leaves. Flowers lilac, in terminal spikes forming a panicle. *Waste places, occasional.*

M. spica'ta L. (**M. vir'idis** L.) 60. Spearmint. Aug.–Sept. An erect glabrous plant with creeping rootstocks and lanceolate sessile leaves. Flowers lilac, in terminal spikes. *Waste places, usually an escape from gardens.*

M. piperi'ta L. 95. Peppermint. Aug.–Sept. Leaves oblong or broadly lanceolate, shortly stalked, glabrous. Flowers lilac; spikes interrupted, solitary or few. *Wet places, occasional.*

M. aquat'ica L. 112. Water Mint. July–Sept. Leaves ovate, stalked. Flowers pale blue or lilac, in globular or ovoid terminal heads. *Wet places, common.*

M. sati'va L. 104. Whorled Mint. July–Sept. Leaves ovate, stalked the upper (floral) ones much smaller than the lower. Flowers lilac, in axillary whorls, calyx teeth narrow. *Damp hedgebanks and wet places, frequent.*

M. arven'sis L. 111. Field Mint. July–Sept. Leaves ovate, stalked and usually but not always approximately equal. Flowers lilac, in axillary whorls, calyx teeth broad. *Cornfields and waste places, common.*

M. Pule'gium L. 50. Pennyroyal. Aug.–Oct. Stem prostrate, with erect flowering shoots. Leaves ovate, seldom exceeding 1 inch. Flowers lilac, in axillary whorls, throat of calyx closed by white hairs. *Damp heaths, occasional.*

II. *LYC'OPUS*

L. europae'us L. 96. Gipsywort. July–Sept. A tall erect plant with narrow deeply-toothed or pinnatifid leaves. Flowers small, white, in axillary whorls; corolla 4-lobed, nearly regular, stamens 2. *Wet places, common.*

III. *ORIG'ANUM*

O. vulga're L. 95. Marjoram. July–Aug. Stem erect to 2 feet. Leaves ovate, entire or nearly so. Flowers purple, in terminal panicles, bracts often purple; corolla 2-lipped; stamens nearly as long, diverging. *Way-sides and hilly pastures on calcareous soil, common.*

IV. *THY'MUS*

T. Serpyl'lum L. 112. Wild Thyme. June–Sept. A low plant with procumbent stems woody at the base and minute ovate entire leaves fringed with long hairs. Flowers small, purple, in terminal leafy heads or whorls; calyx teeth unequal, 2 upper and 3 lower; corolla 2-lipped, stamens diverging, as long as or longer than the corolla. *Dry pastures and heaths, common.*

In *T. ova'tus* (Mill.), a less common plant, the whorls of flowers are in several tiers, and the leaves have few or no hairs.

V. *CALAMIN'THA*

Calyx 2-lipped, with 3 teeth above and 2 below. Corolla 2-lipped, the tube straight and the upper lip longer than the stamens.

Flowers bright rosy-purple, in dense whorls of more than 10,
surrounded by numerous linear bracts . . . C. vulgaris
Flowers pale, whitish or purplish, in whorls of 10 or less; bracts few

(*a*)   (*b*)

2 Calyx tube swollen at base on lower side (*a*) . . C. Acinos
Calyx tube not swollen at the base (*b*) . . . C. officinalis

C. vulga're Druce. **(Clinopo'dium vulgare** L.) 95. Wild Basil. July–Sept. Stem erect or ascending to 2 feet. Leaves ovate, crenate. Flowers bright rosy-purple, in many-flowered whorls surrounded by numerous linear bracts. *Hedgebanks and roadsides, common in England.*

C. A'cinos Clairv. 80. Basil Thyme. June–Sept. A small plant about 6 inches high. Leaves small, narrowly ovate, toothed. Flowers bluish-purple, white in the centre, calyx tube swollen at base on lower side. *Cornfields and waste places on calcareous soil, occasional.*

C. officina'lis Moench. 63. Calamint. July–Sept. Stem erect or ascending to 2 feet. Leaves broadly ovate, obtuse, crenate. Flowers pale purple or whitish, mostly turning to one side. *Hedgebanks and waste places, occasional.*

VI. *MELIS'SA*

M. officina'lis L. 41. Balm. July–Sept. Stem erect or ascending to 2 feet. Leaves ovate, crenate. Flowers white, tinged with pink, in axillary whorls; calyx 2-lipped, with 5 teeth, the 2 lower teeth longer and narrower than the 3 upper; corolla 2-lipped, longer than the stamens. *S. England, escape from gardens.*

VII. *SAL'VIA*

Upper lip of corolla erect or arched, enclosing the 2 stamens each with a long arched connective, at the outer end of which is a fertile anther-lobe, the other being at the base of the connective and generally barren; true filament very short. Lower lip of corolla spreading, 3-lobed.

S. Verbena'cea L. 69. Clary. May–Sept. Leaves ovate, coarsely toothed or lobed, the stem leaves sessile, the radical ones stalked. Flowers small, blue, in terminal spikes, corolla a little longer than the calyx. *Gravelly waste places, occasional.*

S. praten'sis L. 20. Meadow Sage. June–Aug. Leaves mostly radical, ovate or cordate, toothed, much wrinkled. Flowers large, blue, in terminal spikes, corolla about three times as long as calyx. *Dry pastures in S. England, rare.*

VIII. *NEP'ETA*

Calyx with 5 nearly equal teeth. Corolla 2-lipped. Stamens 4, the inner pair longer than the outer.

N. Cata'ria L. 62. Catmint. July–Sept. Erect to about 2 feet. Leaves ovate, coarsely toothed, stalked. Flowers small, whitish, with pink markings, in short terminal spikes. *Hedgebanks, occasional.*

N. hedera'cea Trev. **(N. Glecho'ma** Benth.) 107. Ground Ivy. March–June. Stem trailing and rooting. Leaves reniform, coarsely crenate, long-stalked. Flowers blue, in axillary whorls. *Hedgebanks, common.*

IX. *SCUTELLA'RIA*

Calyx 2-lobed, the upper lobe with a small protuberance on the back. Corolla 2-lipped.

S. galericula'ta L. 106. Common Skullcap. June–Aug. Stem erect or ascending, 6–18 inches. Leaves lanceolate, toothed. Flowers blue, in axillary pairs usually turned to one side. *Wet places, common.*

S. mi'nor L. 74. Lesser Skullcap. July–Sept. A small plant not usually exceeding 6 inches. Leaves small, oblong or lanceolate, entire or nearly so. Flowers small, purplish-pink, in axillary pairs. *Wet heathy places, locally common.*

X. *PRUNEL'LA*

P. vulga'ris L. 112. Self-heal. June–July. Stem procumbent. Leaves ovate, entire, stalked. Flowers purplish-blue (sometimes white), in dense terminal heads; calyx flattened dorsally, with 3 small teeth on the back and 2 larger ones below; corolla 2-lipped. *Meadows and waysides, very common.*

XI. *MELIT'TIS*

M. Melissophyl'lum L. 14. Bastard Balm. May–June. Erect up to 2 feet. Leaves large, ovate or lanceolate, crenate. Flowers large, whitish tinged with pink or purple, in few-flowered axillary whorls; calyx large, broadly campanulate, with 3–4 broad teeth. *Woods in S. England, rare*

XII. *MARRU'BIUM*

M. vulga're L. 75. White Horehound. June–July. Stem and leaves woolly. Leaves orbicular, wrinkled, crenate. Flowers white, in dense whorls; upper lip of corolla bifid, lower 3-lobed; calyx with 10 hooked teeth. *Waste places, occasional.*

XIII. *STA'CHYS*

Calyx with 5 long equal teeth. Corolla 2-lipped, upper lip entire, lower 3-lobed. Stamens with parallel or converging anthers enclosed within the upper lip of the corolla.

Flowers in one or two short dense terminal whorls, leaf pairs few and distant . . . . S. officinali

Flowers in elongated interrupted spikes of several or many whorls .

2 Leaves lanceolate, sessile or nearly so . . . S. palustri
Leaves ovate, lower ones long-stalked . . . .

3 Stem decumbent, leaves small, ovate . . . S. arvensi
Stem erect, leaves large, cordate . . . S. sylvatic

S. officina'lis Trev. (**S. Beton'ica** Benth.) 82. Wood Betony. June–Aug. Stem hairy, erect to 2 feet. Leaves oblong, crenate, those on the stem few and distant. Flowers purple, in a crowded terminal spike or head, occasionally with another whorl of flowers lower down on the stem. *Woods and heathy pastures, common.*

S. palus'tris L. 112. Marsh Woundwort. July–Aug. Stem hollow, hairy. Leaves numerous, lanceolate, toothed, sessile. Flowers reddish-purple variegated with white, the whorls forming a terminal interrupted spike. *Moist places, common.*

Labiatae

S. sylvat'ica L. 111. Hedge Woundwort. June–Aug. A hairy plant up to 3 feet, with solid stems. Leaves cordate, serrate, long-stalked. Flowers dark reddish-purple variegated with white, the whorls forming a long terminal interrupted spike or panicle. *Waysides, very common.*

S. arven'sis L. 106. Field Woundwort. May–Oct. Stems decumbent, spreading. Leaves small, seldom exceeding 1 inch, ovate, crenate. Flowers small, pinkish-purple, the whorls forming a terminal interrupted spike. *Cornfields, frequent.*

XIV. *GALEOP'SIS*

The characters of *Stachys* with the exception of the anthers, the lobes of which split at right angles to the axis of the flower and are hairy.

G. angustifo'lia L. (**G. Lad'anum** L.) 75 Red Hempnettle. July–Oct. Stem seldom exceeding 1 foot. Leaves lanceolate or linear, entire or nearly so. Flowers red variegated with white, in whorls in the upper leaf axils. *Cornfields, frequent.*

    G. du'bia (Leers) has broader leaves with more numerous teeth.

G. Tet'rahit L. 112. Common Hempnettle. July–Sept. A coarse hairy plant up to 2 feet high. Stem swollen below the nodes. Leaves ovate, with a gradually tapering base, serrate, acute. Flowers pinkish-purple or whitish, in short terminal spikes. *Cornfields and waste places, frequent.*

    G. specio'sa (Mill.), Large-flowered Hempnettle, is a variety with larger and usually yellow flowers with purple on the lower lip.

XV. *LA'MIUM*

Calyx with 5 approximately equal teeth. Corolla 2-lipped, upper lip arched and hooded. Ovary and nutlets flat-topped.

Flowers white	L. album
Flowers yellow	L. Galeobdolon
Flowers red or purple	2
2 Upper leaves sessile	L. amplexicaule
Upper leaves stalked	L. purpureum

L. amplexicau'le L. 100. Henbit Deadnettle. May–Sept. Stems decumbent, about 6 inches long. Upper leaves sessile, orbicular, deeply crenate. Flowers pinkish-purple, with a long narrow tube. *Waste places, occasional.*

L. purpu'reum L. 112. Red Deadnettle. Jan.–Dec. Stems decumbent, spreading, 6 inches to 1 foot long. Leaves ovate, stalked, crenate. Flowers purplish-red, with a short tube. *Hedgebanks and waste places, very common.*

    L. hy'bridum (Vill.) is a plant with lobed or deeply crenate leaves and the corolla tube shorter than the calyx.

L. album L. 99. White Deadnettle. March–Oct. Leaves ovate, coarsely serrate, resembling those of the stinging-nettle. Flowers large, white, in axillary whorls; lower lip of corolla with a large bifid terminal lobe. *Waysides, common.*

L. Galeob'dolon Crantz. 68. Yellow Archangel. April–June. Leaves large, ovate, coarsely and irregularly toothed. Flowers large, yellow, in axillary whorls, lower lip of corolla with 3 acute lobes. *Waysides, locally common in England.*

XVI. *BALLO'TA*

B. ni'gra L. 75. Black Horehound. June–Sept. A tall plant up to 3 feet. Leaves ovate, coarsely serrate. Flowers pinkish-purple, in short-stalked clusters in the leaf axils; calyx funnel-shaped, with 5 broad teeth; corolla 2-lipped, tube shorter than calyx. *Hedgebanks, frequent.*

XVII. *TEU'CRIUM*

T. Scorodo'nia L. 110. Wood Sage. July–Sept. Rootstock creeping. Stem erect to 2 feet. Leaves ovate or cordate, wrinkled, crenate, stalked. Flowers pale yellow, in 1-sided racemes often forming a terminal panicle; corolla with a minute upper lip, lower lip long and 5-lobed; stamens 4, protruding beyond the corolla. *Woods and heaths, common.*

XVIII. *AJUGA*

Calyx 5-toothed. Upper lip of corolla very small, bifid; lower lip large, 3–4-lobed. Stamens 4, protruding beyond the corolla.

Flowers yellow	A. Chamaepitys
Flowers blue	.
2 Glabrous, creeping	A. reptans
Hairy, erect	A. pyramidalis

A. rep'tans L. 112. Common Bugle. May–June. Low glabrous plant with creeping runners and entire leaves. Flowers blue, rarely white or pink, in axillary whorls on erect stems, forming a leafy spike. *Pasture and woods, common.*

A. pyramida'lis L. 13. Erect Bugle. May–July. Hairy plant with short runners and numerous erect flowering stems. Leaves ovate. Flowers pale blue, in leafy spikes. *Scottish mountains, rare.*

A. Chamae'pitys Schreb. 9. Ground Pine. May–Aug. Low much-branched hairy plant with leaves dissected into 3 or more linear segments. Flowers yellow, in axillary pairs. *Waste places on calcareous soil in SE. England.*

FAMILY 62. **PLANTAGINA'CEAE**

Leaves all radical. Flowers small; sepals 4; corolla small, scarious, 4-lobed; stamens 4, with long filaments; ovary superior, style 1. Fruit a capsule or nut.

Flowers bisexual, in terminal spikes	Plantago
Flowers unisexual, not in spikes	Littorella

I. *PLANTA'GO*

Flowers bisexual, in a spike on a long leafless peduncle. Fruit a 2-4-celled capsule.

Leaves ovate 2
Leaves lanceolate or linear 3

Leaves long-stalked . . . . . . P. major
Leaves short-stalked or sessile . . . . . P. media

Leaves lanceolate, peduncle furrowed . . . P. lanceolata
Leaves linear, peduncle rounded 4

Leaves pinnatifid . . . . P. Coronopus
Leaves entire . . . . P. maritima

P. **Coron'opus** L. 100. Buck's-horn Plantain. May–July. Leaves pinnatifid. Spikes cylindrical, 1–2 inches long. *Sandy places, common near the sea.*

P. **marit'ima** L. 80. Sea Plantain. June–Aug. Leaves linear, entire, thick and fleshy. Spikes cylindrical, 1–2 inches long. *Salt marshes, locally common.*

P. **lanceola'ta** L. 112. Ribwort Plantain. April–Sept. Leaves lanceolate, with 3–5 parallel ribs. Spikes ovoid or oblong, peduncle furrowed. *Meadows and waysides, very common.*

P. **me'dia** L. 89. Hoary Plantain. June–July. Leaves ovate, greyish-green with hairs, parallel-veined, tapering into a short stalk. Spike cylindrical, much shorter than the peduncle. *Dry pastures on calcareous soils, common.*

P. **ma'jor** L. 112. Greater Plantain. June–Sept. Leaves ovate, glabrous or slightly hairy, parallel-veined, long-stalked. Spikes usually as long as or longer than the peduncle. *Meadows and waysides, very common.*

II. *LITTOREL'LA*

L. **uniflo'ra** Aschers. (L. lacus'tris L.) 94. Shoreweed. June–Aug. A small plant seldom exceeding 3 inches, with bright green linear leaves. Flowers small, unisexual, the male solitary at the end of long peduncles, the female sessile among the leaves. Fruit an indehiscent nut. *Mud and wet sand, occasional.*

FAMILY 63. **ILLECEBRA'CEAE**

Low spreading herbs with small green or white flowers. Sepals 5, petals 5 or none; stamens 5; ovary superior, 1-celled. Fruit a 1-celled capsule.

Leaves ovate . . . . Herniaria I
Leaves linear . . . . Scleranthus II

I. *HERNIA'RIA*

H. gla'bra L. 7. Rupture-wort. July–Aug. A small plant with pro
trate stems and small opposite ovate leaves and scarious stipul
Flowers minute, green, in axillary clusters; sepals 5, petals non
stamens 5, alternating with 5 barren filaments; stigmas 2. *Sandy plac
rare.*

In *H. cilia'ta* (Bab.) the leaves are hairy and broader and the capsu
not longer than the sepals.

II. *SCLERAN'THUS*

S. an'nuus L. 104. Knawel. July–Sept. A small spreading plant 2
inches high, with small opposite linear leaves. Flowers small, gree
in axillary or terminal clusters; calyx ovoid or campanulate, with
teeth; petals none; stamens 5 or less, alternating with barren filament
styles 2. *Fields and waste places, frequent.*

FAMILY 64. **CHENOPODIA'CEAE**

Leaves exstipulate, usually alternate. Flowers small, in clusters, spike
or panicles; sepals 3–5, petals none; stamens 5 or fewer, opposite th
sepals; ovary superior, 1-celled, styles 2–3. Fruit consisting of a sing
seed enclosed in the persistent sepals.

Stem leafless, jointed, fleshy	.	.	.	. Salicornia I
Stem leafy, not jointed or fleshy	.	.	.	.
2 Leaves fleshy, cylindrical	.	.	.	.
Leaves flat	.	.	.	.
3 Leaves ending in a stout prickle	.	.	.	Salsola V
Leaves blunt-ended	.	.	.	. Suaeda
4 Flowers unisexual, seed enclosed in 2 flat triangular bracts				Atriplex I
Flowers bisexual, seed enclosed by 3–5 equal sepals	.	.	.	.
5 Disk fleshy, fruiting perianth enlarged and ribbed	.	.	.	. Beta I
Disk none, fruiting perianth small	.	.	.	Chenopodium

I. *CHENOPO'DIUM*

Leaves alternate. Flowers small, green, bisexual, in axillary cluste
forming spikes or panicles. Fruit of a single seed surrounded by th
small persistent sepals.

Leaves hastate	.	.	.	. C. Bonus-Henricu
Leaves not hastate	.	.	.	.
2 Adult leaves mealy	.	.	.	.
Adult leaves not mealy, green	.	.	.	.
3 Leaves entire, ovate, evil-smelling	.	.	.	C. Vulvar
Leaves toothed or lobed; or if entire, linear or lanceolate			.	.
4 Perianth segments always 5	.	.	.	C. albu
Lateral flowers with 3–4 perianth segments	.	.	C. glaucu

Leaves all entire, ovate . . . . . C. polyspermum
Leaves mostly toothed 6
Leaves with cordate base . . . . . C. hybridum
Leaves with straight or tapering base . . . 7
Inflorescence spreading . . . . . . C. murale
Inflorescence narrow and erect 8
Seed horizontal, perianth segments always 5 . . C. urbicum
Seed vertical, perianth segments 2–5 . . C. rubrum

I. polysper'mum L. 57. July–Sept. Stem procumbent or ascending. Leaves ovate, entire, green, mealy only when young, odourless. *Waste places, occasional.*

2. Vulva'ria L. 56. Stinking Goosefoot. July–Sept. Stem procumbent. Leaves ovate, entire, mealy, with a disagreeable smell. *Waste places, rare.*

3. al'bum L. 112. White Goosefoot, Fat Hen. July–Aug. Stem usually erect up to 2 feet. Leaves pale, mealy, the lower ones ovate and coarsely toothed, sometimes entire, the upper ones lanceolate and entire. Inflorescence a leafy terminal panicle. Seeds smooth. *Waste ground, common.*

4. mura'le L. 50. Nettle-leaved Goosefoot. Aug.–Sept. Leaves mostly green, mealy only when young, sharply serrate. Inflorescence broad and spreading. Seeds rough. *Waste ground, occasional.*

5. hyb'ridum L. 33. Maple-leaved Goosefoot, Sowbane. Aug.–Sept. Leaves large, thick, green, with cordate base and spreading lobes. Seeds rough. *Waste ground, rare.*

6. ur'bicum L. 46. Upright Goosefoot. Aug.–Sept. A stout erect plant with jagged deeply toothed green leaves and a narrow erect inflorescence. Seeds rough, horizontal. *Waste ground, occasional.*

7. ru'brum L. 80. Red Goosefoot. Aug.–Oct. A stout erect plant with narrow erect inflorescence and coarsely toothed green leaves often turning red. Lateral flowers with 2–4 perianth segments. Seeds rough, mostly vertical. *Waste ground, frequent.*

8. glau'cum L. 23. July–Sept. Like *C. album* but stem usually procumbent and leaves all toothed and very white below. Lateral flowers with 3–4 perianth segments. *Waste ground, rare.*

9. Bonus-Henri'cus L. 99. Good King Henry, Allgood. May–Aug. Rootstock thick and fleshy. Leaves large, dark green, triangular, hastate. *Waysides, frequent.*

II. *BE'TA*

1. marit'ima L. 52. Wild Beet. June–Oct. A glabrous plant with erect or spreading stems to about 2 feet high. Lower leaves large, ovate, thick, and green; upper leaves smaller and narrower. Flowers small, green, in terminal bracteate spikes or panicles; sepals 5, becoming large, angular, and almost prickly in fruit; stamens 5; ovary immersed in a fleshy disk. *Common by the sea.*

III. *AT'RIPLEX*

Flowers small, greenish, unisexual; male with 5 sepals and 5 stamens; female with two flattish triangular bracts enclosing the ovary and persisting and enlarging in fruit.

Fruiting bracts 3-lobed at top, leaves all entire and mealy white on both sides .   .   .   .   A. portulacoides
Fruiting bracts triangular, acute; leaves mostly toothed, or if entire, green .   .   .   .

2 Leaves hastate or broadly triangular .   .   .   A. hastata
Leaves with tapering base .   .   .   .   .   .

3 Leaves all linear .   .   .   .   .   .   A. littoral
Lower leaves lanceolate or ovate .   .   .   .   .

4 Leaves all ovate, small, mealy white; fruiting bracts united almost to the top .   .   .   .   .   .   A. laciniata
Leaves mostly lanceolate, green .   .   .   A. patula

A. littora'lis L. 48. Grass-leaved Orach. July–Sept. Stem up to 2 feet. Leaves linear, green, coarsely toothed. Fruit very warty. *Salt marshes, occasional.*

A. pat'ula L. 109. Common Orach. July–Sept. Stem stiff, much branched and spreading, up to 4 feet. Leaves green, lanceolate or narrowly ovate, the lower ones coarsely toothed, the upper entire. Fruit not or scarcely warted. *Waste ground, common.*

A. hasta'ta L. 105. Broad-leaved Orach. July–Sept. An erect or spreading plant up to 4 feet high. Leaves green, broadly triangular or hastate, sharply toothed. *Waste ground, common.*
    A. glabrius'cula (Edmondston), found near the sea, has prostrate reddish stems.

A. lacinia'ta L. (**A. sabulo'sa** Rouy.) 56. Frosted Orach. July–Sept. Stem much branched, 6–12 inches high. Leaves small, broadly ovate or triangular, greyish-white, coarsely and bluntly toothed. Fruiting bracts united almost to the top. *Salt marshes, occasional.*

A. portulacoi'des L. 39. Sea Purslane. July–Sept. Stem 12–18 inches high. Leaves oblong or lanceolate, obtuse, covered with grey meal. Fruiting bracts 3-lobed at the top. *Salt marshes, frequent.*

IV. *SALICOR'NIA*

Stems fleshy, jointed, leafless. Flowers small, bisexual, in threes on each side of a joint on the stem forming terminal spikes; perianth fleshy; stamens 2 or 1.

S. peren'nis Mill. 15. Perennial Glasswort. Aug.–Sept. Stems woody, creeping. Spikes oblong, blunt, sessile. *Muddy sea-shores, occasional.*

S. herba'cea L. 75. Annual Glasswort. Aug.–Sept. Stems herbaceous, erect or spreading. Spikes long, tapering and stalked. *Salt marshes and muddy sea-shores, frequent.*

V. *SUAE'DA*

Leaves small, fleshy, cylindrical. Flowers small, sessile, axillary; sepals , stamens 5, styles 2–3.

. **frutico'sa** Dumort. 16. Shrubby Seablite. July–Sept. A small shrub up to 3 feet. Styles 3. *Sea-coasts in S. and E. England, rare.*

.. **marit'ima** Dumort. 73. Common Seablite. July–Sept. A low much-branched herb seldom exceeding 6 inches. Styles 2. *Salt marshes, frequent.*

VI. *SAL'SOLA*

. **Ka'li** L. 69. Saltwort. July–Aug. A low herb with small fleshy prickly-pointed leaves less than 1 inch long. Flowers small, sessile, axillary; sepals 5, stamens 5, styles 2–3. *Salt marshes and sandy shores, frequent.*

FAMILY 65. **POLYGON'ACEAE**

Leaves alternate, with sheathing stipules. Flowers small, in clusters, pikes, or panicles; sepals 3–6, sometimes coloured; stamens 5–8, opposite he sepals; ovary superior, 1-celled, styles 2–3. Fruit a small nut enclosed n the persistent sepals.

Sepals 5	.	.	.	.	.	.	Polygonum I
Sepals 4	.	.	.	.	.	.	Oxyria II
Sepals 6	.	.	.	.	.	.	Rumex III

I. *POLYG'ONUM*

Stem with swollen nodes and thin semi-transparent stipular sheaths. Flowers small, green, white, or pink; sepals 5, stamens usually 8.

Stem twining, leaves cordate or sagittate .	.	2
Stem not twining, leaves ovate or lanceolate .	.	3
2 Fruit broadly winged, stem round .	. P. dumetorum
Fruit with narrow or no wings, stem angled .	. P. Convolvulus
3 Flowers axillary .	.	4
Flowers in terminal spikes .	.	5
4 Nut glossy, much longer than the sepals	. P. Raii
Nut not glossy, scarcely longer than the sepals	. P. aviculare
5 Spikes solitary or not more than two .	.	6
Spikes several .	.	8
6 Petiole winged .	. P. Bistorta
Petiole not winged .	.	7
7 Leaves linear, margins recurved .	. P. viviparum
Leaves lanceolate, margins not recurved .	. P. amphibium
8 Spike dense and short .	.	9
Spike lax, long and slender .	.	10
9 Peduncles and perianth rough with raised glands	. P. lapathifolium
Peduncles and perianth smooth .	. P. Persicaria

10 Perianth covered with raised dots, leaves with a hot taste like
    pepper . . . . P. Hydropip
   Perianth not dotted, leaves tasteless . . . . P. min

P. Convol′vulus L. 111. Black Bindweed. June–Oct. Glabro
twining herb with angular stems and cordate or sagittate leaves an
small green or pinkish flowers in loose clusters in the leaf axils. Fruitir
perianth not or slightly winged. *Cornfields, common.*

P. dumeto′rum L. 19. Aug.–Sept. Like the preceding species b
stem cylindrical and fruiting perianth with broad white wings. *Hedge
rare.*

P. avicula′re L. 112. Knotgrass. June–Sept. Stems wiry, prostra
or weak. Leaves small, lanceolate. Flowers small, pink or white, i
small clusters in the leaf axils. Nut scarcely longer than the periant
Cornfields and waste places, very common.

P. Raii Bab. 53. July–Sept. Like the preceding species but leaf margi
recurved and nut glossy and longer than the perianth. *Sandy se
shores, occasional.*

P. Hydropi′per L. 107. Water Pepper, Biting Persicaria. July–Sep
Spreading, or erect to 2 feet. Leaves lanceolate, margins wavy, tastin
hot like pepper, stipules glabrous. Flowers greenish, in slender droopin
interrupted spikes; perianth covered with raised dots. *Wet ditche
common.*

P. mi′nus L. 56. Small Persicaria. Aug.–Sept. Spreading, or erect t
1 foot. Leaves narrowly lanceolate, margins not wavy, tasteless, stipule
hairy. Flowers greenish, in erect interrupted spikes, perianth withou
raised dots. *Wet ditches, occasional.*

P. Persica′ria L. 112. Spotted Persicaria. July–Sept. Leaves lan
ceolate, usually with a dark blotch in the middle, stipules fringed wit
long hairs. Flowers usually bright pink, in several short dense termina
spikes, not glandular. *Waysides and ditches, common.*

P. lapathifo′lium L. 110. Pale Persicaria. July–Sept. Leaves lan
ceolate, stipules fringed with short hairs. Flowers white, greenish, o
pinkish, in several dense terminal spikes, the peduncles and pedicel
rough with raised glands. *Waysides and waste places, common.*
   P. nodo′sum (Pers.) having a spotted stem, pink flowers, and no gland
is intermediate between this and the preceding species.

P. amphib′ium L. 111. Floating or Amphibious Persicaria. July–Au
Leaves oblong or lanceolate, with rounded base, either floating o
terrestrial. Flowers pink, in a solitary terminal spike, stamens 5, style
2. *Streams, ponds, and wet fields, common.*

P. Bistor′ta L. 98. Bistort, Snakeweed. June–Aug. Rootstock thic
and often long. Leaves ovate, radical ones with long winged stalks
Flowers pink, in a solitary terminal spike. *Damp meadows, occasiona*

vivip'arum L. 35. Alpine Bistort. June–July. Rootstock tuberous.
Stem simple, erect up to 8 inches, ending in a solitary spike of pale
pink flowers. Leaves linear, with recurved margins. *Mountain pastures
in the north.*

II. *OXYR'IA*

di'gyna Hill. 31. Mountain Sorrel. June–Aug. A small glabrous
plant seldom exceeding 6 inches. Leaves mostly radical, orbicular, or
reniform. Flowers small, greenish, in terminal racemes; sepals 4,
unequal; stamens 6, stigmas 2. Fruit winged. *Mountain pastures in
the north.*

III. *RU'MEX*

Stem furrowed, with thin stipular sheaths. Leaves alternate or radical.
owers small, green or reddish, in whorls forming terminal racemes and
nicles; sepals 6, the 3 inner becoming enlarged in fruit; stamens 6;
les 3, with fringed stigmas.

wer leaves hastate or sagittate	**2**
aves never hastate or sagittate	**3**
Lower leaves ovate or broadly lanceolate, lobes at base in-curved	R. Acetosa
Lower leaves narrowly lanceolate or linear, lobes at base spreading	R. Acetosella
Inner sepals toothed	**4**
Inner sepals entire	**5**
Lower leaves fiddle-shaped (contracted in middle) .	R. pulcher
Lower leaves with rounded base . . .	R. obtusifolius
Lower leaves with tapering base	R. maritimus
Inner sepals with cordate or wide base (*a*)	**6**
Inner sepals with tapering base (*b*)	**7**

(*a*) (*b*)

At least 1 inner sepal with a tubercle . . .	R. crispus
Inner sepals without tubercles . . .	R. longifolius
Panicle erect, lower leaves with tapering base .	R. Hydrolapathum
Panicle spreading, lower leaves with rounded base . . .	**8**
Inflorescence with numerous leafy bracts . .	R. conglomeratus
Inflorescence with few or no bracts . . .	R. nemorosus

conglomera'tus Murr. 107. Sharp Dock. June–Aug. Leaves large,
oblong with rounded base. Flower-whorls distant, in a large spreading
panicle with numerous leafy bracts; inner sepals ovate, entire, all
tubercled. *Waysides and meadows on rich soil, common.*

R. nemoro′sus Schrader. 104. Wood Dock. May–Aug. Like the preceding species but leaves more ovate and less oblong, panicles with few bracts or none, and only 1, if any, of the inner sepals tubercled. *Wood and shady waysides, common.*

A variety in which the veins turn red has been confused with *R. sanguin′eus* (L.) which is a very rare plant of foreign origin.

R. marit′imus L. 50. Golden Dock. July–Aug. Leaves narrow lanceolate or linear, pale yellowish-green. Flowers crowded into dense globular whorls; inner sepals fringed with long fine teeth. *Wet places near the sea, occasional.*

R. pul′cher L. 51. Fiddle Dock. June–Sept. Stems procumbent, spreading, seldom exceeding 1 foot high. Leaves mostly radical, narrowed in the middle. Inner sepals toothed, narrow, some or all tubercled. *Waste places, occasional.*

R. obtusifo′lius L. 112. Broad Dock. June–Sept. A large coarse plant up to 3 feet high. Lower leaves large, broad, and usually obtuse, with rounded base. Flowers in stiff erect racemes forming a large terminal panicle with few or no bracts; inner sepals broadly ovate, toothed. *Waysides and waste places, very common.*

R. cris′pus L. 112. Curled Dock. June–Aug. A large coarse plant up to 3 feet high. Leaves narrow-oblong or lanceolate, acute, with wavy margins. Flowers very numerous, in long narrow panicles; inner sepals entire, with cordate or wide (not tapering) base, with a tubercle on at least 1. *Waysides and waste places, common.*

R. longifo′lius DC. (**R. aquat′icus** Hook. f.) 47. Long-leaved Dock. July–Aug. Lower leaves lanceolate, nearly a foot long. Flowers very numerous, in a long narrow panicle; inner sepals entire, without tubercles. *Wet places in the north.*

R. Hydrolap′athum Huds. 80. Water Dock. July–Aug. A large stout plant up to 5 feet high. Lower leaves lanceolate, very large (2 feet or more), with tapering base. Flowers very numerous, in a long narrow panicle; inner sepals entire, ovate, tubercled. *Wet places, frequent.*

R. Aceto′sa L. 112. Sorrel. May–Aug. Leaves mostly radical, ovate or broadly lanceolate, with 2 pointed incurved lobes at the base. Flowers unisexual, turning red, in long leafless panicles up to 2 feet high. *Meadows, very common.*

R. Acetosel′la L. 112. Sheep's Sorrel. May–Aug. Leaves lanceolate or linear with 2 spreading lobes at the base. Flowers unisexual, turning red, in slender terminal panicles. *Heaths and dry pastures, common.*

Family 66. ARISTOLOCHIA′CEAE

Sepals 3; stamens 6–12; ovary inferior, 3–6-celled. Fruit a capsule.

Flowers regular, stamens 12	Asarum
Flowers irregular, stamens 6	Aristolochia I

I. AS'ARUM

. **europae'um** L. 10. Asarabacca. April–May. A small plant 4–6 inches high with thick shortly creeping stems. Leaves entire, reniform, rather leathery. Flowers solitary, greenish-brown, campanulate, on a recurved stalk. *Woods and shady places, very rare.*

II. ARISTOLO'CHIA

.. **Clemati'tis** L. 12. Birthwort. July–Aug. Stem erect to 2 feet, unbranched. Leaves cordate, entire. Flowers yellow, tubular, irregular, in axillary clusters. *Waste places, especially near ruins, very rare.*

FAMILY 67. THYMELEA'CEAE

Shrubs or woody plants with alternate entire exstipulate leaves. lowers with a tubular 4-lobed perianth and 8 stamens inserted on the erianth tube; ovary superior, 1-celled, with a short style and capitate igma. Fruit a drupe.

DAPH'NE

. **Meze'reum** L. 30. Mezereon. Feb.–April. A small shrub to 3 feet high. Leaves lanceolate, deciduous. Flowers small, purple, fragrant, in clusters on the previous year's twigs, appearing before the leaves. Drupe red. *Woods in S. England, rare.*

. **Laure'ola** L. 59. Spurge Laurel. Jan.–April. A small shrubby plant from 1–4 feet high. Leaves oblanceolate, evergreen, rather thick, crowded towards the top of the stem. Flowers green, in short-stalked axillary clusters among the uppermost leaves. Drupe black. *Woods and shady places, occasional.*

FAMILY 68. ELAEAGNA'CEAE

Shrubs or small trees covered with brown or silvery scales. Leaves ntire, exstipulate. Flowers small, in axillary clusters; calyx 2–4-lobed, amens 4; ovary superior, 1-celled; style 1. with a capitate stigma. Fruit drupe.

HIPPOPH'AE

. **rhamnoi'des** L. 8. Sea Buckthorn. May–June. Shrub or small tree, the branchlets often ending in a spine. Leaves linear, covered with silvery scales. Flowers small, greenish, unisexual, dioecious; sepals 2. Drupe orange-coloured. *Coasts of S. and E. England, occasional, often planted.*

FAMILY 69. LORANTHA'CEAE

Shrubby parasites on branches of trees. Leaves opposite, entire, xstipulate. Flowers small, unisexual; calyx 2–4-lobed; stamens 4, pposite the calyx lobes; ovary inferior, 1-celled. Fruit a 1-seeded berry.

VIS'CUM

V. al'bum L. 48. Mistletoe. Feb.–May. Stems repeatedly forked
Leaves oblanceolate, entire, yellowish-green, leathery. Flowers small
greenish, in sessile clusters between the leaves or in the forks of th
branches; calyx 4-lobed. Berry white, semi-transparent. *Mostly o
apple trees, occasional in S. England.*

FAMILY 70. SANTALA'CEAE

Parasites on the roots of other plants. Leaves entire, exstipulate
Calyx 3–6-lobed. Stamens as many as calyx lobes and opposite them
Ovary inferior, 1-celled. Fruit 1-seeded.

THE'SIUM

T. humifu'sum DC. 24. Bastard Toadflax. May–July. A sma
glabrous plant with stiff spreading stems up to 1 foot. Leaves linea
alternate. Flowers small, greenish-white, in terminal leafy racemes
calyx 4–5-lobed, stamens 4–5. Fruit a small green nut. *Calcareou
pastures in S. England, rare.*

FAMILY 71. EUPHORBIA'CEAE

Flowers small, green or greenish-yellow, unisexual. In *Euphorbia* th
flowers appear to be bisexual, but in reality each stamen is a separat
male flower, indicated by the joint in the filament. Ovary superio
2–3-celled.

Stamens and pistil occur together in what appears to be one flower;
    stem with milky juice .   .   .   .   .   .   Euphorbia
Stamens and pistil in separate flowers; stem without milky
    juice .   .   .   .   Mercurialis

I. *EUPHOR'BIA*

Most of the flowering branches grouped in an umbel of 3–5 or mo
repeatedly forked rays. Flower-head consisting of a cup-shaped caly.
like involucre with 4–5 very small teeth alternating with horizont
yellowish or reddish-brown glands. Stamens (male flowers) 10–1
Ovary (female flower) superior, 3-celled, stalked, projecting beyond th
stamens; styles 3. Fruit of 3 1-seeded carpels.

Glands of involucre convex on outer side .   .   .   .   .
Glands of involucre concave on outer side .   .   .   .

2 Leaves obovate, obtuse, fruit smooth .   .   E. Helioscop
  Leaves oblong, acute, fruit rough .   .   E. platyphyll

3 Bracts connate at base .   .   .   .   E. amygdaloid
  Bracts free at base .   .   .   .   .

4 Main umbel of 5 rays .   .   .   .   .
  Main umbel of 3–4 rays .   .   .   .   .

5 Leaves thick and fleshy, seeds smooth .   .   E. Parali
  Leaves rather thin, seeds rough .   .   .   E. portlandi

Leaves linear .   .   .   .   .   .   E. exigua
Leaves ovate .   .   .   .   .   .   E. Peplus

E. **Heliosco'pia** L. 112. Sun Spurge. April–Nov. Leaves obovate, obtuse, toothed. Main umbel of 5 rays. Glands convex. Fruit smooth. *Cornfields and waste places, common.*

E. **platyphyl'los** L. 30. Warted Spurge. June–Aug. Leaves oblong, acute, minutely toothed. Glands convex. Fruit warted. *Cornfields and waste places in S. England, rare.*

E. **amygdaloi'des** L. 55. Wood Spurge. April–June. Leaves oblanceolate, crowded towards the middle of the stem. Bracts connate at base. *Hedgebanks and woods, common in S. England.*

E. **Para'lias** L. 32. Sea Spurge. June–Sept. Leaves ovate, pale glaucous green, thick and fleshy, crowded and overlapping. *Sand-dunes and sea-shores, locally common.*

E. **portlan'dica** L. 25. Portland Spurge. May–Sept. Leaves oblanceolate, crowded, pale glaucous green. Bracts cordate. Main umbel of 5–6 rays. *South and west coasts, occasional.*

E. **Pep'lus** L. 108. Petty Spurge. May–Nov. Leaves ovate, entire, thin. *Cornfields and waste places, common.*

E. **exig'ua** L. 86. Dwarf Spurge. July–Oct. A small plant seldom exceeding 6 inches. Leaves and bracts linear-lanceolate. *Cornfields, common.*

II. *MERCURIA'LIS*

Leaves opposite, toothed. Flowers small, green, unisexual, dioecious, in spikes or clusters in the leaf axils; sepals 3, stamens 9–12, ovary 2-celled, styles 2. Fruit a 1-celled capsule.

M. **peren'nis** L. 108. Dog's Mercury. Feb.–May. A perennial with a creeping underground rootstock. Stems slender, erect, unbranched. Leaves ovate or lanceolate, finely toothed. Flowers in axillary spikes. *Hedgebanks and woods, very common.*

M. **an'nua** L. 53. Annual Mercury. June-Oct. An annual with an erect branched stem. Leaves ovate, somewhat coarsely and distantly toothed. Male flowers in axillary spikes, females solitary or in pairs hidden among the leaves. *Waste ground, locally common.*

FAMILY 72. **BUXA'CEAE**

Evergreen trees or shrubs. Flowers unisexual, monoecious; sepals 4–6; stamens 4; ovary superior, 3-celled, styles 3. Fruit a 3-horned capsule.

BUX'US

B. **sempervi'rens** L. 7. Box. March–May. Leaves small, opposite, ovate, thick and glossy, dark green above, pale green below, glabrous. Flowers small, greenish, in axillary clusters, the males and females together. *Calcareous hills, rare. Commonly planted.*

FAMILY 73. ULMA'CEAE

Trees with alternate leaves which are usually oblique at the base.
Sepals 4–5, petals none; stamens as many as the sepals, rarely more.
Ovary superior, 1-celled and containing 1 ovule. Fruit 1-seeded.

UL'MUS

Tall rough-barked trees. Leaves ovate, sharply toothed, somewhat
rough to the touch. Flowers small, reddish, bisexual, in clusters on the
previous year's twigs, appearing before the leaves; calyx campanulate or
funnel-shaped; stamens usually 4–5, with straight filaments projecting
beyond the calyx; styles 2. Fruit surrounded by a broad flat wing.

U. gla'bra Huds. (**U. monta'na** Stokes). 109. Wych Elm. March–
April. Twigs glabrous or nearly so, never corky. Leaves large (up to
7 inches), long-pointed, coarsely double-toothed, very oblique at the
base. Fruit about 1 inch long, with the seed in the centre of the wing.
Woods and hedgerows in the north and west, rare in the south-east.

U. proce'ra Salisb. (**U. campes'tris** Mill.). 49. Common English Elm.
March–April. Generally taller and narrower than the wych elm. Twigs
hairy, often corky. Leaves seldom exceeding 3 inches, double-toothed.
Fruit about ½ inch long, with the seed near the top of the wing. *Hedgerows, very common in S. England.*

FAMILY 74. URTICA'CEAE

Flowers small, unisexual; sepals 2–5, stamens as many as sepals and
opposite them; ovary superior, 1-celled, styles 1–2.

Leaves alternate, entire	Parietaria II
Leaves opposite, toothed	
2 Twining plant with lobed leaves	Humulus
Stem erect	Urtica I

I. HU'MULUS

H. Lu'pulus L. 99. Hop. Aug.–Oct. A tall twining plant with rough
stems and opposite palmately lobed leaves. Flowers dioecious; the
males in loose panicles in the upper leaf axils, sepals and stamens 5;
the females in axillary, globular, or ovoid spikes composed of broad
bracts with two flowers in the axil of each bract, styles 2. Fruit a dry
1-seeded nut to which is attached the wing-like persistent bract.
Hedges and open woods, common.

II. URTI'CA

Erect herbs with stinging hairs and opposite ovate coarsely serrate
leaves. Flowers small, green, in axillary clusters, spikes, or panicles,
the males with 4 sepals and 4 stamens, the females with 2–4 sepals and a
flattened ovary with a single stigma

U. **dioi′ca** L. 112. Common Stinging Nettle. June–Sept. A perennial with creeping yellow underground stems sending up tall erect leafy shoots to a height of 3-6 feet. Flowers usually dioecious, in long drooping axillary panicles. *Waste ground, very common.*

U. **u′rens** L. 111. Small Nettle. May–Sept. An annual with erect stems seldom reaching a foot. Leaves deeply toothed, almost lobed. Flowers monoecious, in axillary clusters or short unbranched spikes. *Waste ground, locally common.*

III. *PARIETA′RIA*

P. **officina′lis** L. 94. Pellitory. May–Sept. Stems spreading, downy. Leaves alternate, ovate, entire. Flowers in sessile axillary involucrate clusters; the males with 4 spreading sepals and 4 stamens with thick curved filaments; the females with a tubular or campanulate 4-toothed calyx enclosing the ovary. *Walls, common in England.*

Family 75. PLATANA′CEAE

Trees with alternate palmately lobed leaves. Bark thin, peeling in large flakes. Flowers unisexual, monoecious, in globose heads on a long drooping stalk; perianth of 4–8 small club-shaped scales; stamens as many as the scales; ovary superior, apocarpous, of 3–8 carpels, each with a long simple style. Fruit globular, burr-like.

PLAT′ANUS

P. **acerifo′lia** Willd. London Plane. May. A tall tree with an upright stem and spreading branches. Leaves palmately 3–5-lobed. 2–3 fruiting heads on one stalk. *Commonly planted.*

The London Plane is a hybrid between the Oriental Plane, *P. orienta′lis* (L.) and the American Plane, *P. occidenta′lis* (L.).

Family 76. JUGLANDA′CEAE

Trees with alternate aromatic leaves. Flowers unisexual, monoecious, the male in long drooping catkins, the female solitary or in a small cluster at the end of the shoot; perianth small, irregularly lobed; ovary inferior, 1-celled, stigmas 2. Fruit a large drupe.

JU′GLANS

J. **re′gia** L. Walnut. May. A broad-headed tree with large pinnately compound leaves. Twigs with chambered pith. Fruit ovoid, smooth, green, containing a wrinkled thick-shelled nut inside which is the large edible lobed seed. *Native of SE. Europe, commonly planted.*

Family 77. MYRICA′CEAE

Trees or shrubs with alternate exstipulate leaves, aromatic and resin-dotted. Flowers unisexual, in catkins, dioecious, perianth none; stamens 4–8 within each scale of catkin; ovary 1-celled, 2 to each catkin scale, styles 2. Fruit a small resinous drupe or nut.

MYRI'CA

M. Ga'le L. 88. Sweet Gale, Bog Myrtle. April–June. Shrub to 3 feet
Leaves oblanceolate, toothed near apex. Catkins small, sessile, erect
reddish-brown. *Bogs, locally common.*

FAMILY 78. BETULA'CEAE

Trees or shrubs with alternate stipulate and usually straight-veined
leaves. Flowers unisexual, monoecious, the male in catkins, the female
in catkins, spikes, or clusters; perianth minute or absent; stamens 2–12
within each scale of catkin; ovary 2-celled, 2–3 to each scale of catkin;
styles 2. Fruit a 1-seeded nut.

Nuts small and seed-like, without an involucre . . . .
Nuts large, with an involucral appendage . . . . .

2 Female catkins deciduous, nut winged . . . . Betula
  Female catkins persistent, woody, nut not winged . . Alnus I

3 Nut attached to a 3-lobed bract . . . . Carpinus II
  Nut seated in a cup-like involucre . . . . Corylus IV

I. BET'ULA

B. al'ba L. 111. Common Birch. April–May. A slender graceful tree
with a smooth white bark and very thin twigs. Leaves ovate or
triangular, slender-stalked, coarsely and irregularly toothed. Both
male and female flowers in drooping catkins, the former dropping off
as one, the latter shedding its scales. Fruit a tiny 1-seeded nut with a
wings. *Woods and heaths, common.*

II. AL'NUS

A. glutino'sa Gaertn. 110. Common Alder. March–April. A small
tree with a stiff trunk and short spreading branches. Leaves broadly
obovate, coarsely or vaguely toothed, rather thick and stiff. Male
catkins long and drooping, deciduous; female short, erect, woody, and
persistent. Nut very small, not winged. *Riverbanks and damp woods,
common.*

III. CARPI'NUS

C. Bet'ulus L. 78. Hornbeam. April–May. A small tree with a smooth
fluted stem and numerous spreading branches. Leaves ovate, unevenly
serrate, with 10 or more pairs parallel veins, slightly oblique at the base
Both male and female flowers in drooping catkins. Nut attached to a
large 3-lobed bract. *Woods, occasional but often planted.*

IV. COR'YLUS

C. Avella'na L. 111. Hazel. Feb.–April. A large shrub. Leaves
broadly ovate, with a cordate base, coarsely and irregularly toothed
downy on both sides. Male catkins long and drooping, deciduous;
female small, erect, bud-like, with the red stigmas protruding. Nut
large, in small clusters, each nut seated in a leafy cup-like involucre
Hedges and woods, common.

FAMILY 79. FAGA'CEAE

Trees. Flowers small, unisexual, monoecious; calyx 4–8-lobed; tamens 6–20; ovary 3-celled, styles 3. Fruit of 1–3 nuts enclosed in a up or involucre.

Male flowers in long-stalked heads . . . . Fagus III
Male flowers in slender spikes 2

Male spikes erect, nuts entirely enclosed in a prickly
husk . . . . Castanea II
Male spikes drooping, nut partly enclosed in a scaly cup Quercus I

I. *QUER'CUS*

Male flowers numerous, in long drooping spikes. Female flowers ew, in short erect clusters or spikes. Fruit (acorn) partly enclosed in a caly cup.

Leaves evergreen, mostly entire . . . . . Q. Ilex
Leaves deciduous, toothed or lobed 2

Buds surrounded by long persistent stipules, acorn cup with long
reflexed scales . . . . Q. Cerris
Buds without persistent stipules, acorn cup with short adpressed
scales . . . . Q. Robur

Q. Ro'bur L. 105. Common Oak. April–May. A sturdy tree with rough bark and zigzag branches. Leaves pinnately lobed, the lobes or teeth generally obtuse. Acorn cup covered with small adpressed scales. *Woods and hedgerows, common.*

In *Q. sessiliflo'ra* (Salisb.) the acorns are sessile and the leaves without auricles at the base.

Q. I'lex L. Evergreen or Holm Oak. May. A smaller tree than the preceding, with grey and nearly smooth bark. Leaves ovate or lanceolate, mostly entire, leathery, dark green above, whitish beneath. At least half of nut enclosed in the cup. *Parks and fields, a native of S. Europe.*

Q. Cer'ris L. Turkey Oak. May–June. A large spreading tree with dark furrowed bark. Buds surrounded by long persistent stipules. Leaves narrow, pinnately lobed or coarsely and sharply toothed. Acorn cup with long reflexed scales. *Woods and parks, a native of S. Europe.*

II. *CASTA'NEA*

C. sati'va Mill. 46. Sweet or Spanish Chestnut. June–July. A large tree with twisted fissured bark and spreading branches drooping at the ends. Leaves large, oblong or lanceolate, with numerous pairs of parallel ribs each ending in a fine-pointed tooth. Spikes long, slender, and erect, mostly of male flowers with a few female at the bottom. Nuts large, completely enclosed in a prickly husk. *Woods, locally common but doubtfully native. Often planted.*

III. *FA'GUS*

F. sylvat'ica L. 68. Common Beech. April–May. A tall tree wit'
smooth grey bark, slender twigs and long narrow leaf buds. Leave
ovate, glossy, entire or vaguely toothed, fringed with white hairs whe
young. Male flowers in long-stalked heads; female solitary or in pair
at the end of a short peduncle and surrounded by numerous bracts
Fruit of 2 smooth triangular nuts enclosed in a 4-valved woody hus'
covered with thick bristles. *Woods, common and much planted.*

Family 80. SALICA'CEAE

Trees or shrubs with alternate stipulate leaves. Flowers in catkins
dioecious; perianth none; ovary 1-celled. Fruit a dehiscent 2-valved
capsule containing numerous seeds with tufts of silky hairs.

Leaves short-stalked, catkins not pendulous . . . . Salix
Leaves long-stalked, catkins pendulous . . . Populus I

I. *SA'LIX**

Buds 1-scaled. Leaves ovate, lanceolate, or linear, short-stalked
Flowers dioecious, in erect or spreading catkins; male flowers consistin,
of 2 (rarely 3 or 5) stamens in the axil of a scale; female of a single ovar
with bifid stigma, also in the axil of a scale; the scales entire though usuall
covered with long hairs.

Low bushy plants with creeping and rooting stems . . .
Erect shrubs or trees . . . . . .

2 Leaves lanceolate, hairy . . . . . S. repen
  Leaves ovate or orbicular, glabrous . . S. herbace.

3 Adult leaves hairy or pubescent beneath . . . .
  Adult leaves quite glabrous . . . . .

4 Catkins on short leafy side shoots . . . . S. alb
  Catkins sessile . . . .

5 Leaves linear or lanceolate . . . S. viminali
  Leaves ovate or oblanceolate . . . .

6 Branchlets and buds very hairy . . . S. cinere.
  Branchlets and buds glabrous or pubescent . . .

7 Leaves broadly ovate, with rounded base . . S. Capre.
  Leaves narrowly obovate, with tapering base . . S. aurit

8 Stamens connate or only 1 to each scale . . S. purpure.
  Stamens 3 to each scale . . . . S. amygdalin
  Stamens 5 to each scale . . . S. pentandr.
  Stamens 2 to each scale, distinct . . .

9 Leaves narrowly lanceolate . . . . S. fragili
  Leaves ovate or broadly lanceolate . . . S. phylicifoli.

* The different species interbreed so freely that the exact determination of any on
plant may be impossible.

Salicaceae

. **pentan'dra** L. 86. Bay Willow. May–June. Leaves ovate or broadly lanceolate, toothed, dark glossy green above, midrib yellow. Catkins at the end of short leafy side shoots. Stamens 5. *Riverbanks and damp open woods, occasional.*

. **amygdali'na** L. (**S. trian'dra** L.). 69. Almond-leaved or French Willow. April–May. Leaves lanceolate, toothed. Catkins at the end of short leafy side shoots. Stamens 3. *Riverbanks and damp places, occasional.*

. **frag'ilis** L. 102. Crack Willow. April–May. A small tree with a very broad crown. Twigs stand out from the main branch at an angle of sixty degrees and are easily detached. Leaves lanceolate, toothed, glabrous, often glaucous beneath. Catkins at the end of short leafy side shoots. Stamens 2 to each scale. *Riverbanks, common.*

. **al'ba** L. 108. White Willow. April–May. A tall tree when not pollarded. Leaves lanceolate, toothed, covered with white silky hairs especially when young. Catkins at the end of short leafy side shoots. Stamens 2 to each scale. *Riverbanks and moist meadows, very common.*
   S. caeru'lea (Sm.), the Cricket Bat Willow, is a tall fast-growing variety with branches growing at an acute angle, olive-green twigs and leaves that become glabrous and glaucous when adult. *S. vitelli'na* (L.), the Golden Willow, has yellow or reddish twigs.

. **purpu'rea** L. 95. Purple Willow. March–April. Leaves linear-lanceolate, toothed, glabrous, glaucous-white beneath, often opposite. Catkins sessile, appearing before the leaves. Stamen 1 to each scale or with a forked filament. Ovary hairy. *Riverbanks, locally common, often planted.*

. **vimina'lis** L. 108. Osier. April–June. Leaves linear and very long, entire, with silky hairs beneath. Catkins sessile, short. *Wet places, commonly planted for basket-making.*
   S. mollis'sima (Sm.) with broader lanceolate leaves is a hybrid with *S. Capre'a.*

. **auri'ta** L. 111. Round-eared Willow. April–May. Usually a bush. Leaves narrowly obovate, 1–2 inches long, wrinkled, grey beneath, stipules usually broad and conspicuous. Catkins sessile, ovoid or oblong; ovary hairy. Twigs ridged beneath the bark. *Hedges and woods, common.*

. **Capre'a** L. 110. Sallow, Goat Willow. March–April. A tall shrub with large broadly ovate wrinkled leaves rounded at the base and cottony underneath especially when young, stipules usually broad and conspicuous. Catkins sessile, ovoid or oblong, ovary silky. Twigs smooth beneath the bark. *Hedges and woods, common.*

. **cine'rea** L. 112. Grey Willow. March–April. Like the preceding species but distinguished by the smaller and narrower grey leaves and the grey downy buds. Twigs ridged beneath the bark. *Woods and heaths, common.*

S. re′pens L. 106. Creeping Willow. March–April. A low bush ↑
3 feet with creeping and rooting stems and small narrowly ovate silk
leaves. Catkins sessile, cylindrical. *Heaths, common.*

S. phylicifo′lia L. 41. Tea-leaved Willow. April–May. A shrub ↑
5 feet. Leaves ovate or lanceolate, glossy above, glaucous beneath
1–2 inches long. Catkins cylindrical, at the end of very short side shoo′
or nearly sessile; ovary hairy. *Riverbanks, mostly in the north.*

S. herba′cea L. 37. Dwarf Willow. June–July. A low creeping pla
a few inches high. Leaves small, ovate or orbicular, toothed, glabrou
Catkins very small, ovoid, few-flowered. *Mountain pastures in the nort*

II. *POP′ULUS*

Buds usually pointed and sticky, with several or many scales. Leave
broadly ovate or triangular, on long slender stalks. Catkins pendulou
the scales toothed or lobed; male with 8–20 stamens in the axil of eac
scale.

Leaves white- or grey-felted beneath; buds covered with white or grey
  hairs . . . .
Leaves glabrous or pubescent, buds glabrous . . .

Leaves palmately lobed . . . . P. alb
Leaves coarsely toothed or pinnately lobed . . P. canescer

3 Leaves obtuse, coarsely and irregularly toothed . . P. tremul
Leaves acuminate, finely and regularly toothed . . . P. nig₁

P. al′ba L. 75. White Poplar, Abele. March–April. A tall tree wit
smooth grey bark. Young shoots and under-side of leaves covere
with white felt. Leaves palmately 5-lobed. *Moist woods, occasional.*

P. canes′cens Sm. 65. Grey Poplar, Abele. March–April. Like th
preceding species and perhaps a mere variety, but the leaves are les
white below and not so conspicuously lobed. *Moist woods, occasiona*

P. trem′ula L. 109. Aspen. March–April. Young shoots glabrous o
nearly so. Leaves orbicular, obtuse, coarsely and irregularly toothee
the stalk long and flattened. *Woods, common in the north.*

P. ni′gra L. 112. Black Poplar. March–May. Leaves broadl
triangular or rhomboid, with a translucent edge, evenly toothed, stal
long and flattened. *Commonly planted.*
  P. seroti′na (Hartig), the Black Italian Poplar, is a very commo
hybrid distinguished by the broad fan-like crown. *P. nigra* var. *italic*
(Du Roi) is the well-known Lombardy Poplar, tall and very narrow.

Family 81. EMPETRA′CEAE

Low evergreen heath-like shrubs with small crowded entire leave
their margins much recurved. Flowers small, unisexual; perianth o
6 scales; stamens 3; ovary superior, with spreading divided stigma
Fruit a small drupe.

EMPE'TRUM

. **ni'grum** L. 77. Crowberry. April–June. A low creeping heath-like shrub with crowded and often whorled linear leaves not more than ¼ inch long. Flowers minute, purple, sessile, the stamens in the male flowers protruding on long slender filaments. Fruit a small black berry-like drupe. *Moors, mostly in the north.*

FAMILY 82. CERATOPHYLLA'CEAE

Contains only one genus.

CERATOPHYL'LUM

. **demer'sum** L. 54. Hornwort. June–July. An aquatic submerged plant with whorled leaves, each leaf being once or twice forked into linear finely-toothed segments. Flowers minute, axillary, the male consisting of 12–20 sessile anthers, the female of an ovary with a single undivided style. Fruit a minute ovoid 1-seeded nut. *Ponds and water-channels, occasional.*

FAMILY 83. HYDROCHARIDA'CEAE

Aquatic herbs with floating or submerged leaves. Flowers unisexual; sepals 3, petals 3; stamens 3–12; ovary inferior, with 3 or 6 styles.

Leaves cordate, long-stalked	Hydrocharis II
Leaves lanceolate or linear	2
Leaves entire, opposite or whorled	Elodea I
Leaves toothed, radical	Stratiotes III

I. ELO'DEA

. **canaden'sis** Michx. (**Anach'aris Alsinas'trum** Bab.). 87. Water Thyme, American Waterweed. July–Sept. A much-branched submerged plant with long stems and numerous small opposite or whorled oblong leaves. Flowers small, axillary; the female with a long stalk-like calyx tube provided with a pair of small bract-like bodies (the top of a 2-lobed spathe) in the middle; petals 3, greenish-purple, transparent; stigmas recurved, feathery. Fruit small, indehiscent. *Ponds and slow streams, common.*

II. HYDROCH'ARIS

I. Mor'sus-ra'nae L. 49. Frogbit. July–Aug. A floating plant with entire orbicular deeply cordate leaves on long stalks. Flowers white, projecting above the water; petals 3, very thin. *Still water, locally common.*

III. STRATIO'TES

. **Aloi'des** L. 22. Water Soldier. July–Aug. Leaves all radical, lanceolate, toothed, 6–18 inches long, growing at the bottom of the water. Flowers white, projecting above the surface, petals 3. *Still water, common in the fens of E. England but rare elsewhere.*

FAMILY 84. ORCHIDA'CEAE

Flowers irregular. Perianth segments 6, the 3 outer often called sepa
and the 3 inner, petals; lowest petal known as the lip and sometim
spurred. Stamen 1, consisting of 2 pollen-masses adhering to the pist
by sticky *glands* which are either exposed or enclosed in a pouch. Ova
inferior, 1-celled. (See Fig. 55.)

Plant brownish, without green leaves . . . . Neottia
Plant with green leaves . . . .

2 Lip spurred or saccate . . . .
  Lip not spurred or saccate . . . . . .

3 Flowers normally white or greenish . . . .
  Flowers normally pink or purple . . . . .

4 Lip much longer than whole flower . . . . . Orchis hirci
  Lip not or scarcely longer than flower . . . Habenaria X

5 Pollen-masses with exposed glands (*a*) . . Gymnadenia
  Glands in a pouch (*b*) . . . . . . Orchis V

(*a*)   (*b*)

6 Flowers normally brownish-purple, lip convex . . Ophrys VI
  Flowers green or greenish-yellow . . . .
  Flowers white, or white with coloured markings .

7 Lip 2-lobed . . . . Listera I
  Lip 3-lobed . . . . Herminium I
  Lip 4-lobed . . . . Aceras VI

8 Flowers drooping, ovary stalked . . . . Epipactis
  Flowers erect, ovary sessile . . . . .

9 Spike dense, leafless, spirally twisted . . Spiranthes II
  Spike lax, leafy . . . . . . Cephalanthera I

I. *NEOT'TIA*

N. Ni'dus-a'vis L. 90. Bird's-nest Orchis. June–July. Leaves replace
by brown scales. Flowers brownish, in a spike on a flowering stem u
to 18 inches high, lip bifid. *Woods, occasional.*

II. *LIS'TERA*

Stem with 2 opposite broadly-ovate leaves. Flowers green, in a slende
raceme, lip long and bifid.

L. corda'ta Br. 65. Small Twayblade. June–Aug. A small plant no
exceeding 6 inches. Leaves not more than 1 inch, with rounded o
cordate base. *Moors, mostly in the north, occasional.*

, **ova′ta** Br. 110. Common Twayblade. May–July. Stem up to 2 feet, with a pair of large ovate leaves below the long and narrow raceme. *Woods, common.*

III. *SPIRAN′THES*

. **spira′lis** Koch (**S. autumna′lis** Rich.). 62. Lady's Tresses. Aug.–Sept. Leaves all radical, oblong or ovate. Flowers small, white, almond-scented, in a spirally twisted 1-sided spike to 8 inches high; sepals and petals alike; lip oblong, concave. *Dry pastures, occasional.*

IV. *CEPHALAN′THERA*

Flowers white, erect, not spurred, lip contracted in the middle into ᴏpper and lower portions, ovary sessile.

. **longifo′lia** Fritsch (**C. ensifo′lia** Rich.). 41. Narrow Helleborine. May–July. Leaves long and narrow. Lower bracts shorter than the flowers. *Hilly woods, occasional.*

. **latifo′lia** Janchen (**C. grandiflo′ra** Gray, **C. pal′lens** Rich.). 33. White Helleborine. May–June. Leaves broad. Lower bracts longer than the flowers. *Woods, occasional.*

V. *EPIPAC′TIS*

Stem leafy, root fibrous. Flowers white, tinged with purple and ᴇllow, drooping, not spurred, lip contracted in the middle into upper and ᴠwer portions, ovary stalked.

. **palus′tris** Crantz. 75. Marsh Helleborine. July–Aug. Leaves narrowly lanceolate. Raceme short, lower bracts shorter than the flowers. *Marshy places, occasional.*

.. **Helleborine** Crantz (**E. latifo′lia** Sw.). 91. Broad Helleborine. Aug.–Sept. Leaves ovate or broadly lanceolate. Raceme long, 1-sided, lower bracts longer than the flowers. *Woods, occasional.*

VI. *OR′CHIS*

Stem leafy at base, root with 2 large tubers. Flowers usually pink, red, ʀ purple, in a terminal spike; lip spurred or saccate; glands enclosed in pouch.

ᴘur very slender and longer than the ovary .	O. pyramidalis
ᴘur not longer than the ovary	2
Spur very short (saccate)	3
Spur at least half as long as ovary	4
Lip 1 inch or more, linear	O. hircina
Lip short and broad	O ustulata
Sepals all arching over to form a hood . . .	O. Morio
Lateral sepals spreading	5
Spur directed upwards, spike open . . .	O. mascula
Spur directed downwards, spike dense . . .	6
Stem hollow, lower bracts longer than the flowers .	O. incarnata
Stem solid, bracts shorter than the flowers . .	O. maculata

O. pyramida'lis L. 73. Pyramidal Orchis. June–Aug. Tubers entir
Leaves narrowly lanceolate, acute. Flowers bright crimson, in a den
short pyramidal spike, spur long and slender, lip 3-lobed. *Dry pastur*
frequent.

O. hirci'na Crantz. 22. Lizard Orchis. May–July. A stout plant 1
feet high with entire tubers and leafy stem. Flowers greenish or pu
plish-white, in a long dense spike, lip long and linear, odour of flowe
disagreeable. *Quarries and bushy places, rare.*

O. ustula'ta L. 44. Burnt Orchis. June–July. Small plant abo
6 inches high. Tubers entire. Flowers in a short dense spike which
whitish below but deep purple at top; spur very short, lip 4-lobe
Dry calcareous pastures, occasional.

O. Mo'rio L. 66. Green-winged Orchis. May–June. Tubers enti
Flowers pinkish-purple; sepals veined with green, all converging
form a hood; spur horizontal or directed upwards. *Pastures and woo*
frequent.

O. mas'cula L. 110. Early Purple Orchis. April–June. Tubers entir
Leaves often spotted. Flowers purple, in an open spike, lateral sepa
spreading or reflexed, spur directed upwards. *Pastures and woo*
common.

O. incarna'ta L. 93. Marsh Orchis. June–July. Tubers lobed. Ste
hollow. Flowers purple or flesh-coloured, sometimes almost white, i
a dense cylindrical spike; lower bracts longer than the flowers. *Mo*
meadows and wet places, common.

  O. latifo'lia (L.) has purple flowers and spotted leaves.

O. macula'ta L. 109. Spotted Orchis. May–July. Tubers lobe
Stem solid. Leaves spotted. Flowers lilac or pale purple, sometim
white, in a dense and often pyramidal spike; sepals spreading; brac
shorter than the flowers. *Pastures and woods, common.*

  O. elo'des (Gris.), the Heath Spotted Orchis, is a common varie
with a short pyramidal spike and the middle lobe of the lip muc
shorter than the lateral lobes.

VII. *A'CERAS*

A. anthropoph'ora Br. 18. Man Orchis. June–July. A small pla
about 6 inches high, with entire tubers. Flowers yellowish-green, in
slender spike; sepals converging to form a hood; lip long and narrov
with 4 projections like the arms and legs of a man. *Calcareous pastur*
in E. England, rare.

VIII. *O'PHRYS*

Root tuberous. Stem leafy at base. Flowers with a convex lip marke
with various colours, spur none.

Lip narrow, much longer than the sepals . . . O. muscife
Lip broad, scarcely longer than the sepals . . . .
2 Sepals pink, end of lip turned under . . . O. apife
Sepals green, end of lip scarcely turned under . . O. sphegod

. **apif'era** Huds. 66. Bee Orchis. June–July. Sepals pink. Lip nearly as broad as long, rich velvety brown with yellow markings, resembling a bee alighting on the flower. *Calcareous pastures, occasional.*

. **sphego'des** Mill. (**O. aranif'era** Huds.). 16. Spider Orchis. April–May. Sepals green. Lip broad, dull brown with paler markings, scarcely lobed. *Dry pastures, rare.*

. **muscif'era** Huds. 48. Fly Orchis. May–July. Sepals green; petals linear; lip much longer than broad, purplish-brown, with pale blue or white markings, 2-lobed at the end. *Woods on calcareous soil, rare.*

IX. *HERMIN'IUM*

. **Monor'chis** Br. 22. Musk Orchis. June–July. A small slender plant, seldom above 6 inches, with entire globular tubers, a pair of lanceolate radical leaves, and a slender spike of small yellowish-green flowers with trifid lips. *Calcareous pastures, rare.*

X. *GYMNADE'NIA*

. **conop'sea** Br. (**Habena'ria conopsea** L.). 104. Fragrant Orchis. June–Aug. Tubers lobed. Stem 1–2 feet. Leaves narrowly lanceolate. Flowers rose-coloured, fragrant, in a loose cylindrical spike, pollen-masses with exposed glands, spur long and slender. *Pastures and heaths, frequent.*

XI. *HABENA'RIA*

Root tuberous. Stem leafy. Flowers white or greenish, spurred or saccate, in erect racemes; pollen masses with distant exposed glands.

pur longer than the ovary		.	.	.	.	H. bifolia
pur very short (saccate)	.	.	.	.	.	. 2
Flowers greenish-yellow	.	.	.	.	.	H. viridis
Flowers white	.	.	.	.	.	H. albida

. **al'bida** Br. 57. Small Orchis. June–Aug. Tubers long and narrow like thickened roots. Flowers white, fragrant, in a dense cylindrical spike, lip 3-lobed, spur short. *Hilly pastures, mostly in the north, locally common.*

. **vir'idis** Br. 106. Frog Orchis. June–Aug. Tubers lobed. Flowers yellowish-green, lip 2-lobed, spur a mere pouch. *Hilly pastures, mostly in the north, locally common.*

. **bifo'lia** Br. 99. Butterfly Orchis. June–Aug. Tubers entire. Stem with 2 large ovate or broadly lanceolate leaves near the base. Flowers white, long-spurred, fragrant, in a long loose spike, lip entire. *Woods and pastures, frequent.*
  H. chloran'tha (Bab.) is a larger and more robust variety, with the pollen-masses converging and not parallel.

FAMILY 85. IRIDA'CEAE

Flowers regular. Perianth of 6 petal-like segments. Stamens 3. Ovary inferior, 3-celled, stigmas 3. Fruit a 3-valved capsule.

Cauline leaves present, stiff and sword-like, stigmas petaloid . Iris
Leaves all radical, linear, stigmas jagged . . . Crocus I

I. *I'RIS*

Rootstock thick. Outer perianth segments large and reflexed, inner smaller and erect. Stigmas petaloid, arching over the stamens.

I. foetidis'sima L. 54. Gladdon, Roastbeef Plant. June–July. Flowers purple or yellowish white. Seeds large, orange-scarlet. *Woods, locally common.*

I. Pseudac'orus L. 112. Yellow Flag, Yellow Iris. May–Aug. Flowers bright yellow, large. Seeds pale brown. *Riverbanks and marshes common.*

II. *CRO'CUS*

C. ver'nus Mill. 26. Spring Crocus. March–April. Flowers purple with orange stigmas; perianth tubular, spreading at the top into 6 nearly equal segments. Ovary and capsule buried among the leaves. *Naturalized in meadows in Nottingham, Suffolk, and occasionally elsewhere.*

FAMILY 86. AMARYLLIDA'CEAE

Rootstock bulbous. Leaves radical, linear. Flowers regular; perianth of 6 petal-like segments; stamens 6; ovary inferior, 3-celled. Fruit a 3-valved capsule.

Perianth segments united at base, with a corona . . Narcissus
Perianth segments free, without a corona . . . .
2 Outer perianth segments larger than the inner . . Galanthus I
Perianth segments nearly equal . . . . Leucojum II

I. *NARCIS'SUS*

N. Pseudo-narcis'sus L. 67. Daffodil. March–April. Flowers large, yellow, solitary, with a spreading perianth and conspicuous tubular corona. *Woods, frequent.*

II. *GALAN'THUS*

G. niva'lis L. 55. Snowdrop. Feb.–March. Flowers white, solitary, drooping, inner perianth segments tipped with green and smaller than the outer. *Copses, occasional.*

III. *LEUCO'JUM*

L. aesti'vum L. 11. Snowflake. April–May. Flowers white, drooping, 2–6 on a stalk, perianth segments all equal. *Streamsides, rare.*

   L. ver'num (L.) is similar but the flowers appear earlier and are solitary or in pairs.

Family 87. DIOSCOREA'CEAE

Climbing plants with alternate palmately-veined leaves and unisexual owers. Perianth of 6 segments; stamens 6; ovary inferior, 3-celled.

TA'MUS

. **commu'nis** L. 70. Black Bryony. June–July. Stem twining. Leaves broad, cordate, entire or vaguely lobed. Flowers small, green, the males in slender racemes, the females in short close racemes. Fruit a scarlet berry. *Hedges and open woods, common.*

Family 88. LILIA'CEAE

Flowers regular; ovary superior; in all except *Paris* there are 6 petal-ke perianth segments, 6 stamens and a 3-celled ovary.

hrub with prickly-pointed leaf-like branches . . . Ruscus I
erb 2

Leaves in a single whorl, broadly ovate . . . Paris XI
Leaves not whorled; or if whorled, narrow 3

Perianth segments united into a corolla with short teeth . . 4
Perianth segments free 5

Flowers in drooping axillary clusters . Polygonatum II
Flowers in terminal racemes . . Convallaria III

Flowers yellow 6
Flowers not yellow 7

Flowers in a stiff terminal raceme, filaments of stamens woolly . . . . Narthecium X
Flowers in an umbel-like corymb, filaments of stamens glabrous . . . . Gagea VIII

Flowers solitary on each peduncle 8
Flowers in heads, umbels or racemes 9

Flowers erect, appearing in autumn after the leaves Colchicum IX
Flowers drooping, appearing in early summer with the leaves . . . . Fritillaria VII

Flowers in a head or umbel . . . . Allium IV
Flowers in a raceme 10

Flowers normally blue, purplish, or pink . . Scilla V
Flowers white or greenish . . . . Ornithogalum VI

I. *RUS'CUS*

. **aculea'tus** L. 38. Butcher's Broom. March–June. A shrub to 3 feet with ovate entire prickly-pointed metamorphosed branches on which the small white unisexual flowers are borne. Stamens united into a tube, the anthers forming a cap. Fruit a red berry. *Hedges and copses, occasional, but often planted.*

II. *POLYGONA'TUM*

P. multiflo'rum L. 49. Solomon's Seal. May–July. Rootstock cree[
ing. Stem leafy. Leaves ovate, parallel-veined. Flowers white, tubula
in axillary clusters. Fruit a dark blue berry. *Woods and shady plac
occasional.*

III. *CONVALLA'RIA*

C. maja'lis L. 67. Lily-of-the-Valley. May–June. Rootstock creepin
Leaves usually two, broadly lanceolate. Flowers small, white, droopin
in a terminal raceme, bell-shaped, fragrant. Fruit a red berry. *Wooc
occasional.*

IV. *AL'LIUM*

Rootstock bulbous. Flowers in a terminal head or umbel with 1 or
involucre-like bracts. Fruit a capsule with black seeds.

Bracts longer than the umbel . . . . . A. oleraceu
Bracts not longer than the umbel . . . . . .
2 Leaves cylindrical . . . . A. vinea
Leaves flat . . . .
3 Leaves broad, flowers white . . . . . A. ursinu
Leaves linear, flowers purple . . . . A. Scorodoprasu

A. Scorodop'rasum L. 22. Sand Leek. July–Aug. Leaves linea
flat and keeled. Flowers purple, mixed with bulbils, bracts short
than the umbel. *Pastures and copses in the north.*

A. vinea'le L. 88. Crow Garlic. July–Aug. Leaves cylindrical, hollo
Flowers pinkish-purple, mixed with bulbils and often entirely replac
by them, bracts scarcely longer than the umbel. *Cornfields and was
places, frequent.*

A. olera'ceum L. 63. Field Garlic. July–Aug. Leaves linear, fla
rather thick. Flowers pale brown, mixed with bulbils, bracts mu
longer than the umbel. *Cornfields and waste places, rare.*

A. ursi'num L. 109. Ramsons. April–June. Stem triangular. Leav
ovate or lanceolate. Flowers white. *Woods and shady lanes, common*

V. *SCIL'LA*

Rootstock bulbous. Leaves radical, linear. Flowers normally blue,
a terminal raceme. Fruit a capsule with black seeds.

Flowers narrowly bell-shaped, drooping . . . S. nonscrip
Flowers erect, with spreading perianth segments . . .
2 Flowers bracteate, appearing in spring . . . S. ver
Flowers without bracts, appearing in autumn . . S. autumna

S. autumna'lis L. 10. Autumn Squill. Aug.–Sept. Flowers erec
with spreading perianth segments, bracts none. *Grassy places near t.
sea, rare.*

S. ver'na Huds. 31. Spring Squill. April–May. Flowers erect, wi
spreading perianth segments, bracteate. *Grassy places near the se
locally common.*

S. nonscrip'ta Hoffm. & Link. **(Hyacin'thus nonscriptus** L.) 110. Bluebell. April–June. Flowers drooping, narrowly bell-shaped. *Woods and shady banks, common.*

VI. *ORNITHO'GALUM*

O. umbella'tum L. 51. Star-of-Bethlehem. April–May. Rootstock bulbous. Leaves radical, linear. Flowers white, in a terminal corymb; perianth persistent. Fruit a capsule. *Woods and pastures, rare.*

    O. pyrena'icum (L.) has elongated racemes of greenish-white flowers and occurs locally in the south.

VII. *FRITILLA'RIA*

F. Melea'gris L. 28. Fritillary, Snake's-head. May–June. Flowers large, drooping, solitary on a leafy stem, dull red chequered with purple. Fruit a capsule. *Moist meadows, rare.*

VIII. *GA'GEA*

G. lu'tea Ker. 44. Yellow Star-of-Bethlehem. March–April. Root bulbous. Leaves 1 or 2, radical, long. Flowers yellow, in a terminal corymb or umbel. Fruit a capsule. *Woods and meadows, rare.*

IX. *COL'CHICUM*

C. autumna'lis L. 53. Meadow Saffron. Aug.–Oct. Leaves linear or lanceolate, appearing in spring and dying before the autumn, when the reddish-purple flowers appear. Perianth tube long, rising direct from the ground and spreading at the top into 6 nearly equal segments. Styles 3, long and thread-like. Fruit a 3-valved capsule containing many seeds. *Woods and moist meadows, occasional.* POISONOUS.

X. *NARTHE'CIUM*

N. ossif'ragum Huds. 97. Bog Asphodel. July–Aug. Rootstock not bulbous. Leaves linear, stiff, the upper ones reduced to scales. Flowers yellow, in a stiff elongated raceme; perianth persistent. Fruit a long pointed capsule. *Bogs, frequent.*

XI. *PAR'IS*

P. quadrifo'lia L. 77. Herb-Paris. April–June. Stem with 4 broadly ovate leaves in a single whorl. Flowers yellowish-green, solitary, terminal; perianth of 8 segments, 4 lanceolate and 4 linear; stamens 8. Fruit a bluish-black berry surrounded by the persistent perianth. (The parts of the flower are sometimes in fives.) *Woods, frequent.*

FAMILY 89. JUNCA'CEAE

Stiff grass-like herbs. Perianth of 6 calyx-like segments, persistent in fruit. Stamens usually 6. Ovary superior, style with 3 slender stigmas. Fruit a 3-valved capsule.

Leaves cylindrical or nearly so, glabrous . . . . Juncus I
Leaves flat, hairy . . . . Luzula II

I. *JUN'CUS*

Leaves cylindrical or very narrow. Capsule 3-celled, with numerou
seeds.

Leaves reduced to brown scales near base of stem . . . .
Leaves green, not reduced to scales . . . . . .

2 Stem soft, with continuous pith . . . . J. communi
  Stem rigid, with interrupted pith . . . . J. inflexu

3 Leaves with internal cross-partitions . . . . .
  Leaves without internal cross-partitions . . . . .

4 Stem procumbent, rooting at the nodes . . J. bulbosu
  Stem erect, rigid . . . .

5 Perianth segments acute, shorter than the capsule . J. articulatu
  Perianth segments obtuse, as long as the capsule . J. obtusiflorum

6 Leaves and bracts ending in a stiff, hard, prickly point J. maritimu
  Leaves and bracts without hard prickly points . .

7 Leaves all radical or nearly so . . . . .
  Stem with leaves some distance above the ground . . . 1

8 Flowers 2–3, in a terminal head . . . J. triglumi
  Flowers more numerous, in a loose cyme . . .

9 Bracts much longer than the inflorescence . . J. tenui
  Bracts shorter than the inflorescence . J. squarrosu

10 Flowers in a terminal cyme, fruit longer than the perianth J. Gerard
   Flowers scattered along the stem, fruit shorter than the
   perianth . . . . J. bufoniu

J. bufo'nius L. 112. Toad Rush. June–Sept. A small tufted plan
seldom above 8 inches high, with repeatedly forked stems. Flower
solitary in the forks or along the branches; perianth longer than th
capsule. *Wet places, common.*

J. squarro'sus L. 108. Heath Rush. July–Aug. Leaves all radica
stiff, and grooved, and much shorter than the flowering stem. Flower
in a terminal cyme, distinct, not clustered, bract short and scariou
Heaths, frequent.

J. Gerar'di Lois. 87. Round-fruited Rush. June–Aug. Rootstoc
slightly creeping. Stems tufted, erect. Flowers in a terminal cyme
each flowering stem with a leaf about half-way up; perianth about a
long as the capsule, inner segments obtuse. *Common near the sea.*
  J. compres'sus (Jacq.) is a slightly different inland plant, having th
perianth shorter than the capsule.

J. ten'uis Willd. 43. Slender Rush. July–Aug. Stems tufted, ver
thin. Leaves mostly radical. Flowers pale, in a narrow terminal cym
with a long bract; perianth segments narrow, very acute, longer tha
the capsule. *Damp places, rare, but increasing.*

J. inflex'us L. (**J. glau'cus** Ehrh.). 94. Hard Rush. June–Aug. Stem
thin but hard and stiff, with interrupted pith and a few brown sheathin
scales near the base. Flowers in a loose lateral cyme near the top of th
stem; perianth segments linear. *Stiff soils, frequent.*

. commu'nis Mey. 112. Common Rush. June–Aug. Stems tufted, erect, soft and pliable, with continuous pith, sheathed by brown scales at the base. *Wet places, common.*

Two well-marked varieties are *J. effu'sus* (L.) with the flowers in an open cyme and *J. conglomera'tus* (L.) with the flowers in compact globular clusters.

. marit'imus Lam. 58. Sea Rush. July–Aug. Stems tufted, hard, stiff, and prickly-pointed, the brown sheathing scales at the base continued into prickly-pointed leaves shorter than the stem. Flowers in a terminal cyme with a long stiff bract dilated at the base; capsule about as long as perianth. *Sea-coasts, frequent.*

In *J. acu'tus* (L.) the stems are even more rigid and prickly, the flowers larger and the capsule longer than the perianth.

. bulbo'sus L. (**J. supi'nus** Moench). 112. Lesser Jointed Rush. June–Aug. Stems procumbent or floating, usually with internal cross-partitions, rooting at the nodes. Flowers in clusters among the leaves or in terminal cymes. *Bogs, common.* Perhaps a mere variety of *J. articulatus.*

. obtusiflo'rus Ehrh. 67. July–Aug. Stems cylindrical, erect, hollow, with well marked internal cross partitions. Flowers in small distant clusters forming a spreading cyme; perianth segments obtuse, about as long as the dark brown capsule. *Wet places, frequent.*

. articula'tus L. 112. Jointed Rush. July–Aug. Like the preceding species but stem flattened and perianth segments acute and shorter than the pale brown capsule. *Wet places, common.*

In *J. sylvat'icus* (Reich.) the inner perianth segments are obtuse and the capsule dark brown.

. triglu'mis L. 25. Three-flowered Rush. July–Aug. Stems tufted, about 6 inches. Leaves mostly radical, much shorter than the stem. Flowers in a terminal head. *Mountain bogs in the north.*

II. *LU'ZULA*

Leaves flat. Capsule 1-celled, with 3 seeds.

Flowers in many-flowered clusters, forming a small paniculate cyme	L. campestris
Flowers solitary on each pedicel, or in a large loose panicle-like cyme	2
Flowers solitary on each pedicel	L. pilosa
Two or more flowers on each pedicel . . .	L. sylvatica

. pilo'sa Willd. 111. Hairy Woodrush. April–June. About 6–12 inches high. Leaves mostly radical, fringed with long hairs. Flowers mostly solitary on each branch of the cyme; capsule obtuse. *Woods, frequent.*

In *L. Fors'teri* (DC.) the capsule is acute and the branches of the cyme remain erect after flowering.

. sylvat'ica Gaud. 110. Great Woodrush. April–July. 1½–3 feet high. Leaves mostly radical, fringed with long hairs. Flowers in clusters on each branch of the large panicle-like cyme. *Woods, frequent.*

L. campes'tris Br. 112. Field Woodrush. April–June. 6–18 inches high
Leaves very hairy. Flowers in 3–4 pedunculate clusters. *Pastures and
heaths, common.*

   L. multiflo'ra (Lej.) is a larger plant with more numerous and almost
sessile spikes or heads.

Family 90. TYPHA'CEAE

Marsh or water plants with unisexual monoecious flowers without a
perianth. Ovary tapering into a simple slender style. Fruit small
1-seeded.

Flowers in cylindrical spikes . . . . . . Typha
Flowers in globose heads . . . . . Sparganium I

I. *TY'PHA*

Tall reeds up to 6 feet or more in height. Leaves long and linear. In
florescence a dense cylindrical spike with the male flowers in the upper
and the female in the lower portion. The flowers consist merely of
stamens or ovaries, surrounded by hairs.

T. latifo'lia L. 99. Great Reedmace, Cat's-tail, often mistakenly called
the Bulrush. July–Aug. Male and female flowers in one continuous
spike. *Edges of lakes and ponds, frequent.*

T. angustifo'lia L. 69. Lesser Reedmace. July–Aug. Smaller than
the preceding species, with narrower and stiffer leaves. Male flowers
divided from the female by a distinct gap. *Edges of lakes and ponds,
occasional.*

II. *SPARGA'NIUM*

Erect or floating aquatic plants with linear concave leaves and flowers
in distant globose heads, the upper male, the lower female.

S. erect'um L. (**S. ramo'sum** Curt.) 110. Erect Bur-reed. July–Aug.
Leaves erect, 3-angled at base. Inflorescence branched. *Edges of lakes,
ponds, and streams, common.*

S. sim'plex Huds. 105. Floating Bur-reed. July–Aug. Leaves often
very long and floating on the surface of the water. Inflorescence unbranched. *Ponds and slow streams, common.*

   S. min'imum (Fries) is a slender floating plant with very few male
flower-heads.

Family 91. ARA'CEAE

Flowers in a dense spike (spadix) with a large leaf-like bract (spathe)
either enclosing the spadix, as in *Arum*, or distinct from it, as in *Acorus*

I. *A'RUM*

A. macula'tum L. 89. Cuckoo-pint, Lords-and-Ladies. April–June.
Leaves radical, broadly sagittate, often spotted. Spathe large, green

enclosing the long spadix. The ovaries, or female flowers, are at the bottom of the spadix, with the stamens, or male flowers, immediately above them. The axis of the spadix is prolonged into a purple club-shaped structure, at the bottom of which is a tuft of reflexed hairs. Fruit a short spike of scarlet poisonous berries. *Hedgebanks and woods, common.*

II. A'CORUS

A. Cal'amus L. 39. Sweet Flag. June–July. Leaves long, stiff, and sword-like, aromatic, crinkled on one side. Spike yellowish-green, cylindrical, outside the long linear leaf-like spathe. Flowers bisexual; perianth segments 6; stamens 6; ovary superior, 2–3-celled. *Edges of lakes and streams, rare, except in Norfolk and Suffolk.*

FAMILY 92. LEMNA'CEAE

Tiny floating plants, either solitary or adhering in groups and consisting of a single frond sending down into the water one or more root-like filaments from its under surface. Flowers rarely seen; they appear sometimes on the edge or upper side of the frond; perianth none; stamens 1 or 2; ovary 1-celled.

LEM'NA

Root-like filaments many	L. polyrrhiza
Root-like filaments single	2
2 Fronds oblong or lanceolate, very thin . . .	L. trisulca
Fronds orbicular or broadly ovate	3
3 Fronds thick, convex below	L. gibba
Fronds not thick, slightly convex below . .	L. minor

L. trisul'ca L. 74. Ivy-leaved Duckweed. June–July. Fronds thin, oblong, toothed at one end, shortly stalked at the other. *Ponds and still waters, frequent.*

L. mi'nor L. 108. Common Duckweed. June–Aug. Fronds orbicular, entire, with a single root-like filament, slightly convex below. *Ponds and still waters, common.*

L. gib'ba L. 60. Thick Duckweed. June–Sept. Fronds orbicular, entire, with a single root-like filament, very thick, convex below. *Ponds and still waters, occasional.*

L. polyrrhi'za L. 60. Greater Duckweed. Not known to flower in the British Isles. Fronds ovate or orbicular, entire, up to ¼ inch across, each with many root-like filaments. *Ponds and still waters, occasional.*

FAMILY 93. ALISMA'CEAE

Marsh or water plants with radical leaves, and flowers with a petaloid perianth. Pistil apocarpous, at least in fruit.

Perianth segments all equal and coloured . . .	Butomus III
Perianth of white or coloured petals and smaller green sepals . .	2
Leaves sagittate	Sagittaria II
Leaves ovate or lanceolate	Alisma I

I. *ALIS'MA*

Leaves ovate or lanceolate, long-stalked. Flowers with 3 green sepals and 3 larger white or coloured petals; stamens 6; carpels numerous.

A. Planta'go-aquat'ica L. 103. Water Plantain. June–Aug. Leaves ovate or lanceolate. Flowers pale pink, in a many-flowered panicle with whorled branches. Fruit of numerous achenes arranged in a ring. *Ponds and water-channels, frequent.*

A. ranunculoi'des L. 84. Lesser Water Plantain. June–Aug. Leaves narrowly lanceolate or linear. Flowers large, pale purple, in a terminal umbel. Achenes in a globular head. *Marshes, occasional.*

II. *SAGITTA'RIA*

S. sagittifo'lia L. 59. Arrowhead. July–Sept. Leaves sagittate, long-stalked. Flowers unisexual, large, white, in whorls in a terminal leafless inflorescence; sepals 3, petals 3; stamens numerous; carpels numerous, in a globular head. *Ponds and water-channels, frequent.*

III. *BU'TOMUS*

B. umbella'tus L. 65. Flowering Rush. July–Aug. Leaves linear, triangular in section. Flowers large, pink, in a terminal umbel with 3 involucral bracts; perianth segments 6, all equal and coloured; stamens 9; carpels 6. *Ponds and water-channels, occasional.*

FAMILY 94. NAIADA'CEAE

Water or marsh plants. Flowers small, solitary and axillary, or in spikes; perianth none or of 4–6 small segments; stamens 1, 2, 4, or 6; pistil apocarpous, of 2, 4, or 6 carpels. Fruit of 1 or more achenes.

Stem and leaves erect, rush-like	Triglochin I	
Stem and leaves floating or submerged	. 2	
2 Salt water plant with creeping stem . . .	Zostera IV	
Fresh water plant with floating stem	3	
3 Leaves opposite, linear	Zanichellia III	
Leaves alternate; or if opposite, broad .	Potamogeton II	

I. *TRIGLO'CHIN*

Marsh plants with erect linear leaves and small greenish flowers in a terminal spike or raceme on a leafless peduncle. Perianth of 6 equal segments; stamens 6; carpels 3–6, united at first.

T. palus'tre L. 112. Marsh Arrowgrass. June–Aug. Fruit narrow, of 3 carpels. *Marshes, frequent.*

T. marit'imum L. 80. Sea Arrowgrass. June–Sept. Leaves fleshy. Fruit oblong or ovoid, of 6 carpels. *Salt marshes, frequent.*

II. *POTAMOGE'TON*

Water plants with submerged or floating leaves and small flowers in stalked spikes or heads rising out of the water; perianth of 4 segments; stamens 4, opposite the perianth segments; carpels 4.

Upper leaves floating on the surface of the water .	.	P. natans
Leaves all submerged	.	. 2
2 Leaves all opposite	.	P. densus
Leaves some or all alternate . . .	.	. 3
3 Leaves broadly ovate, clasping the stem all round	.	P. perfoliatus
Leaves oblong, lanceolate, or linear .	.	. 4
4 Leaves with 5 or more longitudinal veins . .	.	P. lucens
Leaves with 1–3 longitudinal veins . .	.	. 5
5 Leaves lanceolate, margins wavy . .	.	P. crispus
Leaves linear, margins not wavy .	.	. 6
6 Leaves strap-shaped, peduncle short .	.	P. obtusifolius
Leaves thread-like, peduncle long .	.	. 7
7 Leaves dilated at base into a long sheath .	.	P. pectinatus
Leaves not dilated at base into a long sheath	.	P. pusillus

P. na'tans L. 112. Broad-leaved Pondweed. June–July. Floating leaves ovate, thick, and opaque, the stalk long and with a joint below the blade, submerged leaves often reduced to a stalk; stipules long, acute. Flowers in a dense cylindrical spike on a stout stalk. *Ponds and streams, common.*

P. polygonifo'lius (Pourr.) has thinner floating leaves without a joint in the stalk. In *P. colora'tus* (Hornem) all the leaves are broad, translucent and beautifully netted, while the stipules are shorter and obtuse.

P. lu'cens L. 84. Shining Pondweed. July–Aug. Leaves all submerged, lanceolate, large and thin, with tapering base and 5 or more pairs of parallel nerves; stipules long and keeled. Flowers in a dense cylindrical spike on a stout stalk swollen at the top. *Rivers, frequent.*

P. praelon'gus (Wulf.) has broader sessile leaves with a rounded base.

P. perfolia'tus L. 102. Perfoliate Pondweed. July–Aug. Leaves all submerged, broadly ovate and clasping the stem all round. Spike about 1 inch long. *Rivers, common.*

P. cris'pus L. 103. Curled Pondweed. July–Aug. Leaves all submerged, lanceolate, 3-nerved, margins wavy. Spikes small, with a few distant flowers. *Ponds and streams, common.*

P. den'sus L. 63. Opposite-leaved Pondweed. July–Aug. Leaves all submerged, opposite, short, in 2 rows. Flowers few, on a short recurved peduncle. *Ponds and streams, frequent.*

P. obtusifo'lius Mert. & Koch. 67. July–Aug. Leaves all submerged, linear, strap-shaped, blunt-ended, or acute. Spikes short, on short peduncles. *Ponds and streams, occasional.*

P. acutifo'lius (Link) is similar but with very acute leaves.

P. pusil'lus L. 107. Small Pondweed. July–Aug. Leaves all submerged, linear, on long thread-like stems. Spike on a long slender peduncle. *Ponds and streams, common.*

P. pectina′tus L. 91. Fennel Pondweed. July–Aug. Like the preceding species but the leaves are longer and even narrower and dilated at the base into a long sheath. *Ponds and streams, frequent.*

II. *ZANNICHEL′LIA*

Z. palus′tris L. 87. Horned Pondweed. May–Aug. A submerged plant with opposite linear leaves and minute unisexual and monoecious flowers sessile in the leaf axils and half enclosed by the stipules. Perianth none, male flower with 1 stamen, female with 4 carpels which are ribbed or warted in fruit. *Ponds and streams, frequent.*

III. *ZOSTE′RA*

Z. mari′na L. 60. Grass-wrack. June–Sept. A submerged sea-water plant with a creeping stem and alternate, ribbon-like, obtuse leaves. Flowers minute, in an axillary spike (spadix) enclosed in a leaf-like sheath (spathe). *Sea-shores at or below low-water mark, locally common.*

FAMILY 95. **CYPERA′CEAE**

Grass-like or rush-like herbs with solid and often 3-angled stems. The leaf sheaths are not split on one side as they are in grasses. Flowers small, green or brown, in small spikes (spikelets) either solitary or in terminal clusters, spikes or panicles, each flower in the axil of a single bract (glume); perianth none; stamens usually 3 (rarely 2); ovary 1-celled, stigmas 2–3. Fruit an achene.

Flowers unisexual (stamens and ovary in separate glumes) (*a*) Carex VII

Flowers bisexual (stamens and ovary in the same glume) (*b*) . . **2**

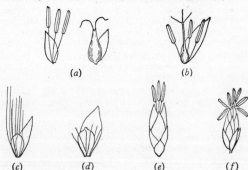

(*a*)　　　　　　　　(*b*)

(*c*)　　　(*d*)　　　(*e*)　　　(*f*)

2 Bristles surrounding the flower lengthen beyond the glume and become cottony in fruit (*c*) . . . . . Eriophorum III

Bristles none, or remain shorter than the glume (*d*) . . . **3**

3 Lowest glumes in each spikelet shorter than the others (*e*) . **4**

Lowest glumes in each spikelet not shorter than the others (*f*) . **6**

Spikelets very numerous, in a compound panicle . Cladium VI
Spikelets few 5
Stems stiff and rush-like, glumes in each spikelet in 2 opposite
    rows (a) . . . . Schoenus V
Stems slender and grass-like, glumes in each spikelet arranged all
    round (b) . . . . Rhynchospora IV
Spikelets arranged in 2 opposite rows in each spike (c) Blysmus II
Spikelets solitary or in heads, clusters or panicles (d) . Scirpus I

I. *SCIRPUS*

Glumes mostly containing bisexual flowers, the lowest ones not shorter
than the upper and arranged all round the spikelet.

Spikelets solitary and terminal on each stem (e) 2
Two or more spikelets on each stem; or if solitary, lateral or apparently
    so (f) 7

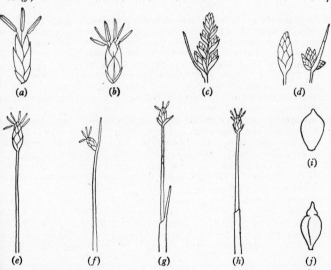

(a)   (b)   (c)   (d)

(e)   (f)   (g)   (h)   (i)

(j)

2 Stems branched, floating . . . . . S. fluitans
  Stems simple, erect 3
3 Sheath at base of stem prolonged into a narrow appen-
    dage (g) . . . . S. caespitosus
  Stem sheath without an appendage (h) 4
4 Stems very slender, hair-like, not exceeding 3 inches S. acicularis
  Stems stiff, mostly more than 3 inches 5
5 Fruit tapering gradually into the beak (i) . . S. pauciflorus
  Fruit crowned by bulbous base of the style (j) . . . 6

6 Stem sheath oblique at end, stigmas 3 (*a*) .   .   . S. multicauli
  Stem sheath square at end, stigmas 2 (*b*) .   .   . S. palustri
7 Less than 6 inches high, hypogynous bristles absent (*c*)   S. setaceu
  More than 6 inches high, hypogynous bristles present (*d*) .   .
8 Stem leafless, or with a few short leaves at the base .   S. lacustri
  Stem leafy .   .   .   .
9 Spikelets large, brown, in clusters .   .   .   . S. maritimu
  Spikelets small, green, in panicles .   .   .   . S. sylvaticu

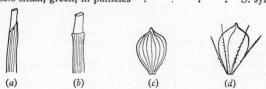

(*a*)   (*b*)   (*c*)   (*d*)

S. acicula′ris L. (**Eleoch′aris acicularis** Roem. & Sch.) 77. June
   Aug. A small plant with creeping thread-like rootstocks and tufts o
   very thin flexible stems seldom exceeding 3 inches. Spikelets solitar
   on each stem; stigmas 3. *Wet sandy places, occasional.*

S. palus′tris L. (**Eleoch′aris palustris** Roem. & Sch.) 112. Creep
   ing Clubrush. June–July. A small plant with creeping rootstock an
   tufts of thin stiff stems up to a foot high. Spikelets solitary on eac
   stem; stigmas 2; fruit crowned by bulbous base of style. *Wet meadow
   and edges of pools, common.*

S. multicau′lis L. (**Eleoch′aris multicaulis** Sm.) 97. June–Aug
   A small densely-tufted plant 4–9 inches high. Stem sheaths oblique a
   the end. Spikelets solitary on each stem; stigmas 3; fruit crowned b
   bulbous base of style. *Wet meadows and bogs, frequent.*

S. pauciflo′rus Lightf. 99. June–July. Like the preceding species bu
   only 3–6 flowers in each spike and without any bulbous thickening a
   the base of the style. *Marshes, mostly in the north, frequent.*

S. caespito′sus L. 104. Deer's-hair. May–July. Stems 6–12 inches
   densely tufted, the sheaths at the base continued into a short narrov
   appendage. Spikelets solitary on each stem; stigmas 3. *Bogs, frequent*

S. flu′itans L. 94. Floating Club-rush. June–Sept. Stems long, slender
   and branching, often floating. Spikelets solitary on each stem; hypo
   gynous bristles none; stigmas 2. *Peaty pools, frequent.*

S. seta′ceus L. (**Isole′pis setacea** Br.) 111. Bristle Club-rush. June–
   Aug. Stems slender, in dense tufts only 2–3 inches high. Spikelets
   solitary or in clusters near the top of the stem; hypogynous bristles
   none; stigmas 3. *Turfy heaths, frequent.*

S. lacus′tris L. 104. Bulrush. June–Aug. Rootstock creeping. Stems
   stout and erect, from 1–8 feet high, leafless, or with a few short leaves
   at the base. Spikelets large, ovoid, in lateral clusters or umbels; stigma
   3. *Edges of lakes, ponds, and streams, frequent.*

   S. Tabernaemonta′ni (Gmel.) is a glaucous variety with 2 stigmas
   found in brackish places near the sea.

. **marit'imus** L. 85. Sea Club-rush. June–Sept. Rootstock creeping. Stems 3-angled, 2–4 feet high, leafy. Spikelets large, brown, in clusters or umbels; stigmas 3. *Salt marshes and brackish water, common.*

. **sylvat'icus** L. 81. Wood Club-rush. June–Aug. Stems 3-angled, 2–3 feet high, leafy. Spikelets green, in large loose panicles. *River-banks, frequent.*

II. *BLYS'MUS*

Spikelets sessile, in 2 opposite rows, glumes arranged all round each ›ikelet.

. **compres'sus** Panz. 63. Compressed Club-rush. July–Sept. A small plant up to 8 inches high, with a 3-angled stem and chestnut-brown spikelets in a terminal spike about 1 inch long. *Bogs, occasional.*

. **ru'fus** Link. 52. Narrow Club-rush. July–Sept. Spikelets dark glossy brown in a terminal spike about ½ inch long. *Marshy places near the sea, mostly in the north.*

III. *ERIOPH'ORUM*

Hypogynous bristles much longer than the glumes and becoming ›ttony in fruit.

. **vagina'tum** L. 91. Hare's-tail Cotton-grass. April–May. Stems tufted, about 1 foot high. Spikelets solitary, terminal. *Bogs, frequent.*

. **polysta'chion** L. 112. Common Cotton-grass. May–June. Root-stock creeping. Stems up to 2 feet high. Spikelets several to each stem. *Bogs, common.*

The two chief kinds are *E. angustifo'lium* (Roth) with narrow leaves and smooth peduncles and *E. latifo'lium* (Hoppe) with tufted stems, broader leaves, and rough peduncles.

IV. *RHYNCHO'SPORA*

. **al'ba** L. 73. White Beak-sedge. July–Sept. Stems tufted, 6–18 inches high. Spikelets few, white, in small clusters, each spikelet containing one or two flowers only, the lower glumes being small and empty; stamens 2. *Bogs, common.*

R. fus'ca (L.), the Brown Beak-sedge, locally common in SW. England, has brown spikelets, with the outer bract projecting an inch beyond the flowers.

V. *SCHOE'NUS*

. **ni'gricans** L. 81. Bog-rush. May–July. Stems tufted, stiff, about a foot high. Spikelets sessile, dark glossy brown, in a compact ovoid head with an involucre of 2–3 bracts one of which is much longer than the head; glumes in each spikelet arranged in two opposite rows. *Turfy bogs, frequent.*

VI. *CLA'DIUM*

. **Maris'cus** Br. 45. July–Aug. A tall plant up to 6 feet. Leaves with rough edges. Spikelets pale brown, in numerous clusters forming a large panicle; each spikelet containing only one or two flowers. *Marshes, rare.*

VII. *CA'REX*

Flowers unisexual, in spikelets, without hypogynous bristles; stamens usually 3 (rarely 2); ovary enclosed in a bottle-shaped sack persistent in fruit

Spikelet solitary, terminal	 2
Spikelets several	 3

2 Spikelet with flowers of one sex only (*a*) . . . C. dioica
  Spikelet with flowers of both sexes (*b*) . . . C. pulicaris

(*a*)   (*b*)   (*c*)   (*d*)

(*e*)   (*f*)   (*g*)   (*h*)

3 Spikelets short, all similar (*c*) 4
  One or more terminal spikelets entirely or chiefly male and usually more slender than the lower female spikelets, especially when the plant is fruiting (*d*) 13
4 Lowers spikelets stalked, inflorescence paniculate (*e*) C. paniculata
  Spikelets all sessile, in a simple spike . . . 5
5 Terminal spikelet with male flowers at the base (*f*) . . 6
  Terminal spikelet with male flowers at the top (*g*) . . 9
6 Lower spikelets with long leafy bracts (*h*) . . C. remota
  Spikelets mostly without bracts 7

7   Spikelets all crowded (*a*) .   .   .   .   .   . C. ovalis
     Lower spikelets distant 8

8   Fruits spreading, beak long (*b*) .   .   .   . C. echinata
     Fruits erect, beak short (*c*) .   .   .   . C. canescens

9   Underground stem long and creeping 10
     Underground stem short, not creeping 11

10   Spike about ½ inch long, bract about as long as spike (*d*).   C. divisa
     Spike 1–2 inches long, bract much shorter (*e*).   . C. arenaria

    (*a*)   (*b*)   (*c*)   (*d*)   (*e*)

    (*f*)   (*g*)   (*h*)   (*i*)

11   Stems not tufted .   .   .   .   . C. teretiuscula
     Stems densely tufted 12

12   Stems stiff, rush-like, 2–4 feet .   .   . C. vulpina
     Stems very slender, grass-like, less than 1½ feet . C. muricata

13   Stigmas 2 .   .   .   .   .   . C. vulgaris
     Stigmas 3 14

14   Fruit hairy 15
     Fruit glabrous 17

15   Leaves hairy, spikelets distant, fruit with a long beak (*f*) .   C. hirta
     Leaves glabrous, spikelets crowded, fruit with a short beak or none   16

16   Female spikelets almost globular (*g*) .   . C. pilulifera
     Female spikelets oblong or cylindrical (*h*) . C. caryophyllea

17   More than 1 male spikelet 18
     Male spikelet solitary, terminal .   .   . 21

18   Fruit obtuse, leaves glaucous (*i*) .   .   . C. flacca
     Fruit acute or beaked 19

19   Fruit flattened .   .   .   .   . C. acutiformis
     Fruit inflated 20

20 Fruit abruptly narrowed into a long beak (*a*) . . C. rostrat
   Fruit gradually tapering into a short beak (*b*) . . C. vesicari

21 Fruit with a very short or no beak 2:
   Fruit with a long beak 2

22 Female spikelets short, oblong, pale (*c*) . . C. pallescen
   Female spikelets long, dark 2

(*a*)   (*b*)   (*c*)

(*d*)   (*e*)   (*f*)   (*g*)   (*h*)

23 Spikelets 4–7 inches long (*d*) . . . C. pendul
   Spikelets less than 2 inches long (*e*) . . C. panice

24 Female spikelets erect, short, usually less than 1 inch long . 2
   Female spikelets spreading or drooping, more than 1 inch long 2

25 Spikelets yellowish, fruits spreading (*f*) . . . C. flava
   Spikelets green or brown, fruits erect 2

26 Bracts exceeding the stem, spikelets fairly close together near the
     top (*g*) . . . . . . C. extensa
   Bracts not exceeding the stem, spikelets all distant (*h*) C. distans

27 Spikelets 4–7 inches long . . . . C. pendul
   Spikelets 3 inches or less 28

8 Glumes linear, toothed (*a*) . . . . C. Pseudo-Cyperus
  Glumes ovate, entire (*b*) . . . . . C. sylvatica

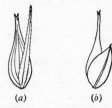

(*a*)   (*b*)

C. **dioi'ca** L. 86. May–July. A small plant with creeping rootstock and very thin stems and leaves. Spikelets solitary on each stem, brown, dioecious; stigmas 2. *Bogs, common in the north.*

C. **pulica'ris** L. 112. Flea Sedge. May–July. Like the preceding species but rootstock not creeping and spikelets with male flowers in the upper and female in the lower half; stigmas 2. *Bogs, common.*

C. **divi'sa** Huds. 68. June–July. Rootstock creeping, hard. Stems about 2 feet. Spikelets few, crowded into an ovoid terminal spike about ½ inch long, the male flowers at the top of each spikelet; stigmas 2. *Marshes near the sea, rare.*

C. **arena'ria** L. 67. Sand Sedge. May–July. Rootstock creeping a long distance. Stems about 1 foot. Spikelets crowded into an ovoid spike, the male flowers at the top of each spikelet; stigmas 2. *Sandy places near the sea, locally common.*
  C. dis'ticha (Huds.) is a somewhat taller inland plant with an oblong interrupted spike.

C. **teretius'cula** Good. 72. May–June. Stems slender, about 1 foot high. Spikelets few, in a narrow panicle or spike, the male flowers at the top of each spikelet; fruit smooth, beaked; stigmas 2. *Bogs, rare.*

C. **panicula'ta** L. 103. Panicled Sedge. May–July. Stems stout, 2–3 feet, in large tufts. Spikelets numerous, brown, in a panicle, the male flowers at the top of each spikelet. Fruit beaked; stigmas 2. *Riverbanks and wet meadows, frequent.*

C. **vulpi'na** L. 97. Fox Sedge. May–July. Stems stout, sharply 3-angled, with rather broad leaves. Spikelets numerous, crowded into a spike interrupted at the base, the male flowers at the top of each spikelet. Fruit beaked; stigmas 2. *Marshes and wet ditches, common.*

C. **murica'ta** Good. 95. Prickly Sedge. May–July. Stems very slender, less than 2 feet. Spikelets few, the male flowers at the top. Fruit beaked; stigmas 2. *Hedgebanks and meadows, frequent.*
  The two chief kinds are *C. contig'ua* (Hoppe) in which the spikelets are crowded into an oval spike with spreading fruits and *C. divul'sa* (Stokes) with distant spikelets and erect fruits.

C. echina'ta L. (**C. stellula'ta** Good.). 111. Star-headed Sedge. May–
July. Stems tufted, about 6 inches. Spikelets few, distant, male flower
at the base. Fruits long-beaked, spreading in star-like fashion; stigma
2. *Wet places, common.*

C. remo'ta L. 102. May–July. Stems slender, about a foot. Spikelet
few and distant, the lower ones with long leafy bracts. *Hedgebanks an*
woods, common.

C. canes'cens L. 85. Grey Sedge. May–June. Stems tufted, about
foot. Spikelets few, pale green, in an interrupted spike, bracts smal
or absent. Fruit not beaked; stigmas 2. *Bogs, occasional.*

C. ova'lis Good. (**C. lepori'na** L.). 112. Oval Sedge. June–July
Stems about a foot. Spikelets few, sessile, crowded into an ovoid spike
the male flowers at the base of each spikelet. Fruit flat, winged; stigma
2. *Damp meadows and open woods, common.*

C. vulga'ris Fries. 112. Common Sedge. May–July. Undergroun
stems creeping. Stems tufted. Spikelets several, the terminal on
male. Fruit flat, not beaked; stigmas 2. *Damp meadows and marshes*
common.

    C. grac'ilis (Curt.) appears to be a more luxuriant variety with longe
and narrower leaves.

C. flac'ca Schreb. (**C. glau'ca** Murr.). 112. Glaucous Sedge. April
July. Stem with creeping runners. Leaves glaucous. Male spikelet
several. Fruit obtuse, not beaked; stigmas 3. *Meadows, common.*

C. pilulif'era L. 110. Pill-headed Sedge. May–July. Stems 6–1
inches. Terminal spikelet male; female spikelets small, ovoid, with
leafy bracts. Fruit hairy, beak very small or none; stigmas 3. *Dr*
pastures and open woods, frequent.

C. caryophyl'lea Latour (**C. prae'cox** Jacq.). 102. Vernal Sedge
April–May. Usually a small plant with creeping rootstock and tuft
of leaves shorter than the flowering stem. Terminal spikelet male
rather thick, the female spikelets oblong and close under it. Fruit hairy
with a short beak; stigmas 3. *Dry pastures and heaths, common.*

C. palles'cens L. 98. Pale Sedge. May–June. Stems about a foot
Terminal spikelet male, the female spikelets short, bracts long an
leafy. Fruit glabrous, pale yellowish-green, not beaked; stigmas 3
Wet places, occasional.

C. pani'cea L. 112. Carnation Sedge, Carnation-grass. May–July
Stems about a foot, with creeping runners. Leaves glaucous. Spikelet
few, long, erect, the terminal one male. Fruit glabrous, with a ver
short beak or none; stigmas 3.

    C. limo'sa (L.) has shorter spikelets on long stalks causing them t
become somewhat drooping and occurs in mountain bogs.

C. pen'dula Huds. 79. Great Drooping Sedge. April–June. A larg
plant from 3–5 feet high with a stout 3-angled stem and bright green
prominently keeled leaves about ½ inch broad. Spikelets long and droop
ing, the terminal one male. Fruit with a short beak; stigmas 3. *Wood*
and hedgebanks, common.

Cyperaceae

C. sylvat'ica Huds. 102. Wood Sedge. May–July. Stem slender, 1–2 feet, with bright green flaccid and prominently keeled leaves. Spikelets slender, rather more than an inch long, drooping and spreading, the terminal one wholly male. Fruits ribbed and beaked; stigmas 3. *Woods, common.*

C. strigo'sa (Huds.), found in similar situations, has longer spikelets, their stalks almost hidden by the sheaths, and the beak short or almost absent.

C. dis'tans L. 110. Distant Sedge. May–Aug. Stems slender, 1–2 feet, leafy. Spikelets few and distant, short and erect, the terminal one male, the lower ones with long bracts. Fruit beaked; stigmas 3. *The typical form is found in marshes near the sea.*

C. helo'des (Link) with long ligule and *C. biner'vis* (Sm.) with green-ribbed fruits are inland plants common on heaths.

C. exten'sa Good. 64. Long-bracted Sedge. June–July. Stems slender, tufted, 1–2 feet, with stiff erect leaves. Spikelets oblong, erect, all near the top of the stem, with long bracts. Fruit beaked; stigmas 3. *Salt marshes, locally common.*

C. fla'va L. 112. Yellow Sedge. June–July. Stems densely tufted, leafy, about 6 inches high, yellowish. Spikelets erect, ovoid or oblong, yellowish, with long leafy bracts sheathing at the base. Fruits beaked, spreading; stigmas 3. *Turfy bogs, common.*

C. hir'ta L. 101. Hairy Sedge. May–July. Rootstock creeping. Stems weak, leafy, 1–2 feet, hairy. Spikelets cylindrical, about an inch long, the upper one or two male, the lower ones female and distant. Fruit hairy, long-beaked; stigmas 3. *Moist meadows, common.*

C. filifor'mis (L.) has bracts without sheaths and fruits with a short beak. It occurs chiefly in the north.

C. Pseudo-Cype'rus L. 58. Cyperus Sedge. June–July. Stem tall, stout, 3-angled, with long comparatively broad leaves. Spikelets about 2 inches long, drooping, the terminal one male but often with female flowers in the upper half. Fruit beaked; glumes linear, toothed, longer than the fruit; stigmas 3. *Marshes, occasional.*

C. acutifor'mis Ehrh. (**C. paludo'sa** Good.). 91. May–July. Rootstock creeping. Stem stout, 3-angled. Leaves long. Male spikelets several. Fruit flattened, beaked; stigmas 3. *Riverbanks, common.*

C. ripa'ria (Curt.) is a taller plant with broader leaves and more pointed glumes.

C. rostra'ta Stokes (**C. ampulla'cea** Good.). 109. Bottle Sedge. May–July. Stems stout, tufted, obtusely 3-angled, with long leaves. Male spikelets several. Fruit inflated, abruptly narrowed into a slender beak; stigmas 3. *Marshes, common.*

C. vesica'ria L. 91. Bladder Sedge. May–July. Like the preceding species but the stem is sharply 3-angled and the fruit tapers gradually into a shorter beak. *Marshes, frequent.*

FAMILY 96. GRAMI'NEAE

Grasses. Stems hollow, swollen at the nodes, leaf-sheath split along 1 side. Flowers in *spikelets*. Each spikelet usually has at the base 1 or empty or *outer glumes* (*g*, Figs. 59, 60). Above these are 1 or more flowers usually called *florets*. Each floret is enclosed by two glumes (paleae), the lower of which is the *flowering glume* (*fg*, Figs. 59, 60). Inside the palea are 2 minute scales which may be a rudimentary perianth. Stamens usually 3, with loose anthers. Ovary 1-celled, with usually 2 feather stigmas. Fruit an achene in which the seed is fused with the wall of the fruit (caryopsis).

Each spikelet with 1 floret . . . .
Most of the spikelets with 2 or more florets 1

  2 Spikelets sessile . . . .
    Spikelets stalked . . . .

(a)   (b)   (c)   (d)   (e)   (f)   (h)   (i)

3 Spike compound (*a*) . . . . . Spartina I
  Spike simple 4

4 Awns much longer than spikelets (*b*) . . Hordeum XXXIII
  Awns shorter than spikelets or none 5

5 Spikelets all on one side of axis (*c*) . . . Nardus XXXII
  Spikelets on both sides of axis (*d*) . . . Lepturus XXXI

6 Inflorescence spike-like (*e*) 7
  Inflorescence paniculate (*f*) 10

7 Stamens 2 . . . . . . Anthoxanthum III
  Stamens 3 8

8 Inflorescence about 6 inches long, tuft of hairs at base of
  floret (*g*) . . . . Ammophila IX
  Inflorescence 3 inches or less, no tuft of hairs at base of floret . 9

9 Flowering glume with a long awn (*h*) . . . Alopecurus IV
  Flowering glume with a very short or no awn (*i*) . Phleum VI

10 Spikelets ovate, blunt, or bluntish (*a*) 11
   Spikelets lanceolate or linear, acute (*b*) 12
11 Spikelets brownish, containing 1 perfect and 1 rudimentary
       floret (*c*) . . . . Melica XXI
   Spikelets pale green, very small, containing 1 perfect and no
       rudimentary floret (*d*) . . . . . Milium V
12 No tuft of hairs at base of floret (*e*) . . . Agrostis VII
   Tuft of hairs at base of floret 13

(*a*)   (*b*)   (*c*)   (*d*)   (*e*)   (*f*)   (*g*)

(*h*)   (*i*)   (*j*)   (*k*)   (*l*)   (*m*)

13 Flowering glumes awned (*f*) . . . Calamagrostis VIII
   All the glumes without awns (*g*) . . . . Phalaris II
14 Spikelets mostly sessile or nearly so, in a single spike . . 15
   Spikelets all stalked or in stalked clusters . . . 18
15 Spikelets in pairs on each tooth of axis (*h*) . Elymus XXXIV
   Spikelets solitary on each tooth of axis 16
16 Empty glume 1 (*i*) . . . . . . Lolium XXIX
   Empty glumes 2 or more 17
17 Outer glumes unequal, spikelets linear (*j*) Brachypodium XXVIII
   Outer glumes equal or nearly so, spikelets ovoid or lanceo-
       late (*k*) . . . . Agropyrum XXX
18 A pinnate involucre below each cluster of spikelets (*l*) .
                                         Cynosurus XVII
   No pinnate involucre 19
19 Spikelets densely clustered at end of long stiff
       branches (*m*) . . . . . . Dactylis XXII
   Spikelets solitary or in short-stalked clusters . . . 20
20 One or more glumes with an awn or long awn-like point . 21
   Glumes all awnless or merely pointed 27
21 Each spikelet with 1 male floret and 1 bisexual floret . 22
   Each spikelet with 2 or more perfect florets . . . 23

22 Upper floret male, awned; lower bisexual, unawned (*a*) Holcus X
   Upper floret bisexual, with a short awn; lower male or barren,
    with a long bent awn (*b*) .   .   . Arrhenatherum XIII

23 Awn inserted on back of flowering glume near the middle   .   24
   Awn terminal or nearly so   25

24 Flowering glume usually small, with a straight awn (*c*)   .   Aira X
   Flowering glume large, usually with a long kneed awn (*d*) Avena XII

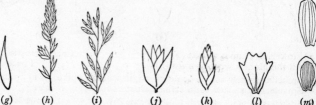

(*a*)   (*b*)   (*c*)   (*d*)   (*e*)   (*f*)

(*g*)   (*h*)   (*i*)   (*j*)   (*k*)   (*l*)   (*m*)

25 Flowering glume surrounded by long hairs (*e*)   Phragmites XV
   Flowering glume not surrounded by long hairs   .   . 26

26 Awn slightly below apex of flowering glume (*f*)   Bromus XXVII
   Awn terminal (*g*)   .   .   .   .   Festuca XXVI

27 Inflorescence narrow and spike-like (*h*) .   .   .   28
   Inflorescence paniculate or racemose (*i*).   .   .   29

28 Inflorescence long and narrow   .   .   Koeleria XVIII
   Inflorescence short, ovoid   .   .   .   Sesleria XVI

29 Outer glumes as long as whole spikelet (*j*)   .   .   30
   Outer glumes shorter than the spikelet (*k*)   .   .   31

30 Outer glumes obtuse   .   .   .   .   Melica XXI
   Outer glumes acute   .   .   .   .   Triodia XIV

31 Leaves obtuse, outer glumes fan-shaped (*l*)   .   Catabrosa XX
   Leaves acute, outer glumes ovate or lanceolate (*m*) .   .   32

2 Spikelets broader than long (*a*) . . . . Briza XXIII
  Spikelets longer than broad 33

33 Flowering glumes keeled and compressed (*b*) 34
  Flowering glumes rounded on back (*c*) 35

34 Ligule replaced by a line of hairs (*d*) . . . Molinia XIX
  Ligule not replaced by a line of hairs (*e*) . . Poa XXIV

35 Flowering glumes obtuse (*f*) . . . . Glyceria XXV
  Flowering glumes acute (*g*) . . . . Festuca XXVI

(*a*)   (*b*)   (*c*)   (*d*)   (*e*)   (*f*)   (*g*)

I. *SPAR'TINA*

S. stric'ta Sm. 11. Cordgrass. July–Sept. Rootstock creeping. Stem and leaves stiff and erect. Spikelets 1-flowered, sessile, in two to four 1-sided spikes; empty glumes 2. *Tidal mud-flats in S. and E. England.*
   S. alterniflo'ra (Loisel.) is taller, with 6 to 8 spikes, while *S. Town-send'ii* (Groves), which is a hybrid largely used to fix mud-flats in Southampton Water and elsewhere, is spreading rapidly.

II. *PHAL'ARIS*

P. arundina'cea L. **(Digra'phis arundinacea** Trin.). 111. Reed Grass. June–Aug. A tall grass with broad leaves. Inflorescence a long and narrow panicle. Spikelets 1-flowered, with a tuft of hairs at the base of the flower; glumes without awns. *Riverbanks and wet places, common.*

III. *ANTHOXAN'THUM*

A. odora'tum L. 112. Vernal Grass. April–June. Leaves flat. Spike-lets 1-flowered, in a narrow spike-like panicle; outer glumes unequal, inner glumes awned; stamens 2. *Meadows, common.*

IV. *ALOPECU'RUS*

  Spikelets 1-flowered, in a compact cylindrical spike; flowering glume with a long slender awn on the back.

Spike thin, acute; outer glumes united from the middle A. myosoroides
Spike thick, obtuse; outer glumes free, or united only at base . 2

2 Stem bent at nodes . . . . . A. geniculatus
  Stem not, or scarcely, bent at nodes . A. pratensis

A. myosuroi'des Huds. **(A. agres'tis** L.). 81. Slender Foxtail. May–Sept. An annual to 2 feet high. Spikes long, thin, and pointed, the awns projecting. *Cornfields and waste places, frequent.*

A genicula'tus L. 112. Bent Foxtail, Marsh Foxtail. May–Aug. A perennial with procumbent stems bent at the nodes. Spikes about 1½ inches long, thick, obtuse, awn 1½–2 times as long as flowering glume. *Moist meadows, common.*

A. praten'sis L. 110. Meadow Foxtail. May–July. A perennial with erect stems. Spikes 2–3 inches long, thick, obtuse, very dense, the awns projecting and twice as long as the flowering glume. *Meadows, common.*

V. *MIL'IUM*

M. effu'sum L. 94. Millet Grass. June–July. Tall and slender up to 4 feet, with rather broad leaves. Spikelets 1-flowered, pale green, very small, in a large loose panicle. *Moist woods, frequent.*

VI. *PHLE'UM*

Spikelets 1-flowered, in a dense spike. Flowering glumes much smaller than, and enclosed in, the 2 keeled and ciliate outer glumes.

P. praten'se L. 112. Cat's-tail Grass, Timothy-grass. July–Sept. A tall perennial grass with narrow flat leaves and cylindrical very compact spikes. The 2 outer glumes of each spikelet abruptly pointed, equal in size and shape and fitting together to form a 2-horned case to the flower. *Meadows, common.*

P. arena'rium L. 49. Sand Cat's-tail. June–July. An annual 6–8 inches high with short leaves and dense spikes tapering to both ends. Outer glumes tapering gradually into converging points. *Sandy shores, occasional*

VII. *AGROS'TIS*

Spikelets small, 1-flowered, in a narrow or spreading panicle.

Awn of flowering glume projecting beyond the spikelet .	A. canina
Awn minute or absent . . , ... 2	
2 Ligule long, acute . . . . . ,	A. alba
Ligule short, obtuse , . . . , .	A. tenuis

A. cani'na L. 110. Brown Bent-grass. June–Aug. A slender, graceful grass up to 2 feet high with very narrow leaves and elegant panicles of small brown spikelets. Flowering glume with a fine awn projecting beyond the spikelet. *Heathy pastures, common.*

A. al'ba L. 112. Fiorin-grass. June–Aug. A perennial with tufted or creeping stems and flat narrow leaves with long acute ligules. Spikelets small, numerous, in a panicle which is contracted before and after flowering into an almost spike-like inflorescence; flowering glumes awnless or with a very small awn near the base. *Meadows, common.*

A. ten'uis Sibth. (A. vulga'ris With.). 112. Fine Bent-Grass. June–Aug. Ligule short, obtuse. Awn minute or absent. Panicle always spreading. *Dry pastures, common.*

VIII. *CALAMAGROS'TIS*

Spikelets 1-flowered, with a tuft of hairs at base of flower, flowering glume awned.

C. epigei'os Roth. 72. Smallreed, Bushgrass. June–Aug. A tall grass with a creeping rootstock and rather broad long-pointed leaves and elegant feathery panicles. Awn inserted some distance from the top of the flowering glume. *Damp woods, occasional.*

C. canes'cens Gmel. (**C. lanceola'ta** Roth.). 39. Purple Smallreed. June–July. Like the preceding species but panicle looser, leaves narrower, and awn inserted close to the top of the flowering glume. *Damp woods, rare.*

IX. *AMMOPH'ILA*

A. arena'ria Link (**Psam'ma arenaria** Beauv.). 75. Marram Grass. July–Aug. Underground stems creeping. Stems and leaves stiff, erect, and glaucous. Spikelets 1-flowered, crowded into a long tapering spike-like panicle; outer glumes lanceolate, chaffy; flowering glume with tuft of hairs at base. *Sand-dunes, common.*

X. *AI'RA*

Spikelets small, 2-flowered; flowering glume with an awn on back near the middle.

Inflorescence spike-like, dense, and narrow .	.	A. praecox
Inflorescence paniculate, loose, and spreading	.	. 2
2 Leaves flat and rough, stem 2–4 feet	.	A. caespitosa
Leaves narrow, rolled, stem 1–1½ feet	.	A. flexuosa
Leaves narrow and short, not rolled, stem 3–6 inches		A. caryophyllea

A. caryophyl'lea L. 111. Silver Hair-grass. June–July. Seldom above 6 inches. Leaves very narrow, short, and flat. Panicles loose, spreading, and branched from near the base. *Dry pastures, common.*

A. prae'cox L. 112. Early Hair-grass. May–June. 3–6 inches. Leaves very narrow, short. Inflorescence spike-like. *Dry pastures, common.*

A. caespito'sa L. 112. Tufted Hair-grass. July–Aug. A tall grass with flat rough leaves in large tufts and large elegant panicles with spreading whorled branches. *Woods and moist meadows, common.*

A. flexuo'sa L. 111. Wavy Hair-grass. June–Aug. A slender grass 1–1½ feet high with narrow rolled leaves and small panicles. *Dry woods and pastures, common.*

XI. *HOL'CUS*

Each spikelet with 2 flowers, the upper one with stamens only, the lower with stamens and pistil. Glume of male flower with a short awn below the apex.

H. mol'lis L. 111. Soft-grass. June–Aug. A slender grass up to 3 feet high, with flat leaves and stems hairy at the nodes. Spikelets in spreading panicles, awn of male flower projecting some distance beyond the outer glumes. *Dry woods and lanes, frequent.*

H. lana′tus L. 112. Yorkshire Fog. May–Aug. Stem and leaves hairy Spikelets in panicles, pale pinkish-purple, softly hairy, awn of male flower scarcely projecting beyond the outer glumes. *Meadows, common.*

XII. *AVE′NA*

Spikelets usually with 3 or more flowers, in a loose panicle; flowering glume with a long twisted and bent awn on the back.

Spikelets drooping	. A. fatua	
Spikelets erect	. 2	
2 Spikelets about ¼ inch long	A. flavescens	
Spikelets about ½ inch long	. 3	
3 Stem and leaves hairy	A. pubescens	
Stem and leaves glabrous or nearly so . . .	A. pratensis	

A. flaves′cens L. 102. Yellow Oat. June–July. Spikelets small, erect, shining, and yellowish, in a spreading panicle up to 2 feet. *Dry pastures, frequent.*

A. pubes′cens Huds. 103. Perennial Wild Oat. June–July. Stem and leaves hairy. Spikelets large, erect, whitish, in a narrow panicle or raceme. *Meadows, common.*

A. praten′sis L. 81. Perennial Wild Oat. June–July. Like the preceding species but glabrous or nearly so. *Meadows, frequent.*

A. fat′ua L. 85. Wild Oat. June–July. Spikelets large, drooping, the flowering glume with long hairs and a very long bent awn. *Cornfields, occasional.*

    A. sati′va (L.), the Cultivated Oat, is similar, but the flowering glume is glabrous and sometimes without an awn.

XIII. *ARRHENATH′ERUM*

A. ela′tius Mert. & Koch. 112. False Oat. June–Oct. A tall, erect perennial to 3 feet, with flat leaves and long narrow panicles; stem sometimes with swollen knobs at the base. Each spikelet with 2 flowers, the upper perfect, the lower containing stamens only and with a fine bent awn on the back of the glume. *Meadows and hedgebanks, common.*

XIV. *TRIO′DIA*

T. decum′bens Beauv. 111. Heath Grass. June–Aug. Leaves narrow. Spikelets large, few, each with 3 or more flowers more or less completely enclosed in the two large outer glumes; awns none; inflorescence a narrow raceme. *Heaths, common.*

XV. *PHRAGMI′TES*

P. commu′nis Trin. (Arun′do Phragmites L.). 112. Common Reed. Aug.–Sept. A tall, stout, bamboo-like grass up to 10 feet high but usually less, with large flat leaves clasping the stem and large purplish-brown panicles. Each spikelet with several flowers surrounded by long silky hairs; flowering glume with a long awn-like point. *Marshes and riverbanks, common.*

XVI. *SESLE'RIA*

S. caeru'lea Ard. 12. Blue Moor-grass. April–June. A small grass seldom exceeding 1 foot, with short stiff radical leaves. Spikelets 2-flowered, in a short bluish-grey ovoid inflorescence; awns none, or mere points. *Mountain pastures in the north.*

XVII. *CYNOSU'RUS*

C. crista'tus L. 112. Dog's-tail Grass. June–Aug. A tall slender grass with narrow short leaves and a 1-sided spike-like inflorescence. Spikelets 2- or more flowered, in short-stalked clusters; below each cluster of spikelets is an involucre of pinnately arranged empty glumes. *Dry meadows, common.*

XVIII. *KOELE'RIA*

K. crista'ta Pers. 101. June–Aug. A small grass about 6 inches high with a dense tuft of short radical leaves and a long narrow spike-like inflorescence consisting of short-stalked clusters of spikelets, each spikelet containing 2 or more flowers, the glumes keeled and pointed but without distinct awns. *Dry pastures, frequent.*

XIX. *MOLIN'IA*

M. caeru'lea Moench. 112. Purple Moor-grass. July–Sept. A tall stiff grass with large tufts of long narrow leaves and loose narrow purplish or purplish-green panicles. Spikelets 3-flowered, the outer glumes shorter than the spikelet, the inner (flowering) glumes narrow and long-pointed. Ligule of leaf replaced by a line of hairs. *Moors, common.*

XX. *CATABRO'SA*

C. aquat'ica Beauv. 103. Water Whorl-grass. May–July. A glabrous pale green grass with stems procumbent or creeping at the base. Leaves short, flat, and blunt-ended. Spikelets 2–5-flowered, in spreading panicles with whorled branches, outer glumes much shorter than rest of spikelet; awns none. *Wet places, occasional.*

XXI. *MEL'ICA*

Spikelets short, about ¼ inch long; outer glumes obtuse; awns none.

M. nu'tans L. 51. Mountain Melic-grass. May–June. Leaves flat and erect. Spikelets 2-flowered, stalked, in a 1-sided raceme or panicle. *Woods in Scotland and W. England, rare.*

M. uniflo'ra L. 97. Common Melic-grass. May–June. Leaves flat. Spikelets solitary at the end of long branches in a panicle or raceme, each spikelet with 1 perfect and 1 rudimentary flower. *Woods and shady places, common.*

XXII. *DACT'YLIS*

D. glomera'ta L. 112. Cock's-foot Grass. June–Sept. A large coarse stiff grass with rough stems and leaves. Spikelets in broad dense clusters at the end of long stiff branches in an open panicle. *Meadows and waysides, very common.*

XXIII. *BRI'ZA*

B. me'dia L. 101. Quaking Grass. June–July. Stem slender. Spikelets several-flowered, broader than long, solitary and drooping at the end of long branches in a spreading panicle. *Meadows, common.*

XXIV. *PO'A*

Spikelets usually with 3 or more flowers in a spreading or narrow panicle, the glumes keeled, compressed and pointed but not awned, the outer pair of empty glumes usually much shorter than the rest of the spikelet.

Stem flattened; panicle narrow, 1-sided . . . P. compressa
Stem rounded 2
2 Annual, 2–6 inches high . . . . . P. annua
  Perennial, 1 foot or more when flowering . . . 3
3 Ligule long and acute, stem usually rough . . P. trivialis
  Ligule short and obtuse, stem usually smooth . . . 4
4 Stems creeping and rooting, upper leaves much shorter than their
    sheaths . . . . P. pratensis
  Stems erect, scarcely creeping; upper leaves usually as long as, or
    longer than, their sheaths, horizontal . . . P. nemoralis

P. an'nua L. 112. Common Meadow-grass. Feb.–Oct. An annual about 6 inches high though taller in especially favourable situations. Panicle spreading; spikelets with 5 or more flowers. *Meadows and waste places, very common.*

P. nemora'lis L. 104. June–July. Stems very slender, with leaves as long as their sheaths, the upper ones horizontal. Panicle slender, rather drooping. *Woods and shady lanes, frequent.*

P. compres'sa L. 81. June–July. Stems flattened. Panicle small, narrow, 1-sided, almost spike-like. *Walls and dry places, frequent in S. England.*

P. praten'sis L. 112. Smooth Meadow-grass. May–July. Stems smooth, creeping and rooting. Leaf with blunt ligule. Panicle spreading, erect. *Meadows and waste places, very common.*

P. trivia'lis L. 112. Rough Meadow-grass. June–July. Stems tufted, usually rough. Leaf with pointed ligule and rough sheath. Panicle spreading; spikelets 2-flowered, scarcely longer than the outer glumes. *Meadows, common.*

XXV. *GLYCE'RIA*

Differs from *Poa* chiefly in the glumes, which are obtuse and not keeled.

Tall aquatic plants 2
Short land plants 3
2 Panicle large and spreading . . . . G. aquatica
  Panicle long and narrow . . . . . G. fluitans
3 Leaves rolled at margins . . . . . G. maritima
  Leaves flat . . . . G. distans

G. flu'itans Br. 112. Flote-grass. June–Aug. Stems long and weak, leaves often floating. Spikelets few, long and narrow, many-flowered, in very long panicles. *Streams and wet ditches, common.*

G. aquat'ica Wahlb. 85. Reed Meadow-grass. July–Aug. A tall reed-like grass up to 6 feet, with flat leaves very rough on the edges. Spikelets very numerous, in a large spreading panicle. *Streams and marshes, frequent.*

G. marit'ima Wahlb. 76. Sea Meadow-grass. June–July. About 1 foot high, with creeping rootstock and leaves rolled at margins. Panicle narrow, erect. *Salt marshes, frequent.*

G. dis'tans Wahlb. 70. June–Aug. About 1 foot high, not creeping. Leaves flat, somewhat glaucous. Panicle spreading. *Pastures near the sea, occasional.*

XXVI. *FESTU'CA*

Spikelets several-flowered; glumes rounded on back and with a terminal awn or point.

Awn as long as, or longer than, the flowering glume		2
Awn none, or shorter than the flowering glume		3
2 Inflorescence narrow, 1-sided		F. Myuros
Inflorescence spreading		Bromus giganteus
3 About 3 inches high, spikelets sessile or nearly so in a stiff 2-ranked inflorescence		F. rigida
Nine inches or more, spikelets stalked		4
4 Radical leaves flat, about ¼ inch broad		F. elatior
Radical leaves rolled, very narrow		F. ovina

F. rig'ida Kunth (**Glyce'ria rigida** Sm.). 75. Hard Fescue. June–July. A small annual with stiff erect tufted stems and narrow inflorescences with the spikelets in 2 rows. *Walls-tops and dry places, common.*

F. Myu'ros L. 112. Rat's-tail Fescue. June–July. A tufted annual 1–2 feet high, with narrow rolled-in leaves. Inflorescence narrow, 1-sided, almost spike-like, the leaves reaching the lowest flowers; flowering glume with long awn. *Walls and dry places, frequent.*

In *F. bromoi'des* (L.), occurring in heathy pastures, the upper part of the flowering stem is bare of leaves.

F. ovi'na L. 112. Sheep's Fescue. June–July. A tufted perennial 6–12 inches high, with very narrow cylindrical leaves and numerous spikelets in a narrow panicle; awn shorter than flowering glume. *Dry pastures, common.*

F. ru'bra (L.), Red Fescue, is a taller plant with reddish and more spreading panicles and the upper leaves often flat.

F. ela'tior L. 105. Meadow Fescue. June–Aug. A tall grass with flat leaves and narrow erect panicles. Flowering glume with a short awn or merely pointed. *Meadows, common.*

F. arundina'cea (Schreb.), Tall Fescue, occurring in wet places, especially near the sea, is a luxuriant variety up to 5 feet, with a spreading panicle.

XXVII. *BRO'MUS*

Spikelets several-flowered; flowering glume with an awn on the back just below the apex.

Awn longer than the flowering glume   2
Awn not longer than the flowering glume   3

2 Glabrous, 3–6 feet high .   .   .   .   .   B. giganteus
  Hairy, less than 3 feet high   .   .   .   .   B. sterilis

3 Flowering glume oblong, with prominent parallel veins   B. mollis
  Flowering glume lanceolate, with faint veins   .   .   .   4

4 Spikelets erect   .   .   .   .   .   .   B. erectus
  Spikelets drooping   .   .   ,   .   .   .   B. ramosus

B. gigan'teus L. (**Festu'ca gigantea** Vill.). 107. Tall Brome-grass. July–Aug. Glabrous, 3–6 feet, with flat leaves ½ inch or more in breadth, and large drooping panicles of long-awned spikelets. *Woods and shady lanes, frequent.*

B. ramo'sus Huds. (**B. as'per** Murr.). 106. Hairy Brome-grass. July–Aug. A tall grass up to 6 feet, with hairy stems and long flat leaves about ¼ inch broad. Spikelets an inch or more in length, drooping, in large loose panicles; flowering glume lanceolate, faintly nerved, with an awn not, or scarcely, longer than itself. *Hedgebanks, common.*

B. erec'tus Huds. 58. Upright Brome-grass. June–July. 1–2 feet high. Leaves very narrow. Spikelets narrow, erect; awn about half as long as flowering glume. *Meadows and hedgebanks, occasional.*

B. ster'ilis L. 99. Barren Brome-grass. May–July. 1–2 feet high. Stem and leaves softly downy. Spikelets drooping, in large panicles; flowering glume with prominent parallel veins and awn longer than itself. *Hedgebanks and waste places, common.*

B. mol'lis L. 112. Soft Brome-grass. May–July. Stem 2–3 feet, hairy. Spikelets broader and stouter than in the other species, with oblong or ovoid strongly-nerved flowering glumes covered with soft down or nearly glabrous; awn scarcely longer than the glume. *Meadows and hedgebanks, common.*

   B. commuta'tus (Schrad.) has a larger and more open panicle, the lowest empty glume being 3-nerved. *B. secali'nus* (L.) is similar but the flowering glumes spread widely in fruit.

XXVIII. *BRACHYPO'DIUM*

Spikelets many-flowered, sessile, linear, on a simple spike, flowering glume awned.

B. sylvat'icum Beauv. 111. False Brome. July–Sept. A tall slender perennial to 3 feet. Leaves flat. Awn usually much longer than flowering glume. *Hedgebanks and woods, common.*

B. pinna'tum L. 38. June–July. Like the preceding species but spikelets with more than ten flowers, more erect, and the awn not longer than the glume. *Dry calcareous pastures, rare.*

XXIX. *LO'LIUM*

Spikelets several-flowered, sessile in the axil of a single outer glume, forming a long interrupted spike.

L. peren'ne L. 112. Rye-grass. May–Sept. Stem 1–2 feet. Spikelets few-flowered, outer glume shorter than spikelet, flowering glume unawned. *Meadows and waysides, common.*

 L. ital'icum (Braun), an escape from cultivation, has awned flowering glumes and 10 or more flowers in each spikelet.

L. temulen'tum L. 45. Darnel. June–July. An annual grass rather like wheat except for the distant spikelets. Outer glume as long as spikelet, flowering glume with or without an awn. *Cornfields, occasional.* POISONOUS TO CATTLE.

XXX. *AGROPY'RUM*

Spikelets several-flowered, sessile, crowded into a spike; empty glumes 2.

Underground stem short, not creeping . . .	A. caninum
Underground stem long and creeping	2
2 Leaves flat, green, not densely tufted . . .	A. repens
Leaves rolled, glaucous, tufted	3
3 Flowering glume obtuse, with a short point . .	A. junceum
Flowering glume acute	A. pungens

A. cani'num Beauv. (**Trit'icum caninum** L.). 98. Wheat-grass. June–Aug. No creeping rootstock. Stem leafy, 1–3 feet, leaves flat. Flowering glume with a long awn. *Occasional.*

A. re'pens Beauv. (**Trit'icum repens** L.). 112. Couch-grass. July–Aug. Underground stems long, white, and creeping. Leaves flat, green, not or slightly tufted. Flowering glume with a short awn. *Hedgebanks and waste places, common.*

A. pun'gens Roem. & Sch. (**Trit'icum pungens** Pers.). 34. June–Aug. Underground stems long and creeping. Leaves stiff, sharp, and densely tufted; glaucous green, the edges rolled inwards. Flowering glumes acute. *Sandy sea-shores.*

A. jun'ceum Beauv. (**Trit'icum junceum** L.). 67. Sea Couch-grass. June–Aug. Like the preceding species but leaves less tufted and the flowering glumes broader, their tips contracted abruptly into a short point. *Sand-dunes, common.*

XXXI. *LEPTU'RUS*

L. filifor'mis Trin. 55. Hard-grass. June–Aug. An annual seldom exceeding 6 inches. Spikelets 1-flowered, adpressed to a linear jointed spike; outer glumes 2, hard and ribbed, awns none. *Salt marshes, frequent.*

XXXII. *NAR'DUS*

N. stric'ta L. 111. Matgrass. June–Aug. A short densely-tufted perennial with stiff bristle-like leaves. Spikelets 1-flowered, sessile, in long 1-sided spikes; empty glumes none, style 1. *Heaths, frequent.*

XXXIII. *HOR'DEUM*

Spikelets 1-flowered, sessile, 3 to each tooth of the spike, 1 or more empty or imperfect; glumes with long awns.

Lateral spikelets perfect . . . . . H. europaeum

Central spikelet perfect, lateral male or empty 2

2 Outer glumes ciliate . . . . . . H. murinum

Outer glumes not ciliate 3

3 Spike about 1 inch long . . . . . . H. marinum

Spike about 2 inches long . . . . . H. nodosum

H. europae'um All. (H. sylvat'icum Huds.). 31. Wood Barley. June–July. Stem erect, 1–3 feet, with flat leaves nearly ½ inch broad; central spikelet barren, lateral perfect. *Woods on calcareous soil, rare.*

H. nodo'sum L. (H. praten'se Huds.). 66. Meadow Barley. June–Aug. Stem 1–2 feet. Leaves narrow, less than ¼ inch broad. Spike about 2 inches long, compressed; central spikelet perfect, lateral empty or male. *Meadows, frequent.*

H. muri'num L. 83. Wall Barley. May–July. Stems tufted, decumbent at base. Spike 3–4 inches, compressed, rough with ciliate awns; central spikelet perfect, lateral rudimentary or empty. *Waysides, common.*

H. mari'num Huds. 28. Sea Barley, Squirrel-tail Grass. June–July. Stems tufted, 6–12 inches. Spike short, 1 inch or less, not or scarcely compressed, central spikelet perfect; glumes rough but not ciliate. *Pastures near the sea.*

XXXIV. *EL'YMUS*

E. arena'rius L. 52. Lymegrass. July–Aug. Stem stiff and glaucous, up to 4 feet high. Leaves stiff, margins rolled inwards. Spikelets 3–4-flowered, sessile in a long spike, 2 to each notch of axis; awns none. *Sandy sea-shores, occasional.*

FAMILY 97. **CONIF'ERAE**

Resinous trees or shrubs with (in the British species) linear leaves. Flowers unisexual, either solitary or in separate catkin-like or cone-like structures; ovules not enclosed in an ovary but attached to an open carpellary scale.

Fruit of a single seed half enclosed in a fleshy scarlet cup . . . Taxus I

Seed or seeds completely enclosed in a bluish berry; leaves opposite or whorled . . . . Juniperus I

Seeds borne on the scales of a woody cone; leaves alternate or in clusters 2

2 Leaves all solitary on each notch of stem . . . Picea IV

Leaves in pairs or clusters (except on the youngest shoots) . . 3

3 Leaves all in pairs . . . . Pinus III

Leaves solitary or in clusters, deciduous . . . . Larix V

I. *JUNIP'ERUS*

J. commu'nis L. 82. Common Juniper. May–June. An evergreen bush or shrub with small prickly-pointed leaves in whorls of 3, jointed at base and each with a single grey band above. Catkins very small, axillary or terminal. Berry small, blue-black, containing 1 or 2 hard seeds. *Downs, locally common.*

II. *TAX'US*

T. bacca'ta L. 50. Yew. March–April. A small evergreen tree with a scaly or peeling bark and spreading branches. Leaves flat, linear, about an inch long, dark glossy green above, bright green below, in 2 opposite rows on the branchlet. Male flowers in small axillary greenish-yellow catkins, female (ovules) solitary. Fruit a bright red fleshy cup containing a single seed. *Much planted in churchyards but indigenous in hilly districts.* POISONOUS.

III. *PI'NUS*

P. sylves'tris L. 18. Scots Fir, Scots Pine. May–June. A tall evergreen tree with a reddish bark, whorled young branches, and a spreading crown when approaching maturity. Leaves (needles) bluish-green, in pairs crowded towards the end of the branch. Male catkins yellow, in clusters near the base of the young shoots; female catkins ovoid, reddish, terminal. Fruit a woody cone with scales much thickened at the apex, each scale bearing 2 winged seeds. *Native in Scotland and formerly over the whole of the British Isles, now much planted.*

IV. *PI'CEA*

P. A'bies Karst (**P. excel'sa** Link). Common Spruce Fir, Christmas Tree. May–June. A tall evergreen tree with a pointed top, whorled young branches, and small dark green sharp-pointed needles borne on alternate pegs. Male catkins yellow or red, in leaf axils near the end of the young shoots; female terminal, green or purple. Fruit a woody cylindrical drooping cone with thin scales, each scale bearing 2 small winged seeds. *Native of central and northern Europe, commonly planted.*

V. *LA'RIX*

L. decid'ua Mill. (**L. europae'a** DC.). Common Larch. April–May. A tall rough-barked tree. Young branches not in whorls. Leaves soft, linear, bright green, deciduous, spirally arranged on young shoots, in clusters on the older shoots. Flowers solitary, appearing on the older shoots, male yellow, female purple. Fruit a small woody cone with thin scales, each scale bearing 2 small winged seeds. *Native of central Europe, commonly planted for its durable timber.*

FAMILY 98. FI'LICES

Plants without true flowers, i.e. without pollen, ovules, or seeds. Reproduction by minute *spores* contained in spore-cases (sporangia) borne in clusters called *sori* on the leaves (fronds) or in separate fructifications.

4565   O

The sori are sometimes covered by a sheath called the *indusium*. In the British species the true stem is confined to an underground rootstock from which the fronds grow up to the light.

Sori in a panicle which is a continuation of the frond . Osmunda XI
Sori in a stalked spike or panicle quite distinct from the frond . 2
Sori sessile on the frond (which may differ somewhat in appearance
from the barren fronds) 3

2 Sori in a spike; frond simple, entire . . Ophioglossum XII
Sori in a panicle, frond pinnate . . . Botrychium XIII

3 Fronds translucent, sori marginal . . Hymenophyllum I
Fronds more or less opaque, sori concealed under rolled margin
of frond . . . . Pteris II
Sori clearly visible on lower surface of frond 4

4 Frond simple, entire . . . . . Scolopendrium VII
Frond lobed or divided 5

5 Fruiting fronds with narrower divisions than those of the barren
ones 6
Fronds all alike 7

6 Fronds once pinnate . . . . . . Blechnum IV
Fronds much divided . . . . . . Allosorus III

7 Segments of frond broad-based and scarcely longer than broad,
covered on the back with rusty shining scales . Ceterach VI
Segments of frond narrow or with narrow base, or with green
showing between the sori 8

8 Sori oblong or merging into irregular masses . . Asplenium V
Sori circular and distinct 9

9 Young sori naked, frond with broad base . . Polypodium X
Young sori covered wholly or partly by an indusium, frond
tapering to base 10

10 Indusium peltate above the sorus . . . Aspidium IX
Indusium attached along one side of the sorus . . . 11

11 Segments of frond obtuse . . . . Cystopteris VIII
Segments of frond acute . . . . . Asplenium V

I. *HYMENOPHYL′LUM*

H. tunbridgen′se Sm. 51. Filmy Fern. June–July. Underground
stem thread-like, creeping. Fronds 2–3 inches long, finely divided,
translucent. Sori ovate, at base of segments or on their inner edge.
Damp rocks, rare.

II. *PTE′RIS*

P. aquili′na L. 112. Bracken, Brake. July–Aug. Fronds tall and erect,
with hard stiff stalks, often growing to 6 feet or more, twice or three
times pinnate, the ultimate segments entire, with the sori concealed
under their rolled margins. *Woods, heaths, and heathy pastures, common.*

III. *ALLOSO'RUS*

A. **cris'pus** Bernh. 55. Parsley Fern. July–Aug. Fronds 3–6 inches, like parsley leaves, twice or three times pinnate; the outer fronds barren, with broad segments, the inner ones with narrow segments under which the sori are borne. *Shady rocks, mostly in the north, occasional.*

IV. *BLECH'NUM*

B. **Spi'cant** Roth. 112. Hard Fern. June–July. Fronds long and narrow, with tapering base, once pinnate, with linear segments. Fruiting fronds with narrower segments than the barren ones. Sori linear, one on each side of midrib of segment on underside. *Hilly woods and heaths, frequent.*

V. *ASPLE'NIUM*

Fronds once or several times pinnate, the sori linear or oblong often merging into irregular masses, indusium attached along one side.

Frond once pinnate		**2**
Frond twice or three times pinnate		**4**
2 Segments of frond thick, ½ inch or more across .	.	A. marinum
Segments of frond thin, less than ½ inch across .	.	. **3**
3 Stalk black		A. Trichomanes
Stalk green		. A. viride
4 Fronds 2–3 feet long		A. Filix-foemina
Fronds less than 1 foot long		. **5**
5 Frond with numerous segments gradually decreasing in size to a		
fine point		A. Adiantum-nigrum
Frond with few segments, all equal or nearly so		A. Ruta-muraria

A. **Adian'tum-ni'grum** L. 110. Black Spleenwort. June–Oct. Fronds tufted, 6–12 inches, twice or three times pinnate, tapering to a point. *Walls and rocks, frequent.*

A. **mari'num** L. 55. Sea Spleenwort. June–Sept. Fronds tufted, 6–12 inches, once pinnate, segments large, thick, and coarsely toothed. *Sea cliffs, occasional.*

A. **vir'ide** Huds. 47. Green Spleenwort. June–Sept. Fronds long and narrow, 2–6 inches, segments ¼ inch or less, broadly ovate or orbicular, finely toothed, stalk green. *Mountain rocks, mostly in the north.*

A. **Trichom'anes** L. 111. Common Spleenwort. May–Oct. Like the preceding species but stalk black and leaves sometimes reaching ½ inch or more. *Walls and rocks, common.*

A. **Ru'ta-mura'ria** L. 112. Wall Rue. June–Oct. Fronds densely tufted, 2–3 inches, rather thick, with scattered ovate stalked segments not differing much in size. *Walls and rocks, common.*

A. **Fi'lix-foem'ina** Bernh. (**Athy'rium Filix-foemina** Roth.). 110. Lady Fern. July–Aug. Fronds 2–3 feet, twice pinnate; segments pinnatifid, acute; stalk with brown scales at base; indusium fringed. *Woods, frequent.*

VI. *CETE'RACH*

C. officina'rum DC. 69. Rusty-back. April–Oct. Fronds thick, tufted, spreading, long and narrow, pinnatifid, with obtuse broad-based lobes covered on the back with rusty shining scales. *Walls and rocks, locally common.*

VII. *SCOLOPEN'DRIUM*

S. vulga're Symons. 105. Hart's-tongue. July–Aug. Fronds tufted, long, narrow, and entire, about 12 inches by 2. Sori in parallel lines on lower surface. *Shady hedgebanks and rocks, common.*

VIII. *CYSTOP'TERIS*

C. frag'ilis Bernh. 90. Bladder Fern. July–Aug. Fronds tufted, 4–12 inches, twice pinnate, with small obtuse segments. Sori distant, near the margin of the frond on the underside; indusium attached to one side and somewhat inflated. *Walls and rocks, occasional.*

IX. *ASPID'IUM*

Fronds pinnately divided, with circular sori dotted on the lower surface and each covered when young with a circular or reniform indusium.

Indusium circular 2
Indusium reniform 3
2 Fronds once pinnate, the segments sharply toothed . A. Lonchitis
  Fronds twice pinnate . . . . . . A. aculeatum
3 Frond 2- or 3-pinnate . . . . . A. spinulosum
  Frond once pinnate, with pinnatifid segments, the lobes broad at
    the base 4
4 Lobes toothed, sori near the middle . . . A. Filix-mas
  Lobes entire, sori near the edge 5
5 Stalk with brown scales, segments glandular and frag-
    rant . . . . A. Oreopteris
  Stalk without brown scales, segments not glandular A. Thelypteris

A. Lonchi'tis Sw. (**Polys'tichum Lonchitis** Roth.). 29. Holly Fern. June–Aug. Fronds tufted, 6–12 inches, narrow, with tapering base, once pinnate; segments short, ovate or oblong, with fine teeth, indusium circular. *Mountain rocks in the north, rare.*

A. aculea'tum Sw. (**Polys'tichum aculeatum** Roth.). 110. Prickly Shield-fern. July–Aug. Fronds tufted, 1–2 feet, twice pinnate, finely toothed, primary segments unequal at base, indusium circular. *Shady hedgebanks and woods, common.*
    A. angula're (Willd.) is a variety with larger, broader, and more finely divided fronds.

A. Thelyp'teris Sw. (**Lastre'a Thelypteris** Bory). 46. Marsh Shield-fern. July–Aug. Fronds not tufted, 1–2 feet, once pinnate, the segments with broad-based entire lobes and sori near the edge; stalk without brown scales. *Bogs, occasional.*

A. Oreop'teris Sw. (**Lastre'a Oreopteris** Bory). 104. Mountain Shield-fern. July–Aug. Fronds tufted, 1–2 feet, once pinnate, the segments gradually decreasing in size towards the base, glandular and fragrant; lobes entire, broad-based; sori near the edge, indusium reniform; stalk with brown scales. *Woods and heaths, occasional.*

A. Fi'lix-mas Sw. (**Lastre'a Filix-mas** Presl.). 112. Male Fern. July–Aug. Fronds large, in circular tufts, 2–3 feet, once pinnate, the segments with broad-based lobes toothed near the apex; sori near the middle of each lobe, indusium reniform; stalk with brown scales. *Woods and shady hedgebanks, common.*

A. spinulo'sum Sw. (**Lastre'a spinulosa** Presl.). 111. Broad Shield-fern. July–Sept. Fronds broad, 1–2 feet long, twice pinnate, finely toothed, primary segments more or less equal at base; sori near the middle, indusium reniform; stalk with brown scales. *Moist woods, common.*
  A. dilata'tum (Willd.) is a variety with larger and broader fronds, 3–5 feet high, and with the scales dark brown in the centre.

X. *POLYPO'DIUM*

Fronds not or scarcely tapering to the base; once pinnate, or ternate with pinnate branches; stalk without or with very few scales; sori circular, indusium absent.

Primary segments of frond entire or slightly toothed . P. vulgare
Primary segments of frond deeply toothed or again divided . . 2

2 Frond once pinnate, with pinnatifid segments . P. Phegopteris
  Frond ternate, with pinnate branches . . . P. Dryopteris

P. vulga're L. 112. Common Polypody. June–Sept. Fronds tufted, 6–12 inches, once pinnate, with long, narrow, nearly entire segments. *Shady walls, hedgebanks, and trunks of trees, common.*

P. Dryop'teris L. 80. Oak Fern. July–Aug. Rootstock slender, creeping. Frond 6–12 inches, with a broad base dividing into 3 main branches, each of which is again divided into pinnate segments, ultimate segments toothed; stalk with a few brown scales at base. *Dry woods, rare.*
  P. calca'reum (Sm.), the Mountain Polypody, with stiffer fronds covered with glandular hairs, occurs occasionally in limestone districts.

P. Phegop'teris L. 82. Beech Fern. June–Aug. Rootstock slender, creeping. Frond 6–12 inches, with a broad base, once pinnate, the segments with broad-based entire hairy lobes. *Shady places, rare.*

XI. *OSMUN'DA*

O. rega'lis L. 86. Royal Fern. June–Aug. Fronds tufted, large, up to 6 feet high or more, twice pinnate; segments long, narrow, entire, and rounded at the base. Sori in a panicle at the upper end of the frond. *Bogs, occasional.*

XII. *OPHIOGLOS'SUM*

O. vulga'tum L. 98. Adder's-tongue. June–Aug. Frond ovate, entire, 3–6 inches. Sori in a terminal spike and not on the frond. *Moist pastures, occasional.*

XIII. *BOTRYCH'IUM*

B. Luna'ria Sw. 106. Moonwort. June–Aug. Frond 3–6 inches, once pinnate, with broad rounded segments. Sori in a panicle attached to, but distinct from, the frond. *Dry pastures, occasional.*

FAMILY 99. EQUISETA'CEAE

Stems jointed, simple, or with whorled branches. Spore-cases in termi-ovoid or oblong spikes.

EQUISE'TUM

Fruiting stems simple, appearing in spring before the branched barren
ones 2
Fruiting stems similar to and appearing in spring or summer at the
same time as the barren ones 3

2 Stem sheaths with 20–30 teeth . . . . E. maximum
  Stem sheaths with 10 or fewer teeth . . . E. arvense

3 Lower branches compound, sheath 3–4-toothed . E. sylvaticum
  Branches all simple or none, sheath with 6 or more teeth . 4

4 Stem sheath with a conspicuous broad black ring . E. hyemale
  Stem sheath with a thin and faint black ring or none . . 5

5 Stem rough, deeply grooved . . . . E. palustre
  Stem smooth, not deeply grooved . . . . E. limosum

E. max'imum Lam. (E. Telmatei'a Ehrh.). 86. Great Horsetail. April–June. Fruiting stem thick, unbranched, 8–10 inches, pale brown, with very large loose sheaths. Spike 2 inches or more. Barren stems 3–6 feet, pale green, much branched, with large loose sheaths. *Wet places, frequent.*

E. arven'se L. 112. Common Horsetail. April–May. Fruiting stem unbranched, brown, with short distant sheaths and a short spike. Barren stems green, 1–3 feet, with simple whorled branches. *Moist stiff soils, common.*

E. sylvat'icum L. 103. Wood Horsetail. April–May. Fruiting stems branched, pale brown at first and nearly simple. Barren stems with very numerous long and slender light green recurved branches, which are again branched giving a plumed appearance. *Wet woods and heaths, occasional.*

E. palus'tre L. 110. Marsh Horsetail. June–Aug. Stems mostly fruit-ing, rough and deeply grooved, with 7–8 simple branches in each whorl. Spike obtuse. *Wet places, common.*

E. limo'sum L. 110. Smooth Horsetail. June–July. Stems mostly fruiting, slightly channelled, either unbranched or with a few short simple branches about the middle. Spike obtuse. *Wet ditches or shallow water, frequent.*

E. hyema'le L. 49. Rough Horsetail. July–Aug. Stems mostly fruiting, rough, faintly channelled, unbranched, with a conspicuous broad black band round base of sheath. Spike acute. *Marshes and wet woods, mostly in the north.*

    E. variega'tum (Schleich.) is probably a mere variety of the above with slender decumbent stems and found in sandy places in the north.

FAMILY 100. LYCOPODIA'CEAE

Low moss-like plants with linear or scale-like leaves. Spore-cases solitary, sessile in the axils of the leaves or of the bracts of a terminal spike.

Bracts entire or nearly so . . . . Lycopodium I
Bracts conspicuously toothed . . . . . Selaginella II

I. *LYCOPO'DIUM*

Spore-cases of one kind only, all containing a large number of small spores.

Spore-cases axillary, stems tufted and scarcely creeping .   L. Selago
Spore-cases in terminal spikes, stems creeping or prostrate .   . 2

2 Fruiting branches usually simple . . . . L. inundatum
  Fruiting branches forked or clustered 3

3 Leaves in 4 rows . . . . . . L. alpinum
  Leaves irregularly arranged . . . . . L. clavatum

L. Sela'go L. 89. Fir Clubmoss. June–Aug. Stems forked, decumbent and rooting at the base but scarcely creeping, forming dense flat-topped tufts 2–6 inches high. Leaves small, lanceolate, crowded, overlapping. Spore-cases in axils of upper leaves not forming a distinct spike. *Moors, mostly in the north, frequent.*

L. inunda'tum L. 60. Marsh Clubmoss. June–Aug. Stems covered with narrow incurved leaves mostly turned to one side, creeping on the surface of the bog and sending up erect simple fruiting spikes. *Heathy bogs, occasional.*

L. clava'tum L. 99. Common Clubmoss. June–Aug. Stems hard, creeping to several feet and covered with stiff narrow leaves. Fruiting branches slender, forked at the top. *Moors, mostly in the north, frequent.*

L. alpi'num L. 65. Alpine Clubmoss. June–Aug. Stems slender, creeping, sending up dense tufts 2–3 inches high. Leaves minute, in 4 distinct rows closely pressed to stem. *Mountains, locally frequent.*

II. *SELAGINEL'LA*

S. selaginoi'des L. 61. Common Selaginella, Lesser Clubmoss. June–
Aug. Stems slender, prostrate, much branched, forming moss-like
patches. Leaves lanceolate, minute. Fruiting branches simple, ascending or erect, upper leaves (bracts) toothed. Spore-cases of 2 kinds, the
larger containing 4 large spores, the smaller numerous small spores.
Moist heaths in the north, occasional.

FAMILY 101. ISOETA'CEAE

Water plants with long subulate leaves growing in a tuft from a
depressed corm. Spore-cases sessile, partly enclosed by the sheathing
base of the leaf. Spores of 2 kinds, large and small.

ISOE'TES

I. lacus'tris L. 41. Quillwort. May–July. A bright green tufted plant
growing under water. Leaves linear, thick, nearly cylindrical, 2–4
inches long. *Edges of lakes and pools, occasional.*

FAMILY 102. MARSILIA'CEAE

Small water plants with creeping stems. Spore-cases globular, sessile
on the stem, containing spores of 2 kinds, large and small.

PILULA'RIA

P. globulif'era L. 65. Pillwort. May–July. Stem creeping and rooting
in the mud and sending up bright green linear cylindrical leaves 1–3
inches long. Spore-cases brown, hairy. *Edges of lakes and pools,
occasional.*

INDEX

(Synonyms in italics)

Abele	154
Acer	51
Aceraceae	51
Aceras	158
Achillea	96
Aconitum	23
Acorus	167
Adder's-tongue	198
Adonis	20
Adoxa	84
Adoxaceae	84
Ægopodium	79
Æsculus	52
Æthusa	81
Agrimonia	65
Agrimony	65
Agrimony, Hemp	94
Agropyrum	191
Agrostis	184
Aira	185
Ajuga	136
Alchemilla	65
Alder	150
Alder Buckthorn	51
Alexanders	77
Alisma	168
Alismaceae	167
Alkanet	118
Allgood	139
All-heal	88
Alliaria	31
Allium	162
Allosorus	195
Allseed	47
Alnus	150
Alopecurus	183
Althaea	46
Alyssum	29
Amaryllidaceae	160
American Waterweed	155
Ammophila	185
Anacharis	155
Anagallis	114
Anchusa	118
Andromeda	110
Anemone	20
Angelica	82
Antennaria	95
Anthemis	96
Anthoxanthum	183
Anthriscus	80
Anthyllis	57
Antirrhinum	123
Apium	78
Apocynaceae	115
Apple	67
Aquifoliaceae	50
Aquilegia	23
Arabis	28
Araceae	166
Araliaceae	83
Archangel	136
Arctium	100
Arctostaphylos	110
Arenaria	42
Aristolochia	145
Aristolochiaceae	144
Armeria	112
Arnoseris	103
Arrhenatherum	186
Arrowgrass	168
Arrowhead	168
Artemisia	97
Arum	166
Arundo	186
Asarabacca	145
Asarum	145
Ash	115
Aspen	154
Asperugo	118
Asperula	87
Asphodel	163
Aspidium	196
Asplenium	195
Aster	94
Astragalus	57
Athyrium	195
Atriplex	140
Atropa	121
Avena	186

Avens	. . . .	63
Awlwort	. . . .	31
Azalea	. . . .	111
Baldmoney	. . .	81
Ballota	. . . .	136
Balm	. . . .	133
Balsam	. . . .	50
Barbarea	. . . .	28
Barberry	. . . .	23
Barley	. . . .	192
Bartsia	. . . .	126
Basil	. . . .	133
Basil Thyme	. . .	133
Bastard Balm	. .	134
Bastard Stone Parsley	.	79
Bastard Toadflax	. .	146
Beak-sedge	. . .	173
Beam	. . . .	67
Bearberry	. . .	110
Bear's-foot	. . .	22
Bedstraw	. . . .	87
Beech	. . . .	152
Beet	. . . .	139
Bellflower	. . .	108
Bellis	. . . .	94
Berberidaceae	. .	23
Berberis	. . . .	23
Beta	. . . .	139
Betony	. . . .	134
Betula	. . . .	150
Betulaceae	. . .	150
Bidens	. . . .	96
Bilberry	. . . .	109
Bindweed	. . . 120, 142	
Birch	. . . .	150
Bird Cherry	. . .	62
Bird's-foot	. . .	58
Bird's-foot Trefoil	. .	57
Bird's-nest	. . .	111
Birthwort	. . .	145
Bistort	. . . .	142
Bittercress	. . .	29
Bittersweet	. . .	121
Blackberry	. . .	63
Black Bindweed	. .	142
Black Bryony	. . .	161
Blackstonia	. . .	116
Blackthorn	. . .	62
Bladderwort	. . .	128
Blechnum	. . .	195
Blinks	. . . .	44
Bluebell	. . . .	163
Bluebottle	. . .	102
Blysmus	. . . .	173
Bog Asphodel	. .	163
Bogbean	. . . .	116
Bog Myrtle	. . .	150
Bog Pimpernel	. .	114
Bog-rush	. . . .	173
Borage	. . . .	118
Boraginaceae	. .	117
Borago	. . . .	118
Botrychium	. . .	198
Box	. . . .	147
Brachypodium	. .	190
Bracken, Brake	. .	194
Bramble	. . . .	63
Brassica	. . . .	31
Brassica	. . . .	32
Briar	. . . .	66
Briza	. . . .	188
Brome	. . . .	190
Bromus	. . . .	190
Brooklime	. . .	126
Brookweed	. . .	114
Broom	. . . .	53
Broomrape	. . .	127
Bryonia	. . . .	74
Bryony	. . . 74, 161	
Buckbean	. . . .	116
Buckthorn	. . . 51, 145	
Bugle	. . . .	136
Bugloss	. . . .	118
Bullace	. . . .	62
Bulrush	. . . 172, 166	
Bunium	. . . .	79
Bupleurum	. . .	77
Burdock	. . . .	100
Bur-marigold	. .	96
Burnet	. . . .	65
Burnet Saxifrage	. .	79
Bur Parsley	. . .	83
Bur-reed	. . . .	166
Butcher's Broom	. .	161
Butomus	. . . .	168
Butterbur	. . . .	98
Buttercup	. . . .	21
Butterwort	. . .	128
Buxaceae	. . . .	147
Buxus	. . . .	147

Cabbage	. . . .	32
Cakile	. . . .	34
Calamagrostis	. .	185
Calamint	. . .	133
Calamintha	. .	132
Callitriche	. .	72
Calluna	. . .	110
Caltha	. . .	22
Campanula	. .	108
Campanulaceae	. .	107
Campion	. . .	40
Candytuft	. .	34
Caprifoliaceae	. .	84
Capsella	. . .	32
Caraway	. . .	79
Cardamine	. .	28
Carduus	. . .	100
Carex	. . .	174
Carlina	. . .	99
Carnation-grass	. .	178
Carpinus	. . .	150
Carrot	. . .	82
Carum	. . .	78
Caryophyllaceae	. .	38
Castanea	. . .	151
Catabrosa	. .	187
Catchfly	. . .	37
Catmint	. . .	133
Cat's-ear	. . .	105
Cat's-tail	. .	166, 184
Caucalis	. . .	83
Celandine	. .	22, 25
Celastraceae	. .	51
Celery	. . .	78
Centaurea	. .	102
Centaury	. . .	116
Centunculus	. .	114
Cephalanthera	. .	157
Cerastium	. .	40
Ceratophyllum	. .	155
Ceterach	. . .	196
Chaerophyllum	. .	80
Chaffweed	. .	114
Chamomile	. .	96
Charlock	. . .	32
Cheiranthus	. .	27
Chelidonium	. .	25
Chenopodiaceae	. .	138
Chenopodium	. .	138
Cherry	. . .	62
Chervil	. . .	80
Chestnut	. .	52, 151
Chickweed	. .	40, 41
Chicory	. . .	102
Chlora	. . .	116
Christmas Tree	. .	193
Chrysanthemum	. .	96
Chrysosplenium	. .	69
Cicely	. . .	80
Cichorium	. .	102
Cicuta	. . .	78
Cinquefoil	. .	64
Circaea	. . .	74
Cistaceae	. . .	35
Cladium	. . .	173
Clary	. . .	133
Claytonia	. .	44
Cleavers	. . .	87
Clematis	. . .	19
Clinopodium	. .	133
Cloudberry	. .	63
Clover	. . .	56
Clubmoss	. .	199
Club-rush	. .	172, 173
Cochlearia	. .	30
Cock's-foot	. .	187
Codlins-and-Cream	. .	73
Colchicum	. .	163
Coltsfoot	. . .	98
Columbine	. .	23
Comfrey	. . .	118
Compositae	. .	90
Coniferae	. . .	192
Conium	. . .	77
Conopodium	. .	79
Convallaria	. .	162
Convolvulaceae	. .	120
Convolvulus	. .	120
Cordgrass	. .	183
Coriander	. .	82
Coriandrum	. .	82
Cornaceae	. .	84
Corn Cockle	. .	40
Cornel	. . .	84
Cornflower	. .	102
Corn Marigold	. .	97
Cornsalad	. .	89
Cornus	. . .	84
Coronopus	. .	33
Corydalis	. . .	25
Corylus	. . .	150
Cotton-grass	. .	173

Cotyledon	.	.	.	70
Couch	.	.	.	191
Cowbane	.	.	.	78
Cowberry	.	.	.	109
Cowslip	.	.	.	113
Cow-wheat	.	.	.	127
Crab Apple	.	.	.	67
Crambe	.	.	.	34
Cranberry	.	.	.	109
Crane's-bill	.	.	.	48
Crassulaceae	.	.	.	70
Crataegus	.	.	.	67
Creeping Jenny	.	.	114
Crepis	.	.	.	103
Cress	.	.	.	33
Crithmum	.	.	.	80
Crocus	.	.	.	160
Crosswort	.	.	.	87
Crowberry	.	.	.	155
Crowfoot	.	.	.	21
Cruciferae	.	.	.	25
Cryptogams	.	.	.	193
Cuckoo-flower	.	.	29
Cuckoo-pint	.	.	.	166
Cucurbitaceae	.	.	74
Cudweed	.	.	94, 95
Currant	.	.	.	69
Cuscuta	.	.	.	120
Cynoglossum	.	.	117
Cynosurus	.	.	.	187
Cyperaceae	.	.	.	170
Cystopteris	.	.	.	196
Cytisus	.	.	.	53
Dactylis	.	.	.	187
Daffodil	.	.	.	160
Daisy	.	.	.	94
Dame's Violet	.	.	30
Dandelion	.	.	.	106
Danewort	.	.	.	85
Daphne	.	.	.	145
Darnel	.	.	.	191
Daucus	.	.	.	82
Deadly Nightshade	.	.	121
Deadnettle	.	.	.	135
Deer's-hair	.	.	.	172
Delphinium	.	.	.	23
Devil's-bit	.	.	.	90
Dewberry	.	.	.	63
Dianthus	.	.	.	38
Digitalis	.	.	.	124
Digraphis	.	.	.	183
Dioscoreaceae	.	.	161
Diplotaxis	.	.	.	32
Dipsaceae	.	.	.	89
Dipsacus	.	.	.	89
Dittander	.	.	.	33
Dock	.	.	.	143
Dodder	.	.	.	121
Dog's Mercury	.	.	147
Dog's-tail	.	.	.	187
Dogwood	.	.	.	84
Doronicum	.	.	.	98
Draba	.	.	.	29
Dropwort	.	.	.	62
Drosera	.	.	.	71
Droseraceae	.	.	.	71
Dryas	.	.	.	63
Duckweed	.	.	.	167
Dyer's Greenweed	.	.	53
Dyer's Weed	.	.	.	35
Earthnut	.	.	.	79
Echium	.	.	.	120
Elaeagnaceae	.	.	145
Elatinaceae	.	.	.	44
Elatine	.	.	.	44
Elder	.	.	.	85
Elecampane	.	.	.	95
Eleocharis	.	.	.	172
Elm	.	.	.	148
Elodea	.	.	.	155
Elymus	.	.	.	192
Empetraceae	.	.	.	154
Empetrum	.	.	.	155
Enchanter's Nightshade	.	74
Epilobium	.	.	.	72
Epipactis	.	.	.	157
Equisetaceae	.	.	198
Equisetum	.	.	.	198
Erica	.	.	.	110
Ericaceae	.	.	.	109
Erigeron	.	.	.	94
Eriophorum	.	.	.	173
Erodium	.	.	.	49
Erophila	.	.	.	30
Eryngium	.	.	.	77
Erysimum	.	.	.	31
Erythraea	.	.	.	116
Euonymus	.	.	.	51
Eupatorium	.	.	.	94
Euphorbia	.	.	.	146

Euphorbiaceae	. . .	146
Euphrasia	. . .	126
Evening Primrose	. .	74
Everlasting	. . .	95
Everlasting Pea	. .	60
Eyebright	. . .	126
Fagaceae	. . .	151
Fagus	. . .	152
False Oat	. . .	186
Fat Hen	. . .	139
Felwort	. . .	116
Fennel	. . .	80
Fenugreek	. . .	54
Fern	. . .	194
Fescue	. . .	189
Festuca	. . .	189
Feverfew	. . .	97
Figwort	. . .	123
Filago	. . .	94
Filices	. . .	193
Fir	. . .	193
Flag	. . .	160, 167
Flax	. . .	47
Fleabane	. .	94, 95
Flixweed	. . .	31
Flowering Rush	. .	168
Fluellen	. . .	123
Foeniculum	. . .	80
Fool's Parsley	. .	81
Forget-me-not	. .	119
Foxglove	. . .	124
Foxtail	. . .	183
Fragaria	. . .	64
Frankenia	. . .	37
Frankeniaceae	. .	37
Fraxinus	. . .	115
French Willow	. .	73
Fritillaria	. . .	163
Fritillary	. . .	163
Frogbit	. . .	155
Fumaria	. . .	25
Fumariaceae	. . .	25
Fumitory	. . .	25
Furze	. . .	53
Gagea	. . .	163
Galanthus	. . .	160
Galeopsis	. . .	135
Galium	. . .	86
Garlic	. . .	162
Garlic Mustard	. .	31
Gean	. . .	62
Genista	. . .	53
Gentian, Gentiana	.	116
Gentianaceae	. .	115
Geraniaceae	. . .	47
Geranium	. . .	48
Geum	. . .	63
Gilliflower	. . .	27
Gipsywort	. . .	132
Gladdon	. . .	160
Glasswort	. . .	140
Glaucium	. . .	25
Glaux	. . .	114
Globe-flower	. . .	22
Glyceria	. . .	188
Gnaphalium	. . .	95
Goat's-beard	. . .	107
Golden Rod	. . .	94
Golden Samphire	.	95
Golden Saxifrage	.	69
Goldilocks	. . .	21
Good King Henry	.	139
Gooseberry	. . .	69
Goosefoot	. . .	139
Goosegrass	. . .	87
Gorse	. . .	53
Goutweed	. . .	79
Gramineae	. . .	180
Grass	. . .	180
Grass of Parnassus	.	69
Grass-wrack	. . .	170
Greek Valerian	. .	117
Gromwell	. . .	120
Ground Elder	. .	79
Ground Ivy	. . .	133
Ground Pine	. . .	136
Groundsel	. . .	99
Guelder Rose	. .	85
Gymnadenia	. .	159
Habenaria	. . .	159
Haloragaceae	. .	71
Harebell	. . .	108
Hare's-ear	. . .	77
Hart's-tongue	. .	196
Hawkbit	. . .	105
Hawk's-beard	. .	103
Hawkweed	. . .	104
Hawthorn	. . .	67
Hazel	. . .	150

Heartsease . . . 37
Heather . . . 116
Hedera . . . 83
Hedge Mustard . . 30
Hedge Parsley . . 83
Helianthemum . . 35
Hellebore . . . 22
Helleborine . . 157
Helleborus . . . 22
Helminthia . . . 103
Helosciadium . . 78
Hemlock . . . 77
Hemp Agrimony . . 94
Hempnettle . . . 135
Henbane . . . 121
Henbit . . . 135
Heracleum . . . 82
Herb-Bennet . . 63
Herb-Paris . . . 163
Herb-Robert . . 49
Herminium . . . 159
Herniaria . . . 138
Hesperis . . . 30
Hieracium . . . 104
Hippocastanaceae . 52
Hippocrepis . . 58
Hippophae . . . 145
Hippuris . . . 71
Hog's Fennel . . 82
Holcus . . . 185
Holly . . . 50
Honewort . . . 77
Honeysuckle . . 85
Hop . . . 148
Hordeum . . . 192
Horehound . . 134, 136
Hornbeam . . . 150
Hornwort . . . 155
Horse Chestnut . . 52
Horseradish . . 30
Horseshoe Vetch . . 71
Horsetail . . . 198
Hottonia . . . 113
Hound's-tongue . . 117
Houseleek . . . 71
Humulus . . . 148
Hutchinsia . . . 34
Hyacinth . . . 163
Hyacinthus . . . 163
Hydrocharidaceae . 155
Hydrocharis . . . 155

Hydrocotyle . . . 77
Hymenophyllum . . 194
Hyoscyamus . . . 121
Hypericaceae . . 44
Hypericum . . . 44
Hypochoeris . . 105

Iberis . . . 34
Ilex . . . 50
Illecebraceae . . 137
Impatiens . . . 50
Inula . . . 95
Iridaceae . . . 160
Iris . . . 160
Isoetaceae . . . 200
Isoetes . . . 200
Isolepis . . . 172
Ivy . . . 83

Jacob's Ladder . . 117
Jack-by-the-hedge . . 31
Jasione . . . 107
Juglandaceae . . 149
Juglans . . . 149
Juncaceae . . . 163
Juncus . . . 164
Juniper . . . 193
Juniperus . . . 193

Kentranthus . . 88
Kidney Vetch . . 37
King-cups . . . 22
Knapweed . . . 102
Knautia . . . 90
Knawel . . . 138
Knotgrass . . . 142
Koeleria . . . 187

Labiatae . . . 129
Lactuca . . . 106
Lady's Fingers . . 57
Lady's Mantle . . 65
Lady's Smock . . 29
Lady's Tresses . . 157
Lamb's Lettuce . . 89
Lamium . . . 135
Lapsana . . . 103
Larch . . . 193
Larix . . . 193
Larkspur . . . 23

Lastrea	. . .	196
Lathraea	. . .	128
Lathyrus	. . .	60
Lemna	. . .	167
Lemnaceae	. . .	167
Lentibulariaceae	. .	128
Leontodon	. . .	105
Leopard's Bane	. .	98
Lepidium	. . .	33
Lepturus	. . .	191
Lettuce	. . .	106
Leucojum	. . .	160
Ligusticum	. . .	82
Ligustrum	. . .	115
Liliaceae	. . .	161
Lily-of-the-Valley	. .	162
Lime	. . .	46
Limnanthemum	. .	116
Limosella	. . .	124
Linaceae	. . .	47
Linaria	. . .	122
Ling	. . .	110
Linnaea	. . .	85
Linum	. . .	47
Listera	. . .	156
Lithospermum	. .	119
Littorella	. . .	137
Livelong	. . .	70
Lobelia	. . .	107
Loiseleuria	. . .	111
Lolium	. . .	191
London Pride	. .	68
London Rocket	. .	31
Lonicera	. . .	85
Loosestrife	. .	72, 113
Loranthaceae	. . .	145
Lords-and-Ladies	. .	166
Lotus	. . .	57
Lousewort	. . .	126
Lovage	. . .	82
Lucerne	. . .	54
Lungwort	. . .	118
Luzula	. . .	165
Lychnis	. . .	39
Lycopodiaceae	. .	199
Lycopodium	. . .	199
Lycopsis	. . .	118
Lycopus	. . .	132
Lysimachia	. . .	113
Lythraceae	. . .	72
Lythrum	. . .	72
Madder	. . .	86, 88
Madwort	. . .	118
Mallow	. . .	46
Malva	. . .	46
Malvaceae	. . .	46
Maple	. . .	51
Marram	. . .	185
Marestail	. . .	71
Marjorum	. . .	132
Marrubium	. . .	134
Marsh Marigold	. .	22
Marshwort	. . .	78
Marsiliaceae	. . .	200
Masterwort	. . .	82
Matricaria	. . .	97
Matthiola	. . .	27
Mayweed	. . .	97
Mazzard	. . .	62
Meadow-rue	. . .	19
Meadow Saffron	. .	163
Meadow Sweet	. .	62
Meconopsis	. . .	24
Medicago	. . .	54
Medick	. . .	54
Melampyrum	. .	127
Melic	. . .	187
Melica	. . .	187
Melilot	. . .	55
Melilotus	. . .	55
Melissa	. . .	133
Melittis	. . .	134
Mentha	. . .	131
Menyanthes	. . .	116
Mercurialis	. . .	147
Mercury	. . .	147
Mertensia	. . .	118
Meum	. . .	81
Mezereon	. . .	145
Midsummer-men	. .	70
Mignonette	. . .	35
Milfoil	. . .	96
Milium	. . .	184
Milk Parsley	. . .	82
Milk-vetch	. . .	58
Milkwort	. . .	37
Mimulus	. . .	124
Mint	. . .	131
Mistletoe	. . .	146
Mithridate Mustard	.	34
Moenchia	. . .	41
Molinia	. . .	187

Moneses	. . . .	111
Moneywort	. . 114,	124
Monkey-flower	. . .	124
Monkshood	. . .	23
Monotropa	. . .	111
Montia	. . . .	44
Moonwort	. . .	198
Moschatel	. . .	84
Mountain Ash	. . .	67
Mountain Avens	. . .	63
Mousetail	. . .	20
Mudwort	. . . .	124
Mugwort	. . . .	98
Mullein	. . .	122
Mustard	. . .	32
Myosotis	. . .	119
Myosurus	. . .	20
Myrica	. . .	150
Myricaceae	. . .	149
Myriophyllum	. .	71
Myrrhis	. . .	80
Naiadaceae	. . .	168
Narcissus	. . .	160
Nardus	. . .	191
Narthecium	. . .	163
Nasturtium	. . .	27
Neottia	. . .	156
Nepeta	. . .	133
Nettle	. . .	149
Nightshade	. . .	121
Nipplewort	. . .	103
Nonsuch	. . .	54
Nuphar	. . .	23
Nymphaea	. . .	23
Nymphaeaceae	. .	23
Oak	. . .	151
Oat	. . .	186
Œnanthe	. . .	80
Œnothera	. . .	74
Old Man's Beard	. .	19
Oleaceae	. . .	115
Onagraceae	. . .	72
Onobrychis	. . .	58
Ononis	. . .	53
Onopordon	. . .	101
Ophioglossum	. .	198
Ophrys	. . .	158
Orach	. . .	149
Orchid	. . .	158
Orchidaceae	. . .	156
Orchis	. . .	157
Origanum	. . .	132
Ornithogalum	. . .	163
Ornithopus	. . .	58
Orobanchaceae	. . .	127
Orobanche	. . .	127
Orpine	. . .	70
Osier	. . .	153
Osmunda	. . .	197
Oxalis	. . .	50
Ox-eye Daisy	. . .	97
Oxlip	. . .	113
Ox-tongue	. . .	103
Oxyria	. . .	143
Oyster Plant	. . .	118
Paigle	. . .	113
Pansy	. . .	27
Papaver	. . .	24
Papaveraceae	. . .	24
Papilionaceae	. . .	52
Parietaria	. . .	149
Paris	. . .	163
Parnassia	. . .	69
Parsley	. . .	78
Parsley Piert	. . .	65
Parsnip	. . .	82
Pasque-flower	. . .	20
Pastinaca	. . .	82
Pea	. . .	60
Pear	. . .	67
Pearlwort	. . .	43
Pedicularis	. . .	126
Pellitory	. . .	149
Penny Cress	. . .	34
Pennyroyal	. . .	132
Pennywort	. . 70,	77
Peplis	. . .	72
Peppermint	. . .	131
Pepper Saxifrage	. .	81
Pepperwort	. . .	33
Periwinkle	. . .	115
Persicaria	. . .	142
Petasites	. . .	98
Peucedanum	. . .	82
Phalaris	. . .	183
Pheasant's-eye	. . .	20
Phleum	. . .	184
Phragmites	. . .	186

Phyteuma	. . .	107
Picea	. . .	193
Picris	. . .	103
Pignut	. . .	79
Pillwort	. . .	200
Pilularia	. . .	200
Pimpernel	. . .	114
Pimpinella	. . .	79
Pine	. . .	193
Pinguicula	. . .	128
Pink	. . .	38
Pinus	. . .	193
Plane	. . .	149
Plantaginaceae	. . .	136
Plantago	. . .	137
Plantain	. . .	137
Platanaceae	. . .	149
Platanus	. . .	149
Ploughman's Spikenard	.	95
Plumbaginaceae	. .	112
Poa	. . .	188
Polemoniaceae	. .	116
Polemonium	. .	117
Polygala	. . .	37
Polygalaceae	. . .	37
Polygonaceae	. . .	141
Polygonatum	. .	162
Polygonum	. . .	141
Polypodium	. .	197
Polypody	. . .	197
Polystichum	. .	196
Pondweed	. . .	169
Poor Man's Weather-glass	.	114
Poplar	. . .	154
Poppy	. . .	24
Populus	. . .	154
Portulaceae	. . .	43
Potamogeton	. .	169
Potentilla	. . .	64
Poterium	. . .	65
Primrose	. . .	113
Primula	. . .	113
Primulaceae	. . .	112
Privet	. . .	115
Prunella	. . .	134
Prunus	. . .	61
Psamma	. . .	185
Pteris	. . .	194
Pulmonaria	. .	118
Purslane	. . 72,	140
Pyrola	. . .	111

Pyrus	. . .	67
Pyrus	. . .	67
Quercus	. . .	151
Quillwort	. . .	200
Radiola	. . .	47
Radish	. . .	35
Ragged Robin	. .	40
Ragwort	. . .	99
Rampion	. . 107,	108
Ramsons	. . .	162
Ranunculaceae	. .	19
Ranunculus	. . .	20
Rape	. . .	32
Raphanus	. . .	35
Raspberry	. . .	63
Red Rattle	. . .	126
Reed	. . .	186
Reedmace	. . .	166
Reseda	. . .	35
Resedaceae	. . .	35
Restharrow	. . .	54
Rhamnaceae	. . .	51
Rhamnus	. . .	51
Rhinanthus	. . .	126
Rhynchospora	. .	173
Ribes	. . .	69
Ribesiaceae	. . .	69
Ribwort	. . .	137
Roastbeef Plant	. .	160
Rockcress	. . .	28
Rocket	. . .	32
Rockrose	. . .	35
Rosa	. . .	66
Rosaceae	. . .	60
Rose	. . .	66
Roseroot	. . .	70
Rowan	. . .	67
Rubia	. . .	86
Rubiaceae	. . .	86
Rubus	. . .	62
Rumex	. . .	143
Rupture-wort	. .	138
Ruscus	. . .	161
Rush	. . .	164
Rusty-back	. . .	196
Rye-grass	. . .	191
Sage	. . .	133
Sagina	. . .	42

Sagittaria	. . .	168
Sainfoin	. . .	58
St. John's Wort	. .	45
Salad Burnet	. .	65
Salicaceae	. . .	152
Salicornia	. . .	140
Salix	. . .	152
Sallow	. . .	153
Salsola	. . .	141
Saltwort	. . .	141
Salvia	. . .	133
Sambucus	. . .	84
Samolus	. . .	114
Samphire	. . .	80
Sand Spurrey	. .	43
Sandwort	. . .	42
Sanguisorba	. .	65
Sanicle	. . .	77
Sanicula	. . .	77
Santalaceae	. .	146
Saponaria	. . .	39
Saussurea	. . .	102
Saw-wort	. . .	102
Saxifraga	. . .	68
Saxifragaceae	. .	67
Saxifrage	. . .	68
Scabiosa	. . .	90
Scabious	. . .	90
Scandix	. . .	80
Schoenus	. . .	173
Scilla	. . .	162
Scirpus	. . .	171
Scleranthus	. .	138
Scolopendrium	. .	196
Scorpion-grass	. .	119
Scrophularia	. .	123
Scrophulariaceae	.	121
Scurvy-grass	. .	30
Scutellaria	. . .	133
Seablite	. . .	141
Sea Buckthorn	. .	145
Sea Heath	. .	37
Sea Holly	. .	77
Seakale	. .	34
Sea Lavender	. .	112
Sea Milkwort	. .	114
Sea Pink	. . .	112
Sea Purslane	.	42, 140
Sea Rocket	. .	34
Sedge	. . .	177
Sedum	. . .	70
Selaginella	. .	200
Self-heal	. .	134
Sempervivum	. .	71
Senebiera	. .	33
Senecio	. . .	98
Serratula	. . .	102
Service	. . .	67
Sesleria	. . .	187
Setterwort	. .	22
Sheep's-bit	. .	107
Sheep's Scabious	.	107
Shepherd's Needle	.	80
Shepherd's Purse	.	32
Sherardia	. . .	88
Shoreweed	. .	137
Sibbaldia	. . .	65
Sibthorpia	. .	124
Silaus	. . .	81
Silene	. . .	39
Silverweed	. .	64
Sinapis	. . .	32
Sison	. . .	79
Sisymbrium	. .	30
Sisymbrium	. .	28, 31
Sium	. . .	79
Skullcap	. . .	134
Sloe	. . .	62
Smallreed	. .	185
Smyrnium	. .	77
Snake's-head	. .	163
Snakeweed	. .	142
Snapdragon	. .	123
Sneezewort	. .	96
Snowdrop	. .	160
Snowflake	. .	160
Soapwort	. . .	39
Solanaceae	. .	121
Solanum	. . .	121
Solidago	. . .	94
Solomon's Seal	. .	162
Sonchus	. . .	106
Sorbus	. . .	67
Sorrel	. . .	144
Sowthistle	. .	106
Sparganium	. .	166
Spartina	. . .	183
Spearwort	. .	21
Specularia	. .	109
Speedwell	. .	125
Spergula	. . .	43
Spergularia	. .	43

Spignel	. . . .	81
Spindle Tree	. .	51
Spiraea	. . . .	62
Spiranthes	. . .	157
Spleenwort	. . .	195
Spruce	. . . .	193
Spurge	. . . .	147
Spurge Laurel	. .	145
Spurrey	. . . .	43
Squill	. . . .	162
Squinancy Wort	.	88
Stachys	. . . .	134
Star-of-Bethlehem	.	163
Star Thistle	. .	102
Starwort, Water	.	72
Statice	. . . .	112
Stellaria	. . .	41
Stinkweed	. . .	32
Stitchwort	. . .	41
Stock	. . . .	27
Stonecrop	. . .	70
Stork's-bill	. . .	50
Stratiotes	. . .	155
Strawberry	. . .	64
Strawberry, Barren	.	64
Suaeda	. . . .	141
Subularia	. . .	31
Succory	. . . .	103
Sundew	. . . .	71
Swede	. . . .	32
Sweet Briar	. .	66
Sweet Chestnut	. .	151
Sweet Cicely	. .	80
Sweet Flag	. . .	167
Sweet Gale	. . .	150
Swine-cress	. . .	33
Sycamore	. . .	51
Symphytum	. . .	118
Tamaricaceae	. .	44
Tamarisk	. . .	44
Tamarix	. . . .	44
Tamus	. . . .	161
Tanacetum	. . .	97
Tansy	. . . .	97
Taraxacum	. . .	106
Tare	. . . .	59
Taxus	. . . .	193
Teasel	. . . .	89
Teesdalia	. . .	34
Teucrium	. . .	136

Thale Cress	. .	34
Thalictrum	. . .	19
Thesium	. . .	146
Thistle	. . . .	100
Thlaspi	. . . .	34
Thrift	. . . .	112
Thyme	. . . .	132
Thymeleaceae	. .	145
Thymus	. . . .	132
Tilia	. . . .	46
Tiliaceae	. . .	46
Toadflax	. . .	123
Toothwort	. . .	128
Torilis	. . . .	83
Tormentil	. . .	64
Touch-me-not	. .	50
Tower Mustard	. .	28
Town Clock	. .	84
Tragopogon	. . .	107
Traveller's Joy	. .	19
Treacle Mustard	.	31
Trefoil	. . . .	57
Trientalis	. . .	114
Trifolium	. . .	55
Triglochin	. . .	168
Trigonella	. . .	54
Trinia	. . . .	77
Triodia	. . . .	186
Triticum	. . . .	191
Trollius	. . . .	22
Turnip	. . . .	32
Tussilago	. . .	98
Tutsan	. . . .	45
Twayblade	. . .	156
Twin-flower	. . .	85
Typha	. . . .	166
Typhaceae	. . .	166
Ulex	. . . .	53
Ulmaceae	. . .	148
Ulmus	. . . .	148
Umbelliferae	. .	74
Urtica	. . . .	148
Urticaceae	. . .	148
Utricularia	. . .	128
Vacciniaceae	. .	109
Vaccinium	. . .	109
Valerian	. . .	88
Valerianaceae	. .	88
Valerianella	. . .	88

Venus's Comb	80
Venus's Looking-glass	109
Verbascum	122
Verbena	129
Verbenaceae	129
Veronica	124
Vervain	129
Vetch	59
Vetchling	60
Viburnum	85
Vicia	58
Vinca	115
Viola	36
Violaceae	36
Violet	36
Viper's Bugloss	120
Viscum	146
Wahlenbergia	108
Wallflower	27
Wall Mustard	32
Wall Rocket	32
Wall Rue	195
Walnut	149
Watercress	27
Water Dropwort	81
Waterlily	23, 116
Water Milfoil	72
Water Parsnip	79
Water Pepper	142
Water Plantain	168
Water Purslane	72
Water Rocket	28
Water Soldier	155
Water Thyme	155
Water Violet	113
Waterwort	44
Wayfaring Tree	85
Weld	35
Welsh Poppy	24
Wheat-grass	191
Whin	53
White-rot	77
Whitlow-grass	30
Whortleberry	109
Willow	153
Willow-herb	73
Wintercress	28
Wintergreen	111
Wolfsbane	23
Woodbine	85
Woodruff	87
Woodrush	165
Wood Sage	136
Wood Sorrel	50
Wormwood	97
Woundwort	134
Yarrow	96
Yellow Rattle	126
Yellow-wort	116
Yew	193
Yorkshire Fog	186
Zannichellia	170
Zostera	170

PRINTED IN GREAT BRITAIN AT THE UNIVERSITY PRESS, OXFORD
BY CHARLES BATEY, PRINTER TO THE UNIVERSITY